ECOCIDE
IN
INDOCHINA

ECOCIDE IN INDOCHINA

The Ecology of War

Barry Weisberg

BAY AREA INSTITUTE
SAN FRANCISCO, CALIFORNIA

CANFIELD PRESS • SAN FRANCISCO
a Department of Harper & Row, Publishers, Inc.

ECOCIDE IN INDOCHINA

Preface

Although individual members of the scientific community have been concerned with chemical and biological warfare for some time, only recently has public attention been focused on America's chemical warfare in Southeast Asia, crop destruction, and defoliation. Herbicides, together with the "application of massive fire power" and forced urbanization, have evolved into ecological warfare in which the Military's old strategy of "search and destroy" has given way to the incentive to simply destroy.

This could not have been accomplished with ground combat troops—that is, "fighting the enemy on his own terrain." We had to eliminate the terrain. One acquires the awful feeling now that the concern of America in Indochina is no longer deterence, or even counterinsurgency—but rather total destruction. There seems no other way to describe the complexity and sheer volume of havoc described in this book. The materials included in this book describe the destruction of the "living landscape" by war as well as the effects of such a war upon the people and culture of Southeast Asia, most specifically South Vietnam. Peter Farb in *The Living Earth* understood well the interdependence when he wrote: "the wholeness of what we call life is like a delicate fabric with many simple strands. The wonder is not that so many threads are necessary in the fabric, but rather that the fabric manages to exist at all." The nature of the interdependence between the threads and the highly precarious nature of the entire fabric is made clear in the articles of this book.

In Asia the unraveling of this fabric is a strategy geared not only to the destruction of the enemy with his present settlements and culture but also to the breakdown of the biological fabric required to sustain any possible adversary in the future. What we have now accomplished in Indochina is to make vast areas of a rural society uninhabitable for decades to come, pushing refugees into a consumer economy in the urban slums.

Perhaps after ten years of the growing awareness that there is no longer a means by which to distinguish friend from foe in Indochina, there has evolved a strategy to combat "peoples wars of national liberation"—the elimination of the people.

But Southeast Asia merely provides a telescopic preview of conditions on a planetary scale. Our destruction of the life support system of Indochina parallels America's destruction of the air, water, and land of the entire world through chemical contamination. Such a manipulation of nature is unique.

Within the last few years the human race has achieved a totally unprecedented influence on the course of all life on this planet. For several billions of years the processes of life and death—the cycle of regeneration— remained woven in the unpredictable, unmanageable legend of evolution. No single animal, or species of animal, could at will bid the journey or termination of other forms of life. This has changed. Man's relationship to nature is no longer determined by nature but is subject to the rule of political management on a scale beyond normal comprehension. This awesome realization forms the foundation for understanding not only our willful destruction of Indochina but also the ecological peril that faces the entire Earth from America's pre-eminent role in the chemical poisoning of the life support systems. No other event of our time has more clearly marked this unprecedented power than the dawn of the atomic age, twenty-five years ago. But perhaps in Indochina, during these last five years, we have taken another qualitative step along the terminal path of aborting the multi-billion years of evolutionary process. The threat of atomic warfare is self evident. But with Ecocide, more consciously in Indochina, less consciously elsewhere, we are slowly, though steadily, altering the organic chemistry of the life process, and we are approaching a point beyond which regeneration is impossible. During these past few years the threat of atomic holocaust has been held in check, but the threat of ecological oblivion proceeds almost without reservation. Ecocide may be less dramatic, less immediately apparent than atomic war—but it is every bit as conclusive. Again, Southeast Asia only mirrors a larger, more pervasive, but related issue. The forces at work now in Indochina are at work around the world, in the towns of America as well as the jungles of Asia. The chemical poisoning of Indochina by the Military parallels the poisoning of America by our Chemical industry. To believe for an instant that one will stop without the other would be a grave miscalculation. It is toward this realization that this book was written. It is tragic that many of America's environmental crusaders have not fully realized the interconnection between the destruction of Indochina and the destruction of our total environment. The power of this destruction cannot be circumvented by consumer boycotts or draft resistance alone. The power of the Military, the power of excess production, as well as imperial consumption, must be broken at the source.

Put in the most simple terms, we can never hope to stop the destruction of the environment in America unless we stop America's destruction of the environment of Indochina.

This entire book was assembled in about two months. Although some academics and professionals were quite unwilling to cooperate with such a project, many others eagerly lent their encouragement and assistance. Both Karen McNally and Malcolm Somerville of the Ad Hoc Committee of Earth Scientists at the University of California at Berkeley, provided continual aid in searching out and gathering materials. Franz Schurmann and Orville Schell, both colleagues of mine at the Bay Area Institute, taught me much of what little I know about Asia. The patience and support shown by Gail Weisberg toward me was no small contribution.

Contents

Legend is that the illustrious King Lac Long,
grandson of the god of the seas,
married an immortal called Au Co,
a descendent of the angels of the mountains.
From this union one hundred boys were hatched from one hundred eggs. . . .
Then the King and the Fairy, conscious of
the transitory nature of human existence,
and the elusiveness of human happiness,
decided to part.
Au Co went up to the mountains along with fifty of her sons,
and Lac Long went down to the sea with the others.
From this separation, the kingdom of Bach Viet (now Viet Nam) came into
being. . . .

This book is written for the people of Vietnam,
of all Indochina,
who struggle toward liberation

ECOCIDE
IN
INDOCHINA

PART 1

Introduction

On Ecocide

The War in Viet Nam! For ten years everything about our lives and our society has been colored by this one event. An entire generation of children grew up to the evening news of Viet Nam. An age of protest in the United States has centered on Viet Nam. It has dominated the economy, the social structure, the universities, and the role of America around the world. America was Viet Nam in the 1960's.

Yet, after daily press reports, evening television, and a torrent of articles; after protests, bombings, and long jail sentences, the war persists. It not only persists but grows. It has become nothing short of a cancer within American life—with no cure in sight. It is no longer Viet Nam, but Laos, Cambodia and Thailand. It is now the Second War in Indochina.

But how little we know of this precious land, this ancient peninsula jutting out from the body of China. What of its people, landscape, the history of its culture? The extent of destruction?

Bertrand Russell once remarked that "it is in the nature of imperialism that the citizens of the imperial power are always among the last to know—or care—about the circumstances in the colonies."[1] Now, after ten years, we know almost nothing short of news reports, "body counts," missions flown, and our own protest movement. Southeast Asia today seems a blur of facts and military records. Old newspapers we have discarded. Little wonder then that we are so pitifully incapable as a people of grasping the magnitude of what has happened there, what continues to happen. This is not the case with other catastrophic events of recent warfare. Few historical moments evoke the universal images such as mark the events of Guernica, Auschwitz, or

---

[1]Bertrand Russell, *Against the Crime of Silence*, ed. John Duffett, O'Hare, 1966, p. 3.

1

Hiroshima. Unlike other times, other places, these events stand out as unique, crystalline examples of what man does to man and woman.

With Guernica for the first time, aircraft were employed in a conscious manner to completely demolish an urban population. With Auschwitz, and what it symbolizes, we see the efforts of one culture to exterminate another. But Hiroshima completely distinguishes itself from all previous human experience. There, in Asia, instruments of war were employed against a civilian population with the capacity not only of destroying a city, a people, and a local environment, but the planet, earth. With Hiroshima, and its sister city, Nagasaki, the image of destruction is clearly emblazoned in the memory of most every person on the earth—a mushroom cloud.

But with Viet Nam, there is no such image, no such date, by which to mark or measure what has happened, what continues to happen. There is no mushroom cloud, no stench from the gas chambers. While the weapons being employed in Viet Nam appear, in a sense, to be of a more "limited" nature, they are every bit as profound in their impact as were the devices dropped on Hiroshima or the "final solution" selected to deal with the "Jewish problem."

Many people believe that current American activities in Southeast Asia fall under Article 2 of the 1948 Geneva Convention which defines genocide on the basis of intent; genocide being a term coined to describe the Nazi extermination of the Jews. Others cite the Nuremburg Principles which affirm that War Crimes and Crimes Against Humanity are crimes under international law. Still others cite the Geneva Protocol of 1925 against poisonous gases or the United Nations Convention on Genocide. Three years ago the Bertrand Russell War Crimes Tribunal was convened in Stockholm to consider American war crimes.

Still, such principles seem almost irrelevant to the magnitude of saturation bombing and chemical warfare in Indochina. This book asks simply, does American policy in Indochina represent an intentional and rationally executed assault against the people and culture of Viet Nam (the pacification programs, forced urbanization, saturation bombing, Operation Phoenix, defoliation ...), a strategy employed not only to eliminate the enemy but destroy the environment which supports him? If so, not since the Romans salted the earth at Carthage can such a tactic be recalled.

Many international agreements seem applicable to American involvement in Indochina. But the United States still refrains from ratifying most of them, such as the 1925 Geneva Protocol against "asphyxiating, poisonous or other gases. . . ." To date, some 84 nations have ratified that Protocol.[2] And although the World Health Organization has condemned the use of herbicides and tear gas in warfare, as well as suggesting that 2,4,5-T was a "possible cause of birth defects in children,"[3] the United States continues to

---

[2]Thomas Whiteside, *Defoliation*, Ballantine, 1970, p. 168.
[3]*New York Times*, December 5, 1969.

employ 2,4,5-T in Viet Nam[4] in complete disdain for possible pathological consequences, even when officially banned from use in Viet Nam by Deputy Secretary of Defense David Packard on April 15, 1970:

> ... in a quarter of a century since the Department of Defense first developed the biological warfare uses of this material (2,4,5-T) it has not completed a single series of formal tertological tests on pregnant animals to determine whether it has an effect on their unborn offspring.[5]

This is but one example of the almost complete neglect for investigation or inquiry into the consequences upon humans, plants, and animals of the large scale ecological disruption in progress in Viet Nam and throughout Southeast Asia. Taken together, the "ecological warfare"[6] against both the people and the biological fabric which supports them, there seems no adequate concept by which to describe, let alone judge, what is happening in that particular corner of Asia.

Every indication suggests that South Viet Nam is a preview for what is now happening in Laos, Cambodia and parts of Thailand: forced urbanization, saturation bombing, defoliation. . . . Consequently, by examining in detail the ecology of war in South Viet Nam, we can begin to construct what is likely to become fact for all of Southeast Asia.

The purpose of such an inquiry is not related to matters of law. Before man can achieve the orderly and moral regulation of his behavior, he needs to first understand the complexity of his condition. Viet Nam demonstrates more than anything else in the American experience that law holds no sway in the modern world of force, particularly nuclear force. Through all of what has been described in these pages, the United States has never legally declared war, though our involvement in Southeast Asia today far surpasses the commitment made in Korea,[7] the tonnage of munitions used in World War II,[8] even, perhaps, the monetary cost of World War II.[9] As Cambodia demonstrates, the President of the United States has it within his power to

---

[4]From a conversation with E. W. Pfeiffer after his return from a visit to Viet Nam in June, 1970. His evidence indicates that 2,4,5-T had been used in South Viet Nam up and until June 2, 1970.

[5]Whiteside, *op. cit.*, p. 41.

[6]The term "ecological warfare" appeared in *Scientific American*, January, 1968, p. 44.

[7]At the height of Korea we dropped a "mere" 17,000 tons of bombs a month, compared to well over 100,000 tons a month in Laos and South Viet Nam. Casualties for Americans totaled 142,091, compared to over 150,000 in South Viet Nam alone so far. Malvern Lumsden, *The Vietnamese People and the Impact of War*, Institute for Peace and Conflict Research, Denmark, December 1969, mimeo.

[8]The total tonnage of all bombs dropped against the Axis powers during World War II was surpassed in North and South Viet Nam alone by December 10, 1967, mounting to 1,554,463 tons. This is before the heavy bombing began. Reported in the *Washington Post*, December 10, 1967.

[9]The projected cost of the War in Indochina, given present patterns of expenditures, including future veteran payments, may amount to $330 billion, reported in "Vietnam: The 200 Year Mortgage," *Nation*, May 26, 1969. This estimate was made in May of 1969. Given the recent invasion of Cambodia and the widening war, we have every indication that the $330 billion will rise to surpass the total of $381 billion for World War II.

4

unleash untold destruction and devastation almost at will, without the consent of Congress, without even the consent, and in some cases the knowledge, of his own Cabinet. The Secretary of State, William Rogers, was not even aware of the bombing of North Viet Nam that occurred on May 2 and 3, 1970 until after it occurred.[10]

If the Secretary of State is not aware of the bombing of North Viet Nam, it is little wonder we are so desperately ignorant of Southeast Asia. So we, the people of America, are left with the task of not only constructing for ourselves what happens there but also with creating some measure by which to judge the acts which are carried out in our name.

Appearing at the Conference on War and National Responsibility in Washington, D. C., February, 1970, Professor Arthur W. Galston of Yale University "proposed a new international agreement to ban 'Ecocide'—the willful destruction of the environment."[11] (The precise origins of this term seem unknown. No doubt "Ecocide" originated in the recent concern that chemical warfare in Viet Nam required a concept similar to that of Genocide, relating to the theory of war crimes.)

Ecocide is a measure of what is happening to Indochina. Ecocide is the premeditated assault of a nation and its resources against the individuals, culture and biological fabric of another country and its environs. But we must hasten to add that by its very nature such warfare knows no simple boundaries. National demarcations, programs, military operations have no purview over the order of the natural world.

Therefore, it is almost impossible to talk rationally about Ecocide in terms of limited warfare. The ascribed limits of national conflict do not apply to the over-arching natural interface of environmental systems. With "ecological warfare," national confrontations become global survival issues.

Chemicals dispersed over South Viet Nam find their ecological path into Cambodia and throughout the Mekong River. Some persist in the soils for decades. Thus to understand Ecocide requires a breadth of imagination and scope of understanding which is now not present in our conception of the war in Vietnam. It simply is not enough to consider news events in isolation. To understand the destruction of Indochina as ecocide requires that we come to understand that the "ecosystem of Southeast Asia is one organic fabric in which all living things are tied together by an infinite number of interdependent strands."[12] The events portrayed in this book are some of those strands.

Origins of Ecocide

Is Ecocide a tragic but unexpected consequence of a limited policy, as some maintain, or is it rather a strategic choice of tactics on the part of Americans in Asia? To answer this question, it is important to consider

[10]*New York Times*, May 5, 1970.
[11]*New York Times*, February 26, 1970, see editorial.
[12]Orville Schell and Barry Weisberg, "Ecocide in Indochina," see Part 2 of this book.

briefly the origins both of American interest and its present military tactics in Indochina.

American entanglement in Southeast Asia did not arise overnight. As early as March 12, 1947, President Harry S. Truman said, "It must be the policy of the United States to support free people who are resisting attempted subjugation by armed minorities or by outside pressure." The Truman Doctrine set the stage for Korea and our later involvement in Indochina.[13] The determination of America to involve itself in Southeast Asia spans more than two decades. Gabriel Kolko in *The Roots of American Foreign Policy* traces American involvement in Viet Nam to the period after World War II. He points out that America paid half the French bill for their unsuccessful involvement in the First Indochina War.[14] In April of 1954, Vice President of the United States Richard M. Nixon said:

> If in order to avoid further Communist expansion in Asia and particularly in Indochina, if in order to avoid it we must take the risk by putting American boys in, I believe that the Executive Branch of the Government has to take the politically unpopular position of facing up to it, and I personally would support such a decision.

How similar these words sound to President Nixon's recent decision to send "American boys" to Cambodia.

In the preceding year, Richard Nixon expressed the Government's growing concern that Southeast Asia was a most critical source of materials and markets:

> If this whole part of Southeast Asia goes under Communist domination or Communist influence, Japan, who trades and must trade with this area in order to exist, must inevitably be oriented toward the Communist regime.[15]

Eisenhower further orchestrated this theme:

> The loss of Vietnam, together with Laos on the west and Cambodia on the southwest ... would have spelled the loss of valuable deposits of tin and prodigious supplies of rubber and rice. It would have meant that Thailand, enjoying buffer territory between itself and Red China, would be exposed on its entire Eastern border to infiltration and attack. And if Indo-China fell, not only Thailand but Burma and Malaya would be threatened, with added risks to East Pakistan and South Asia as well as to all Indonesia.[16]

Military advisors were assigned to Viet Nam by President Eisenhower in 1955. There is no need here to recount what has now become record. By the time President Kennedy took office, the stage was set for massive American involvement in Viet Nam, and throughout all Southeast Asia.

---

[13]"The Trouble with Harry," by Phil Dion, *Far Eastern Economic Review*, June 25, 1970. Along with *Le Monde*, this is the best regular source on Asia.
[14]Kolko, Gabriel, *The Roots of American Foreign Policy*, Beacon, 1968, Boston, p. 97.
[15]Kolko, *op. cit.*, p. 100.
[16]Kolko, *op. cit.*, p. 100.

Prior to the Presidency of John F. Kennedy the kind of warfare described in this book could not have occurred. The weapons of Ecocide reflect a fundamental shift in American military priorities that occurred between the Eisenhower and Kennedy Administrations. Put simply, it meant a shift from a basic philosophy of "massive retaliation" and nuclear deterrence to the innovation of a counterinsurgency strategy to enable America to fight "brushfire" guerrilla warfare around the globe.

The weapons of counterinsurgency: defoliation, napalm, anti-personnel and incendiary bombs, and later massive air power replacing ground combat troops, reflect a marked shift in military thinking whose leading proponents included Maxwell Taylor, Walt Whitman Rostow and Henry Kissinger (presently Special Assistant to the President for Security Affairs). When President Kennedy concluded that the Pentagon under Robert McNamara was not responding rapidly enough to his desired shift from deterrence to counterinsurgency, he initiated a "Special Group for Counterinsurgency" and the Green Berets.

Thus, for the first time since Korea, large numbers of ground combat troops played a strategic role in American military operations. A variety of special weapons were developed to assist these troops in counterinsurgency warfare against movements for national liberation. Viet Nam became the test site, as explained by General Maxwell Taylor in 1963:

> Here we have a going laboratory where we see subversive insurgency, the Ho Chi Minh doctrine, being applied in all its forms. This has been a challenge not just for the armed forces, but for several of the agencies of government, as many of them are involved in one way or another in South Vietnam. On the military side, however, we have recognized the importance of the area as a laboratory. We have had teams out there looking at the equipment requirements of this kind of guerrilla warfare. We have rotated senior officers through there, spending several weeks just to talk to people and get the feel of the operation, so even though not regularly assigned to Vietnam, they are carrying their experience back to their own organizations.[17]

The extent to which various governmental and civilian agencies of the society were involved in this affair was reflected in a speech by General William Westmoreland to the Association of the United States Army, in Washington, D. C., on October 14, 1969, when he spoke of the "military industrial-academic-scientific cooperation," which was so vital in the development of the new techniques required for the counterinsurgency warfare in Viet Nam. This, I presume, refers to the cooperation of major universities and corporations in the production of war-related knowledge and products. George Wald has suggested in this connection that companies such as Dow Chemical are in some sense as responsible for War Crimes as is the Military.[18]

---

[17]U.S. House Comm. on Appropriations, Subcommittee, Department of Defense Appropriations for 1964, 88th Congress, Session 1, Part 1, pp. 483-484.

[18]George Wald, "Corporate Responsibility for War Crimes," *New York Review of Books*, July 2, 1970.

Adding to the "military advisors" sent by President Eisenhower in 1955, President Kennedy in May, 1961 assigned 100 Green Berets to South Viet Nam, thus assigning the first U. S. combat troops to that country. The first "official" United States casualty in Viet Nam was reported by Dean Rusk, five years later, as having occurred in 1961.[19] The first major offensive action taken by America since Korea occurred in May, 1964 with the bombing of Laos.[20] The rest is record. These actions were consistent with a long standing ideological commitment in the U. S.: "For more than twenty years, the United States has carried on a global campaign against revolution and native insurgency movements, conducting a major military campaign or CIA operation in an underdeveloped country about once every eighteen months."[21]

But Viet Nam is unique. Writing in *Ramparts (December, 1965)*, *Bernard Fall captured, prophetically, the meaning of American operations in Viet Nam. ". . . the situation in Vietnam isn't Munich; it is Spain. There is in Vietnam a test of wills . . . there is a test of military technology and military ideas." He goes on to conclude:*

> The incredible thing about Viet Nam is that the worst is yet to come. (It is strictly a one way operation in the South. The Viet Cong do not have a single flying machine. We can literally go anywhere and bomb anything. The possibilities of devastation are open ended.)
>
> Looking back at the Viet Nam I left, I can see the means only too clearly, and so can everyone else who is not altogether blind. But I cannot say that I have found anyone who seems to have a clear idea of the end—of the 'war aims'—and if the end is not clearly defined, are we justified to use any means to attain it?

Bernard Fall wrote that in 1965. Two years later he was killed by a land mine in Viet Nam. What he described was only the beginning of the single and most critical American military decision after the initial involvement in Southeast Asia—the shift from combat ground troops to massive saturation bombing. This is what is called "Vietnamization."

For it is only with massive air power in 1965 that the strategy of counterinsurgency assumes its full Ecocidal dimensions. The "means" of this strategy is the subject of this book.

It is practically impossible to convey the sense of devastation that massive bombing can wreak. The following quote describes the bombing of Khe San in early 1968.

> In about six weeks, US aircraft had dropped 100,000 tons of bombs (some five times the equivalent of the device dropped on Hiroshima) and fired 700,000 rounds of machine gun fire into a circular area roughly five miles in diameter. . . . An Air Force colonel said, 'The tonnage of ordnance placed in that circle is unbelievable. In mid-February, the area looked like the rest of Vietnam, mountainous and heavily jungled with very little visibility through the canopy. Five weeks later, the jungle had become literally a desert—vast stretches of

[19]Senate Comm. on Foreign Relations, February 18, 1966.
[20]Peter Dale Scott, "Cambodia—Why the Generals Won," *New York Review of Books*, June 18, 1970.
[21]Richard J. Barnett, *The Economy of Death*, Atheneum, p. 42.

scarred, bare earth with hardly a tree standing, a landscape of splinters and bomb craters!'[22]

This is the "scorched earth" policy. Originally employed as an anti-crop weapon, herbicides, devastatingly dispersed by aircraft, soon became a critical defoliation agent by removing the foliage canopy that would hide insurgent forces.

Khe San and incidents of chemical warfare illustrate increasingly that such "means" all but negate any possible ends. Many tactics utilized in Viet Nam defy reasonable understanding. Thomas Whiteside writes in the *New Yorker* (July 11, 1970) about recent food denial programs:

> ... it can be estimated that the American military destroyed the rice supply of a million people with the aim of denying food to twenty thousand Viet Cong. Or, to put it another way, in order to deprive the Viet Cong of one ton of rice the American military has to destroy fifty tons of rice that would ordinarily support members of the civilian population.

Whiteside also indicates that those deprived turn out not to be soldiers but children and women. Dr. Jean Mayer of Harvard also has discussed the results of food denial programs.

Not only do these tactics defy reason, they defy as well conventional estimates as to effects and objectives. Not only is the unanticipated result far more drastic than supposed on the battlefield—chemicals spreading for hundreds of miles from the target zone—but equally unanticipated and profound are the implications in store for those who set forth the "aims" in Washington, D. C.

The Ecocidal Boomerang

While there can at this point be no doubt that America has inflicted extensive injury upon the lands, people and culture of Southeast Asia, it is also clear that the war abroad has profound implications for life here at home. The complete ecology of war in Indochina would explore both sides of this conflict, in Southeast Asia and in America. This would be the full ecological overview to the War in Southeast Asia.

Evidence accumulates daily about the brutalization of GI's in Asia,[23] the growing racial overtones of American treatment of Asians,[24] the haz-

---

[22]Scott, *op. cit.*, p. 32.

[23]and [24] Robert Jay Lifton in his book *The Circle of Deception* talks both about the brutalization of GI's and the racial overtones implied in the terms "gooks" and "dinks." Wallace Terry II writes in nationally carried articles about racial tension in the Armed Forces, see *San Francisco Chronicle*, June 29, June 30 and July 2. Still further substantiation comes from a junior officer on the Carrier Hancock describing the behavior of his fellow pilots, "They (pilots) are mainly anaesthetized ... They would go out on a mission and come back to white linen tablecloths. There was the attitude that those (Vietnamese) were less than people ... Each meal was punctuated with war stories from pilots, whose bombing victims were referred to as 'crispy critters.' I particularly remember the account of a boy on a bicycle who was strafed and reported as a 'mechanical vehicle.'" *San Francisco Chronicle*, June 26, 1970.

ardous domestic effects of CBW weapons development[25] and nuclear fall out,[26] the hazard from "Broken Arrows" (accidents with nuclear weapons),[27] complete disruption of the universities, as well as the severe impact the War has had upon the economy:[28]

> Vietnam is the cause for the deficit in our federal budget, the need for a tax increase, the heavy spending that is causing inflation. These problems, in turn, are behind the deficiency in our balance of payments, the lack of confidence in the dollar, the run on our gold supply. . . .[29]

Richard J. Barnett has calculated that since 1946 "taxpayers have been asked to contribute more than one trillion dollars for national security."[30]

During the last six years America has spent nearly $115 billion to wage the war in Southeast Asia, with total costs approaching $330 billion[31] before Americans can stop paying. This amounts to $600 for every American family yearly. Since 1965 corporate taxes have risen 43.9% while individual taxes have soared by a full 78.6%. Corporate taxes rose from $35.5 billion to $37.0 billion in 1970. Individual income taxes in the same period jumped from $48.8 billion to $92.2 billion. The $30 billion increase in individual income taxes is roughly equivalent to the annual increase in defense expenditures due to the war in Southeast Asia. At the same time, however, corporate profits increased by 33% while weekly gross earnings for nonagricultural workers increased by 15.2%—before taxes![32] This is just the beginning of the domestic effects of the war.

---

[25]There have been several incidents in recent years indicating the hazards from CBW weapons testing and disposal. The famous Dugway accident of 1968 where 6400 sheep were killed is the most publicized, but there have been others infecting humans with less dramatic consequences.
[26]Nuclear arms development has been spurred by military preparedness, prior to and during Viet Nam. Since the first atomic testing of weapons in the domestic United States, fallout has had a pronounced impact upon infant mortality in the surrounding areas. Dr. Ernst L. Sternglass, a Professor of Radiation Physics at the University of Pittsburg (Roy Bongartz, "Muckuppery Along the Potomac," *Esquire*, June 1970) suggests that those states directly under the fallout cloud from the first New Mexico blast in 1945: Texas, Arkansas, Louisiana, Mississippi, and the Carolinas, witnessed a forty to fifty percent rise in the infant mortality rate within five years of the blast. Similar results are reported on the West Coast following Bikini in 1954.
[27]Since 1945 the Pentagon has announced 13 accidents involving nuclear weapons, or "Broken Arrows," as they are called. Other records indicate more than 22. These include the crashes of B-52 planes carrying atomic or hydrogen bombs over North Carolina in 1961, over Spain in 1966 and over Greenland in 1968 (Bongartz, *op. cit.*).
[28]For sources about the influence of the war upon the economy, consult the publications of the US Budget Bureau and the Department of the Treasury, and Douglas Dowd, "Recession and War," *Liberation*, March 3, 1970.
[29]From "Vietnam: The Impact on American Business," p. 1, quote of Marriner Eccles, former Chairman of the Federal Reserve Board of Governors, a study commissioned for the BEM by the Institute for Policy Studies, mimeo, by Benjamin J. Cohen, Department of Economics, Princeton University.
[30]Barnett, *op cit.*, p. 1.
[31]James L. Clayton, "Vietnam: The 200 Year Mortgage," *Nation*, May 26, 1969.
[32]The figures cited in this paragraph, except for the $330 billion cost figure, all come from the Bureau of the Budget or the Department of the Treasury Publications.

These events, from all evidence, were completely unanticipated by the "national defense planners" over the past few years, much in the same way that the ecological effects of defoliants in Viet Nam were never anticipated. In 1966, in response to an inquiry by the Board of Directors of the American Association for the Advancement of Science about the possible consequences of defoliants in Viet Nam, Dr. John S. Foster Jr., Director of Defense Research and Engineering, the Department of Defense, stated:

> As you know, we have considered the possibility that the use of herbicides and defoliants might cause short or long term ecological impacts in the areas concerned. The questions of whether such impacts exist, and if they do, whether they are detrimental or advantageous, have not yet been answered definitely, even though these chemicals have been used in large quantities for many years. Qualified scientists, both inside and outside the government, and in the governments of other nations, have judged that seriously adverse consequences will not occur. Unless we had confidence in these judgments, we would not continue to employ these materials.[33]

It is only the thirst of the Department of Defense for these chemicals which has prevented even larger portions of the United States from being sprayed.[34] Thomas Whiteside estimates that three percent of the United States has been sprayed with herbicides already, and that, for example:

> In Texas alone more than a million acres of range land and pasture land are being sprayed with 2,4,5-T this year, probably a quarter of a million head of cattle will graze on that sprayed land; and the cattle will produce something like a hundred and fifty million pounds of meat that will be sold to Americans as edible.[35]

While officially banned from "use" in the United States, Whiteside concludes that its "use and sale" continues almost without exception.

The first on-the-spot government investigation of possible damage was not conducted until 1968,[36] and then during the dry season, when the effects of defoliation were least apparent. The first nongovernmental scientific mission was conducted by E. W. Pfeiffer of the University of Montana and Gordon Orians of the University of Washington in March of 1969.[37]

The American Association for the Advancement of Science has—after ten years—done little but express concern.[38] If the response of the professional scientific community has been less than satisfactory, the traditional

---

[33]John S. Forster, Jr., *Science, 161*, July 19, 1968, pp. 243-256.

[34]*Business Week*, April 22, 1967.

[35]Thomas Whiteside, in a letter to the *New Yorker*, June 18, 1970.

[36]The first Government on-the-spot investigation was carried out by Fred A. Tschirley in 1968.

[37]A visit by E. W. Pfeiffer and Gordon Orians to South Vietnam under the auspices of the Society for Social Responsibility in Science.

[38]An excellent description of the American scientific community's response to defoliation can be found in "Vietnam: Progress of the Chemical War" J. B. Neilands, *Asian Survey* 10:209-229.

conservationist-ecology organizations all but ignored the ecological effects of American operations in Southeast Asia until the Cambodian adventure.

The Board of Directors of the Sierra Club, the largest conservationist organization in the country with more than one hundred thousand dues paying members, has taken no public stand on the war, though its staff has urged this move. By and large, America's environmental crusade last Spring ignored what most certainly is the most extensive, pre-meditated, ecological catastrophe in the history of this planet, the war in Southeast Asia. The much heralded "Earth Day" in reality was concerned with a very little part of that earth, the United States. From campus to campus where teach-ins were held, little if any mention was directed toward the War. The *Environmental Handbook*, the teach-in bible, contained nothing regarding the ecological devastation of Southeast Asia.

The "battle" against the shipment of Nerve Gas from Okinawa through the Pacific Northwest last May reflects the rather narrow, nationalistic, self-interested attitude on the part of many "ecologically minded" people.[39] The day before a major rally was to occur in Portland, Oregon, in protest of the Northwestern route, President Nixon announced that the gas would be diverted from the Northwest to Alaska. Consequently, because the gas was no longer seen as a "direct threat," many speakers did not appear, and the rally fizzled, with scant attendance compared to what was expected. They in their "victory" ignored the facts that the Okinawans and other people of Asia had been terrorized by the gas for many years and that their present "victory" had merely passed the gas onto the shoulders of the Eskimos in Alaska. Nor did they consider the cause of the rerouting of the gas which was in fact not their patient petitions but the threat of large scale violence in Seattle, as contended by Senator Henry "Scoop" Jackson of Washington.

As indicated earlier, we should not be surprised that the Federal Government is incapable (or unwilling) of enforcing prohibitive regulations against the use of 2,4,5-T in Asia when they find the same difficulty in enforcing similar regulations here in the United States. Add the mounting evidence of our national failure to cope with increasing air pollution, water contamination, lead and mercury poisoning, DDT, the destruction of the oceans, not to mention the SST, and the present American "population control" of Indochina assumes perspective.

Moreover, a look at the background of the duly elected authorities responsible for ecological regulation in the United States, makes the connection between Ecocide and our lack of ecological concern more apparent. The Chairman of the Senate Committee on the Interior and Insular Affairs, the Congressional watchdog, is Senator Henry M. Jackson.

---

[39]An expression of this sentiment is the concern of many conservationists I have talked with in the Pacific Northwest who will not oppose Senator Jackson for reelection on the grounds that they might jeopardize their standing with him if he were reelected, even though he takes a hawkish position on the war which they do not support.

The Senator has a long and distinguished record in the development of American air power. He was instrumental in the development of the B-47 and the B-52 bombers, as well as numerous other weapons systems developed by Boeing Aircraft, his "home town constituency." Air power is *the* central component of counterinsurgency warfare.

We must conclude that there exists an intimate relationship between the mounting destruction of American life at home and the devastation of Southeast Asia.

If we are ever to put a stop to the growing war in Indochina, we must come to comprehend that the traditional distinction between victim and victimizer loses its meaning in "ecological warfare." Previous warfare was rather neat, Just the people and a few buildings were demolished. Even the highly sophisticated forms of CBW might eliminate the people without even touching buildings or foliage. But Ecocide is less limited, more over-arching, more complete. By tampering with the rivers, streams, food chains and cultures of a region, we set in motion chains of events which may, in time, have profound global consequences. Not in the halls of Congress or the tables of Paris, but in the body of every living organism.

In this sense, if the war subsides, we then may be considered "survivors" of the war in Indochina as well as the people of Southeast Asia. Previous warfare could be terminated by political agreement. Ecocide may know no termination in its implications for the "web of life."

> Long after the US withdraws her troops and technology, America will remain in Asia in the soils, air, water, biological fabric and agony of her scarred people.[40]

Warfare may finally have achieved its ultimate objective in Ecocide—the very negation of life itself.

Consequently our notions about postbellum reconstruction must be reexamined. There can be no Mekong TVA[41] to restore the nutrient value of the soils of Indochina, no Marshall Plan to restore the natural growth of a generation of children starved into intellectual retardation.

Our primary task if the war subsides is not the reconstruction of Indochina, but of America. Finally, we should heed the observation of Mark Twain, "It is easier to stay out than to get out."

Viet Nam has now endured a long history of foreign domination, whether through war or foreign aid. Ten centuries of Chinese rule, the French colonization, and now American "pacification." And yet they have managed to carry on as a people. "Viet" is the Vietnamese pronunciation of a Chinese character which means "far off, to traverse, to go beyond, to draw oneself up, to pass through, to sit up again...." "Nam" means south. "Viet Nam" means then a country to the south of China which passes over obstacles, sits up again and spreads. Better we accept the vision Asians have of themselves than our illusions of postwar aid programs.

---

[40]Schell and Weisburg, *op. cit.*
[41]Refer to the map of the Mekong Plan in Part 2.

Can we, after the war (if that can be imagined), with any respect to the people we have devastated, send our teams of scientists and social engineers into Indochina to patch up the damage: to study the Vietnamese as we did the Japanese after Hiroshima?

And to what extent will those who have made the "hard decisions" come to regret the nature of their acts, such that together we might find a way to forever prevent the repetition of such warfare? Do hawks hatch doves?

Edward R. Murrow, in a radio broadcast on February 2, 1958, asked Harry S. Truman about his afterthoughts on the decision to use the atomic bomb; "Any regrets?" Truman responded, "Not the slightest—not the slightest in the world."[42] Eleanor Roosevelt, a noted humanitarian, when asked about such weapons, responded, "No one can be sure that the atomic bomb, or even a greater weapon, would not be used. . . . In order *to defend peace*, it may be necessary to use the Atomic Bomb."[43]

All indications suggest still, as Bernard Fall believed in 1965, the "worst is yet to come," for Indochina. From the very beginning of the war we have been told by successive Presidents that this is the beginning of the end. Yet the end remains more elusive than ever. As Peter Dale Scott suggests in the *New York Review of Books* (June 18, 1970), "there has never been a genuine US de-escalation in Southeast Asia." While the absolute numbers of troops may diminish somewhat, the air and chemical war not only intensifies but spills over into adjacent nations. Movements of "national liberation" burgeon throughout Southeast Asia. The pressures of additional refugees in Viet Nam from the Delta area, resulting from defoliation now in process, may well push Saigon beyond the breaking point. As American soldiers are withdrawn from Saigon, so will the liquid supply of capital. At least the soldiers distributed the wealth amongst bars and lower class merchants. When the soldiers leave, American aid programs will increase—income which goes not to bar girls but into the pockets of Saigon bureaucrats behind desks. Income distribution will then become an even more severe problem than at present. And, later rather than sooner, pacification will be replaced by development, in the form of the Mekong River Development Project,[44] which may well displace another two million people in addition to millions of existing refugees throughout Southeast Asia. Finally, one must not ignore the fact that to this date some 5500 nuclear weapons are positioned in Southeast Asia.[45]

As for America, similar symptoms seem likely. As the war continues to spread throughout Asia, protest will no doubt swell to the proportions following the invasion of Cambodia in May. Economic stress will not sudside readily. Resistance to the military is just beginning in Congress, and the military themselves shuffle about fretting over which weapons systems will

---

[42]Robert Jay Lifton, *Death in Life*, Random House, p. 333 (Italics added).
[43]Lifton, *op. cit.* p. 335.
[44]A thirty-five year plan involving 12 Nations and UN Agencies to build 40 dams.
[45]Richard J. Barnett, "Nuclear War Games," *Hard Times*, #79, May 25, 1970.

survive the "de-escalation." In short, the results of our military operations in Asia will become increasingly more apparent at home. For this, albeit tragically, we must be grateful.

It is time we realize that any war waged against the biological fabric of the earth is a war against the very means of life itself. We have realized this about human beings before:

> It is terrible, an inexorable law that one cannot deny the humanity of another without diminishing one's own: in the face of one's victim, one sees oneself. [46]

An ecological perspective reveals the same interdependence between man and the entire natural world. The continuing escalation of the war in Indochina means a continued escalation of the means to bring about the eventual destruction of the earth: people, land, air, water, plants and animals. The war in Indochina has become a war against all life. Ecocide in Indochina turns around to be Ecocide in America as well.

---

[46]James Baldwin, *Nobody Knows My Name.*

PART 2

Overview*

In Vietnam the chemical weapons of a technologically advanced society are being used massively for the first time in a guerrilla war ... The current extent of the defoliation program is not determined by military demand nor by any considerations of saving the ecology and viability of the land and natural resources of Vietnam, but solely by competition for equipment and personnel ...

We consider that the ecological consequences of defoliation are severe ...

The government of the Republic of Vietnam and American officials have not disclosed information to the Vietnamese about the agents used, areas sprayed, and the nature of the chemical action of defoliants and herbicides. The most concerned Vietnamese scientists did not know the chemical composition of the herbicides even though they have tried to ascertain it from their government.

*From "Ecological Effects of the War in Vietnam," Gordon H. Orians and E. W. Pfeiffer, *Science*, Vol. 168, May 1, 1970, pp. 553-554.

Ecocide in Indochina

Orville Schell and Barry Weisberg

The War in Indochina will leave the imprint of America pressed on Vietnam for many years. What has happened to Vietnam: saturation bombing, defoliation, napalm, forced urbanization, has not escaped the people of Laos, Thailand, and Cambodia. The invasion of Cambodia by American and ARVN troops only dramatizes the lesson that there are no simple boundaries or battle lines by which to distinguish war from peace, soldier from civilian. The ecology of war in Vietnam, by natural law, effects the entire Southeast Asian peninsula.

The war reports speak of particular battles, a defoliated hamlet, increasing refugees, casualty figures, corruption in Saigon, and give very little orchestration to the full complexity or scope of what America is doing in Southeast Asia. We have understood the war more in terms of isolated events than as complex patterns. We have matter of factly come to assume that the changed structure of a village, the altered chemistry of the jungle, the destroyed tissue of a napalmed child or the shattered economy of a nation do not affect one another. We still see the war in Southeast Asia in terms of boundaries, nations, programs and operations, without really understanding that the ecosystem of Southeast Asia is one organic fabric in which all living things are tied together by an infinite number of interdependent strands.

The mountains, rivers, jungles, plants, animals and human society of this region form a single community. The extent to which we have tampered with this community—the extent to which reconstruction is possible—this is not known. But any reasonable estimate must conclude that never before in the history of mankind has such a magnitude of destruction been wrought upon any people, at any time, in any single place. Herbicides, free fire zones, anti-personnel and fragmentation bombs, napalm, urbanization, food denial programs, all together form an unprecedented strategy of counterinsurgency which relies increasingly upon air technology rather than ground combat warfare. The current American destruction of Southeast Asia represents a new and unprecedented strategy, aimed not at the destruction of an enemy, his territory, a food crop or a culture but of an entire ecosystem. This is Ecocide.[1]

The two critical agents of this new strategy are chemical and biological warfare, primarily the use of herbicides known as defoliants, and the saturation bombardment of people and landscape with high explosives.

Beginning in 1961 the United States began the "experimental" use of herbicides in South Vietnam as a weapon to exterminate forests and crops. The initial objective was to undermine the economic resources of the national liberation movement. In 1962 defoliants became "a central weapon" in the overall Chemical and Biological Warfare (CBW) strategy of America throughout Southeast Asia. Known as "Operation Ranch Hand," some of the converted C-123 cargo planes used to spray the herbicides were inscribed with the motto, "Only we can prevent forests."

Present estimates suggest that between 1965 and 1970 more than 50,000 tons of herbicides were dropped on South Vietnam alone.[2] The Pathet Lao report defoliation in parts of Laos as early as 1966.[3] The "accidental" defoliation of rubber plantations in Cambodia predated the United States invasion of that country.[4]

Although the defoliation program began with the intention of merely destroying the economic base of the NLF, it was soon expanded into a critical aspect of the shift from ground to air power in South Vietnam. Besides destroying crops, defoliants were used to destroy the forest canopy that hid NLF forces from detection by air.[5] Since 1961, official American reports state that five million acres of land have been "sterilized," or 12% of South Vietnam.[6] These figures are quite conservative when compared to Vietnamese statements. In the first two months of 1969 alone some 37 of the 44 provinces of South Vietnam were sprayed, contaminating 285,000 people, with death resulting in at least 500 cases. In these raids more than 905,000

---

[1]Ecocide is the premeditated assault of a nation and its resources against the individuals, cul- and biological fabric of another country and its environs. *Scientific American* in January of 1968 described American activities in Southeast Asia as "ecological warfare." The first public recognition of the term Ecocide occurred in an editorial of the *New York Times* on February 26, 1970.

[2]*New York Times*, December 6, 1969.

[3]*New York Times*, February 6, 1966.

[4]T. Whiteside, *Defoliation*, Ballantine, 1970, p. 168, and *New York Times*, January 14, 1970.

[5]The shift from ground combat troops to air power required the massive defoliation to find enemy troops that might be hidden by natural foliage.

[6]These are "official reports" on the area sprayed which are far lower than Vietnamese reports noted in Footnote 8. Official statistics obtained from the U. S. Department of Defense Data (MACV) and N. Gruchow, "Curbs on 2,4,5-T Use Imposed," *Science* 168:453.

hectares of rice, orchards and other crops were destroyed.[7] Between late 1961 and October of 1969, Vietnamese estimate that 43% of the arable land and 44% of the total forest area of South Vietnam were sprayed at least once and in many cases two or three times with herbicides. Over 1,293,000 people were directly contaminated.[8] Besides forest and mountain areas, large populated areas in the Delta have been sprayed as well, including the outskirts of Saigon itself.

The agents used consist of "Orange" (50:50 mixture of 2,4-D and 2,4,5-T), used on general crops and reported as amounting to 50% of the defoliation program; "White" 20% picloram and 80% isoprophlamin salt from 2,4-D), used for 35% of the missions; and "Blue" (a form of arsenic) for 15% of the missions; as well as a host of other agents including Phenal compounds of the type DNOC, arsenates and arsenites, and "earth sterilizing compounds," such as Bromacil and Urox. At the peak of the defoliation program, the United States spent $70.8 million on defoliation in 1968 alone.[9]

On April 15, 1970, Deputy Secretary of Defense David Packard announced the immediate "suspension" of the use of 2,4,5-T in Vietnam. This action resulted from domestic evidence that 2,4,5-T constituted a possible hazard to women of child bearing age. Fetal damage to animals had been linked to 2,4,5-T. On June 22, 1970, American military sources in Saigon announced that the nine-year defoliation program in Vietnam had been "temporarily suspended." The C-123 cargo planes were reportedly diverted to move men and supplies in and out of Cambodia. After the June 30 withdrawal from Cambodia, defoliation would resume. The *New York Times* of June 23, 1970, reported that 90% of the defoliation program had consisted of 2,4,5-T. This figure far surpassed the 50% formerly reported. Consequently, the possibility of widespread fetal damage to the population of areas sprayed is far more likely than anticipated.

Contrary to official reports, there is little reason to believe that the use of 2,4,5-T has been actually stopped. Thomas Whiteside reports in the June 20, 1970 issue of the *New Yorker* that although the domestic use of 2,4,5-T was officially prohibited on April 15, 1970, both its use and sale continue within the United States practically uninhibited.

The extent to which these herbicides affect their intended target is unknown. But the indications are that virtually every aspect of the organic fabric is affected in some way. Herbicides can affect people through eating contaminated foods, drinking poisoned water, breathing contaminated air or by direct skin contact. The results have been described by a Vietnamese:

[7]Communique issued in South Vietnam by the Committee to Reveal U. S. Puppets War Crimes in Vietnam, 1969, issued on January 5, 1970.
[8]Statement of Mme. Nguyen Thi Binh, Chief of the Delegation of the Provisional Revolutionary Government of the Republic of Vietnam at the 55th Plenary Session of the Paris Conference on Vietnam, February 19, 1970.
[9]*San Francisco Chronicle*, July 4 and July 27, 1968.

Those who were in the sprayed area found it difficult to breathe, difficult to stay awake, got fever and were thirsty. These symptoms hit mainly in older people, children, and pregnant women. Many vomited and had cholic type pains. Others got muscle paralyzation and became numb around the hands and feet. Also other symptoms have been reported, such as the loss of hair, pains in the heart area, pains in the back, bleeding in the esophagus. Those exposed to poisonous chemicals directly in the skin got red rashes and thereafter blistering skin adhesion. The women have often suffered disturbances in the menstrual cycle, and many cases of miscarriage have been reported.[10]

Reports of "women giving birth to monsters" are not uncommon, though most occurrences are not reported because of nonexistent procedures. The Saigon Ministry of Health classified the files of malformed babies as "secret" in 1969.[11]

Herbicides directly damage the soil. They either destroy the microorganisms needed to prevent erosion, or remove the humus material (decomposing vegetation on the forest floor), which turns the soil into a hard rock-like substance. Reports indicate that chemicals entering the Mekong River upstream have all but eliminated biological life in the estuary. The damage to livestock has been severe, especially among swine and poultry. Wild animal life has been altered through the interruption of food chains and the near extinction of several rare species. This in turn affects the regeneration of the forests which are pollinated by animals rather than the wind. Elephants are shot on sight, as they are often used by both sides for transportation, while the tiger population has soared as a consequence of an abundant supply of fresh human meat.

Agricultural productivity has been severely curtailed in many regions. The Delta area of South Vietnam, once considered the rice bowl of Southeast Asia, now imports rice from California growers. Crops of rice, corn and other cultivated food stuffs such as manioc, sweet potatoes, pepper, banana, and coconut are all adversely affected.

Besides defoliants, more than 7,000 tons of other poisonous gas have been used between 1964 and 1969.[12] The most common are CS-1 and CS-2; however, CN, DM and bromoacetoethyl, and other gases "affecting the central nervous system" have been reported used. When employed in a heavily concentrated form, such gases cease to function as "tear gas" and become lethal. The rate of use has increased 2300% between 1964 and 1969. The application of chemicals to the life fabric of South Vietnam has been limited both by the available supply of 2,4,5-T as well as the shortage of chemical spraying aircraft. Defoliation missions are backlogged for months. However, while defoliation may be said to be limited to technological capaci-

---

[10]"Document Concerning the U. S. Chemical Warfare in South Vietnam," issued by The South Vietnamese Committee for the Revealing of the U. S. imperialists' war crimes in South Vietnam, February, 1970, p. 3.
[11]Sunday *London Times*, November 30, 1969.
[12]*Associated Press*, January 3, 1970.

ty, saturation bombing is not. The massive tonnage combined from both air and artillery fire in many areas of Southeast Asia is unprecedented—dwarfing tonnage figures for all of World War II.

The battleship "New Jersey," which was taken out of mothballs several years ago for duty off the coast of Vietnam, put together a press kit. On its cover were emblazoned the words, FIREPOWER FOR FREEDOM.[13]

If nothing else, the war in Indochina has proved that United States firepower is almost limitless. Our inability to win the war has not stemmed from an absence of ordnance but from an absence of bona fide targets. The basic problem has remained unsolved: how to distinguish our "free world allies" from the "Red aggressors." Perhaps the distinction itself is meaningless in the context of Indochina. In any case, it has been ignored. In this technological warfare, our lethal firepower has turned on society itself like a broad spectrum antibiotic that makes no distinction between wanted and unwanted germs. Pinpoint bombing has given way to saturation bombing. Artillery strikes, once called in only on specific targets, have evolved into Harassment and Interdiction (H&I) fire which is shot around the clock into "free fire zones" from coastal and inland firebases. Navy guns are now computerized to fire continuously at whole counties for several days running, rather than just at isolated targets. Single snipers are incinerated along with whole villages by napalm strikes. Armed helicopters of days gone by have been replaced by gun ships capable of launching rockets, grenades and machine gun fire. Unarmed DC-3s, or Puff the Magic Dragons, have been armed with multiple 50-caliber machine guns capable of laying a withering blaze of fire, 300 rounds a second, into several acres at a time. B-52s, designed for nuclear warheads, have become a common household weapon used to "prep" huge areas.

UPI reports that in May 1969 alone, B-52s dropped 24,500 tons of bombs on South Vietnam. They were reported to have "struck" 272 times that month, an average of nine times a day. In one day, July 4, 1969, B-52s dropped 1,000,000 pounds of bombs on jungle areas in the Central Highlands.

On January 28, 1970, the *New York Times* quietly reported that:

> " . . . acting on intelligence assessments of enemy supply movements in South Vietnam, United States B-52 bombers made their heaviest raids in nine months. Planes struck at North Vietnamese supply depots inside Laos, ranged across the frontier over the Ashau Valley, and farther south along the Cambodian border. Sixty B-52's (4/5's of the SAC bomber fleet in Asia) dropped nearly 2,000 tons of explosives on the North Vietnamese depots, the official report said, to slow an enemy build-up for a *possible* new offensive." (Italics added.)

Since the cessation of the bombing of North Vietnam, United States aircraft from South Vietnam, Thailand, Guam and the 7th Fleet have been diverted to Laos and the Ho Chi Minh trail where they have been flying an

---

[13]*Minneapolis Tribune*, Ronald Ross, June 11, 1969.

estimated 20,000-27,000 sorties monthly. This is seven times the level reputedly flown in 1968.[14]

In Admiral Sharp's and General William Westmoreland's final report on the war *(Report On The War In Vietnam, 1964-1968)* Admiral Sharp (p. 21) wrote of Operation Rolling Thunder, the bombardment of North Vietnam officially begun in 1965. "As the campaign got under way and more targets were made available, up to 1,600 tons of ordnance were dropped each week."

After Ho Chi Minh's death in 1969, Nixon called a 36-hour halt of United States B-52 raids. A few days afterwards, on September 13, an AP dispatch reported that "One military source had said that since records of daily flights had begun in 1968, there was never a day in which B-52s were not flown in South Vietnam except for truce periods."

As of September 1968, AP reported that we had dropped 2,825,824 tons of explosives on North and South Vietnam,[15] twice the tonnage dropped on all of Europe during World War II. This amounts to nearly 180 pounds of explosives for every person in North and South Vietnam as well as upwards of 20 tons of explosives for each square mile. The figures do not even include the escalations of the air war during the last two years, artillery fire, and the extensive bombings of Laos and Cambodia.

In March 1970, US Command reported that conventional military aircraft flew an average of 250 to 300 sorties daily over South Vietnam.[16] Presumably this refers to fighter bombers, that is, F-4s, F-105s, and F-100s. But what is a sortie? What is a mission? What is a raid? How big are these planes, and what kind of ordnance did they carry? The U.S. military does not carefully make this distinction in their press releases. The average American is left completely bewildered to interpret the significance of this massive destruction as he will. There is a great deal of difference between one B-52 half loaded with 500 pound bombs and ten B-52s fully loaded with 1,000 pound block busters. As Drummond Ayres reported last October 13th in the *New York Times*, "The U.S. Command has consistently refused to disclose any statistics on bomb loads or numbers of planes on each mission."

The Indochinese War is an impenetrable jungle of half statistics, lies, meaningless definitions and censored transcripts. In one transcript, for instance, of the Senate Foreign Relations Committee hearings on *U.S. Security Agreements and Commitments Abroad, Kingdom of Laos*, held last October, there is a chart listing air strikes conducted over Northern and Southern Laos for the period 1964-1969. But the chart is blank. There are no figures in any of the neatly laid out boxes.

But even when the military does provide crude statistics, they are impossible to visualize in human or concrete terms. In his report,

---

[14]*New York Review of Books*, June 18, 1970.
[15]*San Francisco Chronicle*, November 24, 1968.
[16]*New York Times*, March 2, 1970.

Westmoreland says that during the 77 day siege of Khe Sanh, "Increasing numbers of B-52s were demonstrating their ability to neutralize a large area. The B-52s flew 2,602 sorties and dropped 75,000 tons of bombs" (p. 71). He casually reports also that 100,000, 175 mm artillery rounds were fired into the area. What can a man reading his morning paper make of this?

Almost daily one reads a few small lines tacked onto the end of battle reports to the effect that "enemy strongholds were softened up by waves of B-52 Stratofortresses." And yet it is difficult to appreciate what these raids mean. Even if one has been up on air strikes, it is hard to grasp the extent of the destruction on the ground. The B-52s flying at over 30,000 feet (above the cloud cover) are unheard from the ground, and undetectable by sophisticated infrared devices, therefore, even the men in the plane can have no real awareness of what happens below. The pilots make their long routine flights from Guam or Sattahip, in Thailand, drop their thousands of tons of bombs, and return home to a hot shower and the officers' club by evening. Even in a fighter bomber or a Forward Air Control spotter one is detached. One feels as though he is witnessing events under water. There is no sound, no concussion, no smell and little feeling as the bombs send their grey clouds of smoke and earth skyward, or as a splattering cannister of napalm churns a boiling black cloud filled with orange flame up over the green land below. And yet, on earth below, a cataclysm is taking place.

The bombing, H&I fire and defoliation have had a devastating effect on the civilian population of Vietnam, Laos and Cambodia. And yet no attempt has ever been made to keep comprehensive figures on civilian deaths, just as there has never been a realistic effort to deal with the civilians who finally make up this unknown statistic (the military tabulates only those admitted to hospitals). In Westmoreland's report there are eight entries in the index under "Civilian casualties." Three entries seem to be nonexistent in the text. The other five refer to civilians killed by the Viet Cong. On the report forms which unit commanders file after coming in from an operation, there is no box to fill in for dead civilians. The same is true of Bomb Damage Assessment Reports filled out by the Forward Air Control (FAC) pilots. All dead (unless they are ARVN or US troops) are simply listed as enemy KBA, Killed by Air. Civilian houses ("hootches") are listed as Military Structures.

In recent years, it is difficult to recall prewar Vietnam. It was a country largely made up of small decentralized rural villages which were concentrated on the coastline and the fertile Mekong River Delta in the South. The village was the essential unit of Vietnamese life. Most people seldom left their village. Fewer left their county or province. Although simple, most villages gave one a sense of peace and beauty. Many were accessible only by path or canal. Over the last few centuries the countryside had changed little. But the inhabitants gave the impression of having worked out an accommodation with the natural world around them. Palm trees and bamboo groves were planted around the houses for shade and shelter. Small houses of split bamboo and thatch, some even on stone foundations, were clumped together in an agreeable way so as to allow for both privacy and communality. The rice fields, the life blood and the reason for existence of the peasant, surrounded the village. And, of course, not far from each village were the ancestral tombs. Here a peasant farmer was born, married, raised his family, grew his crops and died. He lived in a relatively simple universe, but in one which gave him dignity.

One of the most important aspects of communal life in rural Vietnam has been the water works. It is the one undertaking which makes cooperation within the village, and even between adjacent villages, absolutely essential. As in all Asian countries, the irrigation system for the rice fields is extremely complicated. Water runs from the higher paddies to the lower paddies through scores of fields on which hundreds of different people and families depend. Disruption at any point of the long chain threatens the survival of everyone further down the line.

It was this single feature that, since the advent of Chinese hydraulic technology hundreds of years ago, made a social fabric out of the patchwork of villages in the Vietnamese countryside. Disruption of the water works meant a fundamental disruption of every aspect of rural life. The crops, land and society could not exist without the intricate systems of dams, dikes and canals to temper the heavy monsoon rains and assure water during the long dry months.

Almost without noticing it, the US military has destroyed this system in much of Indochina. They have even talked of bombing the huge dikes of the Red River in North Vietnam. In the South, as one flies over the country, one sees brownish yellow rivers and streams flowing aimlessly across paddy field and eroded land. Other areas are scorched dry and pitted with craters like some lifeless planet. One looks down on mile after mile of uncultivated rice fields, pock marked with millions of water filled craters (30 feet by 45 feet) in which malarial mosquitoes have been breeding in epidemic numbers. Reportedly, some 2.5 billion cubic yards of earth has been removed. This is 10 times the size of Suez Canal excavation. In the coastal areas of I Corp, one searches for signs of life in the vast "sanitized" free fire zones. On the borders where the treeline meets the fields one can often see evidence of pathetic gardens where people, who live like moles in bomb shelter holes beneath the ground, attempt to grow basic foods like sweet potatoes, taro or squash. They do not dare work the rice fields for fear of being shot by Americans in bubble choppers who are out "squirrel hunting." In free fire zones these people are subject to bombardment 24 hours a day.

The whole nature of Indochinese agriculture is slowly being changed by the aerial destruction. In 1964 South Vietnam *exported* 48,563 million metric tons of rice. The following year, largely because of bombing and defoliation, South Vietnam *imported* 240,000 million metric tons of rice.[17]

---

[17]*Europa Yearbook*, 1964, 1965.

The role of rice in the Asian culture has no parallel to any food product in the Western world. The people of Asia have been growing and eating rice for 5,000 years. The earliest record describes the Chinese invoking the spirits to help bring in a good crop. One crop, grown once a year, feeds an entire village and is *the* staple, three times a day. Rice is central not only to diet but the entire spiritual relationship between the people and the natural world. If a Vietnamese has not eaten rice, even though they may have eaten other food-stuffs that day, they consider themselves not to have eaten at all. During the eating hours of the day, Vietnamese often greet each other with the expression, "An Com Chua," literally, "Eat cooked rice yet?"

While the short term consequences of insufficient food are important, the long term interference with their culture may be more critical:

> We are people who live by farming alone and have fallen into a deficient, indigent situation because of the influence of defoliation. . . . It takes years to teach a farmer how to plant properly and then this happens. What does the farmer do when his crop fails—send his daughter into town to be a prostitute? Is this what President Johnson wants? [18]

The Vietnamese view their world in a historical continuum. Past is linked to present and future through tradition and mythology. Destruction of the forests of Vietnam will certainly have a profound impact upon the folk-lore of the forest. In such critical ways the war has all but eliminated the traditional transmission of culture inherent within the folklore and mythology which an adult normally passes on to a child.

The moral and philosophical consequences of uprooting millions of Vietnamese people will severely affect their culture. The world of a Vietnamese is ordered to an extent unknown in the western world. Each person is a part of a larger, completely ordered environment, in which man and nature exist symbiotically. The natural laws of harmony and equilibrium dictate the social patterns of life. Thus the villages are perfectly ordered, each structure in its proper place. People become rooted in the village that their family, and their family's family lived in. They do not uproot themselves every five years and move, as do Americans. The war has changed all that. People cease to become attached to the village because the war has destroyed their village. Rather than being securely fixed in the ancestral site of both lineage and culture, they become wanderers, refugees. They are severed from both their physical and spiritual foundation.

So deep is the relationship between person and place that one of the most appalling plights to befall any man is eternal wandering. The ancestor worship, codified by Confucius, states that if a man does not leave a male descendant, the ancestral souls of the dead are doomed to eternal wandering —the worst of all afflictions.

No element of the social fabric of Vietnam has been more severely affected than the children. In 1964 UNESCO reported that 47.5% of the

---

[18]*Christian Science Monitor*, November 25, 1967.

population were under 16 years, that figure has no doubt subsequently increased. The Food Denial Program, or starvation, originally waged against troops, will have the most severe effect upon the present and future generations of children. Abundant studies indicate the correlation between nutritional deprivation and intellectual retardation.

In a country where filial devotion is considered sacred, family structure has all but been obliterated. Men are away fighting the war, thus removing the traditional source of family authority. Women increasingly are forced to turn to prostitution as the only source of income, "the biggest industry in Saigon." Consequently, children by the tens of thousands are socialized at an early age into stealing, pimping, black marketeering and drug peddling. Some graduate to more violent crimes. The sight of children running "in packs" throughout the streets of Saigon is not uncommon.

At present there are 77 orphanages in South Vietnam. An administrator in the Bien Hoa province described the situation as follows: "The children are automated to robot status. But how else could you run an orphanage of 2,500 children?"[19] Present estimates, considered conservative, suggest that 50% of the children of South Vietnam do not reach the age of five years.

Psychiatrist Robert Jay Lifton has written of what he calls "psychic numbing—the loss of the capacity to feel—and of general brutalization."[20] The war has left this impact on both native Vietnamese and the American GI. A Vietnamese student described this affliction in a student publication, "People die in many ways . . . bombs, bullets, and gas. But there is something called living death. Living, but living as if one were dead."[21]

This state of nonbeing is the product of dislocation and refugee camp life. Such camps are usually located in "secure areas" away from all trees or hills. They are placed in the baking sun on bulldozed earth lots surrounded by barbed wire. Small houses with tin roofs, which cause them to heat up like ovens under the tropical sun, are lined up like cars on a parking lot. Foreign food (cornmeal, bulgarwheat, diet food banned in the US because of cyclamates) is brought in to replace their native rice. A refugee, or "detainee," is left without any reason to live, frequently separated even from friends and family in the evacuation shuffle. During 1967 and 1968, through the aftermath of the TET offensive when American bombing leveled many provincial capitals, the resettlement camps were unable to provide even potable water, food and shelter, much less medical aid, clothing and a new life.

Hundreds of thousands of these refugees fled from such camps back into the free fire zones to their old villages. There they fended for themselves, with the bombs and artillery shells raining down on them, because as one pilot put it, "If they're out here, they gotta be Cong, 'cause we told 'em this is a free fire zone."

---

[19]*Los Angeles Times*, May 29, 1970.
[20]Robert Jay Lifton, *"The Circle of Deception," Trans Action*, March 1968.
[21]"One Morning in the Hospital," Saigon University Student Union, published in Saigon, mimeo, June 1, 1967.

As in every other aspect of the war, statistics on refugees have almost no real meaning because they fail to reflect reality. Authorities in Vietnam have compiled statistics in a feeble attempt to give the illusion that the problem is not totally out of hand. These figures are dutifully quoted to the press and Congressional investigations—to men who seldom have either the time or wherewithal to check them. They suffice as an incomplete shadow picture of the devastating reality they purport to represent.

On December 28, 1967 the *New York Times* reported that the military had "classified" two million Vietnamese as refugees, but that a "competent source" put the figure at four million. Meanwhile officials claimed that 309,000 were in camps and 475,000 were "elsewhere." When asked where "elsewhere" is, a journalist is usually informed in Saigon that they are "staying with relatives." One begins to understand what this means only after seeing the depressing, squalid, overcrowded conditions in most South Vietnam cities.

In February, 1970, RAND anthropologist Gerald Hickey said, "Just 15 years ago all but 15% of the South Vietnamese people lived in rural areas. Now 60% live in urban areas. Saigon has grown from a city of 300,000, which it was designed to be, to more than 3 million."[22] The pattern is the same in all Vietnamese cities. Da Nang has grown from a city of 25,000 to 300,000 in five years.[23] This is forced urbanization, a tactic which Samuel Huntington, a long time supporter of the war and chairman of the Department of Government, Harvard University, advocated in *Foreign Affairs*, July, 1968. He claimed that the Viet Cong's support could be denied if there was "direct application of mechanical and conventional power ... on such a massive scale as to produce a massive migration from the countryside to the city."

The city of Saigon perhaps best illustrates the total perversity of this military urbanization. In December of 1964 an article in the *Christian Science Monitor* described Saigon as the "Paris of the East." In a mere two years the same paper constantly ran articles describing Saigon as a city in which "labor shortages due to the war have made services worse than usual. The streets are very dirty. Huge piles of uncollected trash and rotting garbage lie about, and sanitation is sadly lacking." Saigon is the "most congested city in the world," with an average of 140 persons per acre (Tokyo with 63) running as high as 830 in the ghettos. Saigon itself is less than one third the geographic size of the District of Columbia, half the size of San Francisco.

Life in Saigon in some ways is no less horrific than in the countryside. In the first nine months of 1969, no less than 19 Saigon newspapers were closed. In the first five months of 1969, there were more than 3,000 police raids in Saigon against intellectuals, Buddhists and students. On January 20, 1969, 10,000 people were searched and arrested. In January, 1967, a former police

[22]*New York Times*, February 2, 1970.
[23]Kennedy Hearings on Refugees, June 24-25, 1969, p. 44.

chief of Saigon was arrested on suspicion of being the head of a "narcotics ring stretching across Central America and Europe."[24] And there is the constant stream of homeless refugees, the absence of city wide sanitation facilities, no running water for the vast majority of people, and smog so dense that it kills trees inside Saigon just as in Los Angeles.

The economy of Saigon and South Vietnam also reflects the chaos of war. Methods employed to fight inflation have consistently failed. While the official exchange rate is 118 piastre to the American dollar, the Black Market rate has soared from 150 in 1967, to 200 in 1968, 250 in 1969, to near 470 by March 1970, and as of June 1, 1970 is reported to verge on 600 piastre to the dollar, or almost six times the official rate. Flooded by consumer goods, the South Vietnamese economy reflects a complete dependence upon the United States. The average monthly military expenditure in South Vietnam is about U.S. $2,000 million, not counting weapons, ammunition and equipment to the South Vietnamese Army. Total aid between July 1954 and December 1969 totalled about $4,000 million. The budget deficit has sky rocketed from a minus 8,726 million piastre to a minus 41,731 million in the last three years. From 1958 through 1965 South Vietnamese imports rose from 8,125 million piastre to 12,507 million. In 1966 they jumped to 28,385 million, and in 1967 to 43,044 million, with exports remaining somewhat constant. These were U.S. imports directly attributable to the growing military commitment.

The overriding problem of civilian dislocation, euphemistically called "pacification," is one which the American military has never taken seriously. In the index of his report, Westmoreland makes five references to "Refugees," and all are listed under the misleading subtitle of "Care of." Nowhere is there a serious discussion or even statistical reference to the tremendous disruption that has been taking place in the countryside because of U.S. fire power.

In June 1969, John Hannah, head of AID, told Kennedy's Senate Judiciary Subcommittee on Refugees that 3.2 million Vietnamese had "become homeless" since 1965. A chart accompanying the testimony (*Refugee Statistics*) lists 1,328,517 of these people as "current temporary refugees" for 1968. Then, there is a miniscule asterisk referring to a footnote in miscroscopic print: "Refugees are defined as persons who leave their home for *war related* reasons, and have not yet reestablished a permanent home. Statistics do not include victims of the TET and MAY offensive numbering in excess of 1,000,000" (p.12).

Hannah's report further states that 612,101 of these "current temporary refugees" are "in camp." The other 600,105 are listed as "out of camp" or "elsewhere." It all sounds like a reasonably manageable proposition. But as any honest refugee advisor in the provinces of Vietnam is quick to point out

---

[24]*The Observer*, January 15, 1967.

(since he has to work with actual figures, not fantasyland figures), official statistics deal only with "registered" refugees.

Conservative estimates place the real figure of dislocated people at twice the number of registered refugees. This means that as of 1969 (using 3.2 million as a base), roughly 7,000,000, out of a population estimate of 16 million, have been rendered homeless. But the madness of the statistic juggling does not end there. By a new system of double entry bookkeeping AID and CORDS (Civil Operations and Revolutionary Development Support) are able to slim down the ballooning figures to acceptable levels by a process which Senator Edward Kennedy outlined in the hearings with John Hannah. Joseph A. Mendenhall, Acting Asst. Administrator for Vietnam AID, had been waxing optimistic about the progress of pacification and its success shown in the "declining figures for new refugees" when Kennedy broke in:

> When referring to the earlier figures about the reduction in numbers of refugees, you are too good a student of this whole problem to be putting great significance on reductions of the total number of refugees, because you know as well as I do that the reclassification of refugees to resettled refugees is just the question of payment. So, you can fiddle around with these figures and say that you get so many hundreds of thousands of refugees one month and then they are deemed to have been paid a certain amount for resettlement, and then they are considered resettled and then they are not refugees any longer.
>
> I am sure, Mr. Hannah, and all of you who have been to Vietnam, that you have gone to places where on one side of the street you will see almost the same exact living conditions of refugees who are refugees, and on the other side of the street they are considered resettled. If you can tell the difference between the two camps you are a better man than I am. (p. 31)

The story in Laos is much the same. According to Royal Laotion Government officials, since the U.S. started intensive bombing of the Plain of Jars region in 1968 (which has no geographic or strategic relation to the Ho Chi Minh trail) 150,000 Laotions (or half the population of Laos) have been displaced. Most have been forced into the cities. In January, 1968, the *New York Times* described Vientiane, the capitol of Laos, as a "river port of 88,000." By November, 1969, the *Times* put the population of Vientiane at 160,000. Only some 180,000 dislocated people are said to be living in the "refugee villages."[25] According to Jacques Decornoy of *Le Monde*, who was in the liberated areas of Laos in 1968, all but two villages in the Pathet Lao held province of Sam Neua had been destroyed. Recent reports from Laos speak of thousands of people struggling over the incredibly rough mountain terrain, harassed by frequent U.S. strafing attacks, trying to reach the safety of Sam Thong, Luang Prubang, Vientiane, and southern Laos.

Secretary of State Rogers replied candidly (April 15, 1970) to Kennedy's subcommittee, which was holding further hearings on the refugee prob-

[25]*New Republic*, May 9, 1970.

lem in Laos, saying that "the current situation relating to civilian war casualties is serious and getting worse, although we do not have meaningful figures." But the rest of the transcript of the hearings is rendered almost incomprehensible by seven "censored" sections, again because it was allegedly "in the interest of national security." One wonders how the Ship of State might founder by releasing statistics on Laotian civilian casualties and refugees.

For Cambodia, there are no statistics on refugees whatsoever, although we do know that the Lon Nol regime did "generate" some 100,000 refugees from the ethnic Vietnamese living in Cambodia in a xenophobic preparation for his ill fated anti-Vietnamese drive on the NLF sanctuaries. We also know that some of the heaviest B-52 raids of the war have been carried out in Cambodia during the past months. With the withdrawal of U.S. troops one has every reason to believe that they will continue. Destruction of cities like Snuol, Tonle Bet, Kompong Thom, etc. have been reported. Thousands of people once inhabited these cities. In the wake of their destruction and the B-52 raids on the countryside, *Le Monde* carried numerous reports of uprooted Cambodians joining the National United Front of Kampuchea (Cambodia) which is led by Sihanouk.

In spite of this obvious escalation of the air war, and thus the increase in rural dislocation, U.S. authorities in Indochina have been recently claiming that the refugee problem is under control.

In his report to the Kennedy subcommittee, Hannah claimed that in 1968 there were 311,057 "new refugees," whereas in the first five months of 1969 there were only 53,283 "new refugees." One wonders where all the refugees went. They seemed to have disappeared just as the Air Force's B-52 raids got into full swing. One is justified in wondering whether or not the thousands of refugees are not simply being killed in the villages rather than being "sand bagged," tied up and brought into the pacification camps by GIs?

At the same time another statistical miracle was announced to buoy up the pacification effort. A recent report from the computerized Hamlet Evaluation System claimed that over 85% of the population was "secure."

What does all this mean? Is it possible that we are withdrawing at the same time that we are escalating the destruction?

What appears to have happened is that with the firing of General Westmoreland, and his replacement by General Creighton Abrams, a shift of tactics began in Vietnam. The massive and much publicized "search and destroy" operations which were the heart and soul of the Westmoreland tenure, began quietly to be phased out in favor of "cordon and search" operations. The high U.S. casualties (300 to 400 during an average week) had become too great a political liability at home. There was a pull back on the ground away from the bloody Dak To, Khe San, Iadrang Valley type of military operation. Planes that had been flying daily strikes over North Vietnam were diverted, after the bombing halt, to Laos and South Vietnam. B-52s began to be used as tactical weapons on daily runs. Bomb tonnage soared and U.S. casualty figures dropped. Nixon began to speak effusively about withdrawal and of Vietnamization.

At the same time Americans began to hear less and less about the troubling refugee problem. The My Lai Massacre broke almost as though it were news from another war fought years ago in which U.S. soldiers were killing civilians en masse in the field. CORDS began to shift its emphasis from resettlement to control as though the pacification millenium had arrived. Strategic Hamlets, New Life Hamlets, Revolutionary Development, winning the hearts and the minds of the people through good works, all gave way to Operation Phoenix. Only Operation Phoenix was more than a new rhetorical packaging job. It was a program of organized assassination of political opposition carried out in the remaining villages and refugee colonies under Thieu-Ky control. It was reminiscent of the early Diem days. Its stated purpose is "to destroy the enemy infrastructure, root out the shadow government, and identify and arrest infrastructure agents where they exist."[26] CORDS administers the refugee program and its chief, William Colby, claims that through Operation Phoenix 19,500 civilians "have been neutralized." He later told the Senate Foreign Relations Committee in an evasive and almost unintelligible testimony that ". . . I would not want to say that no one was ever actually executed. You have not had convictions of members of the enemy apparatus in which executions followed."(?)[27]

With Operation Phoenix constituting the "other war" on the ground, and the B-52s in the air, the whole problem of refugees has seemed to melt away from public consciousness. With fewer soldiers on operations in the field in Indochina, there was no one to "generate" refugees, or bring people into the resettlement camps. Refugees and pacification had just gotten to be too much trouble and caused too much bad publicity to continue. The public relations logic seems to be that civilians are a lot less visible if they remain in the free fire zones or in urban suburbs "with relatives" where few Americans can observe them.

From the point of view of the Indochinese peasant, Vietnamization has not meant cessation of U.S.-caused destruction. It has meant a clear escalation of the murderous assault on the countryside by U.S. air power. Aerial bombardment has increased, and in many instances replaced the presence of American ground forces. H&I fire has not ceased. When Kennedy asked G. Warren Nutter, Asst. Secretary of Defense, whether H&I fire still continued, he replied: "We do still have some, Mr. Chairman, but it has been reduced. This kind of tactic is not being employed in populated areas" (p. 27). The message seems to be that we only kill civilians in the countryside. Whatever selectivity the military exercised in picking targets, putting in air

[26]*New York Times*, February 14, 1970.
[27]San Francisco Chronicle, February 18, 1970.

strikes or defoliants, it has disappeared with the advent of massive and continuous saturation bombing.

What used to be an unforgivable war against individuals, specific targets, and enemy units has become a war against all life. Indochinese society has become our target, and in turn our enemy. We are waging a war against an abstraction which has turned out to be a war against the people and the land itself. Westmoreland's technological nightmare has arrived, where America can commit ecocide while reducing its own casualties, and thus hardly noticing what it is doing. As Westmoreland told the Association of the U.S. Army on October 15, 1969, "I see battlefields on which we can destroy anything we can locate through instant communications and almost instant application of highly lethal firepower. . . . With first round kill probabilities approaching certainty, and with surveillance devices that can continually track the enemy, the need for large forces to fix the opposition will be less important."[28]

As Senator William Proxmire noted in a July 5th press conference, the only trouble with this new $2 billion "electronic battlefield" was that these "secret weapons still cannot distinguish between enemy soldiers and innocent civilians."

The near complete destruction of the living landscape and the human society throughout all of Southeast Asia is proceeding at such a staggering rate that it is really impossible to estimate its true scope, severity or long-range consequences. The destruction of the nutrient values of the land, air, and water, the complete and increasing dependence of the economies of the region on foreign capital and goods, the destruction of the cultural heritage and family structure, the sheer volume of misery and death, constitute an attempt at total disruption of the biological and social fabric of the land. So far reaching is the destruction that finally one is forced to ask whether or not the American military has not in fact found a way of dealing with wars of national liberation: the destruction of the people and the land itself.

---

[28]*New York Times*, October 15, 1969.

On Genocide*

Jean-Paul Sartre

The word "genocide" is relatively new. It was coined by the jurist Raphael Lemkin between the two world wars. But the fact of genocide is as old as humanity. To this day there has been no society protected by its structure from committing that crime. Every case of genocide is a product of history and bears the stamp of the society which has given birth to it. The one we have before us for judgment is the act of the greatest capitalist power in the world today. It is as such that we must try to analyze it—in other words, as the simultaneous expression of the economic infrastructure of that power, its political objectives and the contradictions of its present situation.

In particular, we must try to understand the genocidal intent in the war which the American government is waging against Vietnam, for Article 2 of the 1948 Geneva Convention defines genocide on the basis of intent; the Convention was tacitly referring to memories which were still fresh. Hitler had proclaimed it his deliberate intent to exterminate the Jews. He made genocide a political means and did not hide it. A Jew had to be put to death, whoever he was, not for having been caught carrying a weapon or for having joined a resistance movement, but simply *because he was a Jew.* The American government has avoided making such clear statements. It has even claimed that it was answering the call of its allies, the South Vietnamese, who had been attacked by the communists. It is possible for us, by studying the facts objectively, to discover implicit in them such a genocidal intention? And after such an investigation, can we say that the armed forces of the United States are killing Vietnamese in Vietnam for the simple reason that they are Vietnamese?

*Reprinted with permission from: *Ramparts Magazine*, S. F., Calif.

This is something which can only be established after an historical examination: the structure of war changes right along with the infrastructures of society. Between 1860 and the present day, the meaning and the objectives of military conflicts have changed profoundly, the final stage of this metamorphosis being precisely the "war of example" which the United States is waging in Vietnam.

In 1856, there was a convention for the protection of the property of neutrals; 1864, Geneva: protection for the wounded; 1899, 1907, The Hague: two conferences which attempted to make rules for war. It is no accident that jurists and governments were multiplying their efforts to "humanize war" on the very eve of the two most frightful massacres that mankind has ever known. Vladimir Dedijer has shown very effectively in his study "On Military Conventions" that the capitalist societies during this same period were giving birth to the monster of total war in which they express their true nature. He attributes this phenomenon to the following:

1. The competition between industrial nations fighting for new markets produces·a permanent antagonism which is expressed in ideology and in practice by what is known as "bourgeois nationalism."

2. The development of industry, which is the source of this hostility, provides the means of resolving it to the advantage of one of the competitors, through the production of more and more *massively* destructive weapons. The consequence of this development is that it becomes increasingly difficult to make any distinction between the front and behind the lines, between the civilian population and the soldiers.

3. At the same time, new military objectives—the factories—arise near the towns. And even when they are not producing materiel directly for the armies, they maintain, at least to some extent, the economic strength of the country. It is precisely this strength that the enemy aims to destroy: this is at once the aim of war and the means to that end.

4. The consequence of this is that everyone is mobilized: the peasant fights at the front, the worker fights behind the lines, the peasant women take over for their husbands in the fields. This *total* struggle of nation against nation tends to make the worker a soldier too, since in the last analysis the power which is economically stronger is more likely to win.

5. The democratic facade of the bourgeois nations and the emancipation of the working class have led to the participation of the masses in politics. The masses have no control at all over government decisions, but the middle classes imagine that by voting they exercise some kind of remote control. Except in cases of defensive wars, the working classes are torn between their desire for peace and the nationalism which has been instilled in them. Thus war, seen in a new light and distorted by propaganda, becomes the ethical decision of the whole community. All the citizens of each warring nation (or almost all, after they have been manipulated) are the enemies of all those of the other country. War has become absolutely total.

6. These same societies, as they continue their technological expansion, continue to extend the scope of their competition by increasing communications. The famous "One World" of the Americans was already in existence by the end of the 19th century when Argentine wheat dealt a final blow to English agriculture. Total war is no longer only between all members of one national community and all those of another: it is also total because it will very likely set the whole world up in flames.

Thus, war between the bourgeois nations—of which the 1914 war was the first example but which had threatened Europe since 1900—is not the "invention" of one man or one government, but simply a necessity for those who, since the beginning of the century, have sought to "extend politics by other means." The option is clear: either *no* war or *that* kind of total war. Our fathers fought that kind of war. And the governments who saw it coming, with neither the intelligence nor the courage to stop it, were wasting their time and the time of the jurists when they stupidly tried to "humanize" it.

Nevertheless, during the First World War a genocidal intent appeared only sporadically. As in previous centuries, the essential aim was to crush the military power of the enemy and only secondarily to ruin his economy. But even though there was no longer any clear distinction between civilians and soldiers, it was still only rarely (except for a few terrorist raids) that the civilian population was expressly made a target. Moreover, the belligerent nations (or at least those who were doing the fighting) were industrial powers. This made for a certain initial balance: against the possibility of any real extermination each side had its own deterrent force—namely the power of applying the law of "an eye for an eye." This explains why, in the midst of the carnage, a kind of prudence was maintained.

However, since 1830, throughout the last century and continuing to this very day, there have been countless acts of genocide whose causes are likewise to be found in the structure of capitalist societies. To export their products and their capital, the great powers, particularly England and France, set up colonial empires. The name "overseas possessions" given by the French to their conquests indicates clearly that they had been able to acquire them only by wars of aggression. The adversary was sought out in his own territory, in Africa and Asia, in the underdeveloped countries, and far from waging "total war" (which would have required an initial balance of forces), the colonial powers, because of their overwhelming superiority of firepower, found it necessary to commit only an expeditionary force. Victory was easy, at least in conventional military terms. But since this blatant aggression kindled the hatred of the civilian population, and since civilians were potentially rebels and soldiers, the colonial troops maintained their authority by terror—by perpetual massacre. These massacres were genocidal in character: they aimed at the destruction of "a part of an ethnic, national, or religious group" in order to terrorize the remainder and to wrench apart the indigenous society.

After the bloodbath of conquest in Algeria during the last century, the French imposed the *Code Civil*, with its middle-class conceptions of property and inheritance, on a tribal society where each community held land in common. Thus they systematically destroyed the economic infrastructure of the country, and tribes of peasants soon saw their lands fall into the hands of French speculators. Indeed, colonization is not a matter of mere conquest as was the German annexation of Alsace-Lorraine; it is by its very nature an act of cultural genocide. Colonization cannot take place without systematically liquidating all the characteristics of the native society—and simultaneously refusing to integrate the natives into the mother country and denying them access to its raw materials and agricultural products at a reduced price to the colonizing power. The latter, in return, sells its manufactured goods to the colony at world market prices. This curious system of trade is only possible if there is a colonial subproletariat which can be forced to work for starvation wages. For the subject people this inevitably means the extinction of their national character, culture, customs, sometimes even language. They live in their underworld of misery like dark phantoms ceaselessly reminded of their subhumanity.

However, their value as an almost unpaid labor force protects them, to a certain extent, against physical genocide. The Nuremberg Tribunal was still fresh in people's minds when the French massacred 45,000 Algerians at Setif, as an "example." But this sort of thing was so commonplace that no one even thought to condemn the French government in the same terms as they did the Nazis.

But this "deliberate destruction of a part of a national group" could not be carried out any more extensively without harming the interests of the French settlers. By exterminating the subproletariat, they would have exterminated themselves as settlers. This explains the contradictory attitude of these *pieds-noirs* during the Algerian war: they urged the Army to commit massacres, and more than one of them dreamed of total genocide. At the same time they attempted to compel the Algerians to "fraternize" with them. It is because France could neither liquidate the Algerian people nor integrate them with the French that it lost the Algerian war.

These observations enable us to understand how the structure of colonial wars underwent a transformation after the end of the Second World War. For it was at about this time that the colonial peoples, enlightened by that conflict and its impact on the "empires," and later by the victory of Mao Tse-tung, resolved to regain their national independence. The characteristics of the struggle were determined from the beginning: the colonialists had the superiority in weapons, the indigenous population the advantage of numbers. Even in Algeria—a colony where there was settlement as much as there was exploitation—the proportion of *colons* to natives was one to nine. During the two world wars, many of the colonial peoples had been trained as soldiers and had become experienced fighters. However, the short supply and poor quality of their arms—at least in the beginning—kept the number of fighting units low. These objective conditions dictated their strategy, too: terrorism, ambushes, harassing the enemy, extreme mobility of the combat groups which had to strike unexpectedly and disappear at once. This was made possible only by the support of the entire population. Hence the famous symbiosis between the liberation forces and the masses of people: the former everywhere organizing agrarian reforms, political organs and education; the latter supporting, feeding and hiding the soldiers of the army of liberation, and replenishing its ranks with their sons.

It is no accident that people's war, with its principles, its strategy, its tactics and its theoreticians, appeared at the very moment that the industrial powers pushed total war to the ultimate by the industrial production of atomic fission. Nor is it any accident that it brought about the destruction of colonialism. The contradiction which led to the victory of the FLN in Algeria was characteristic of that time; people's war sounded the death-knell of conventional warfare at exactly the same moment as the hydrogen bomb. Against partisans supported by the entire population, the colonial armies were helpless. They had only one way of escaping this demoralizing harassment which threatned to culminate in a Dien Bien Phu, and that was to "empty the sea of its water"—i.e. the civilian population. And, in fact, the colonial soldiers soon learned that their most redoubtable foes were the silent, stubborn peasants who, just one kilometer from the scene of the ambush which had wiped out a regiment, knew nothing, had seen nothing. And since it was the unity of an entire people which held the conventional army at bay, the only anti-guerrilla strategy which could work was the destruction of this people, in other words, of civilians, of women and children.

Torture and genocide: that was the answer of the colonial powers to the revolt of the subject peoples. And that answer, as we know, was worthless unless it was thorough and total. The populace—resolute, united by the politicized and fierce partisan army—was no longer to be cowed as in the good old days of colonialism, by an "admonitory" massacre which was supposed to serve "as an example." On the contrary, this only augmented the people's hate. Thus it was no longer a question of intimidating the populace, but rather of physically liquidating it. And since that was not possible without concurrently liquidating the colonial economy and the whole colonial system, the settlers panicked, the colonial powers got tired of pouring men and money into an interminable conflict, the mass of the people in the mother country opposed the continuation of an inhuman war, and the colonies became sovereign states.

There have been cases, however, in which the genocidal response to people's war is not checked by infrastructural contradictions. Then total genocide emerges as the absolute basis of an anti-guerrilla strategy. And under certain conditions it even emerges as the explicit objective—sought either immediately or by degrees. This is precisely what is happening in the Vietnam war. We are dealing here with a new stage in the development of imperialism, a stage usually called neo-colonialism because it is characterized by aggression against a former colony which has already gained its independence, with the aim of subjugating it anew to colonial rule. With the beginning of independence, the neo-colonialists take care to finance a *putsch* or *coup d'état* so that the new heads of state do not represent the interests of the masses but those of a narrow privileged strata, and, consequently, of foreign capital.

Ngo Dinh Diem appeared—hand-picked, maintained and armed by the United States. He proclaimed his decision to reject the Geneva Agreements and to constitute the Vietnamese territory to the south of the 17th parallel as an independent state. What followed was the necessary consequence of these premises: a police force and an army were created to hunt down people who had fought against the French, and who now felt thwarted of their victory, a sentiment which automatically marked them as enemies of the new regime. In short, it was the reign of terror which provoked a new uprising in the South and rekindled the people's war.

Did the United States ever imagine that Diem could nip the revolt in the bud? In any event, they lost no time in sending in experts and then troops, and then they were involved in the conflict up to their necks. And we find once again almost the same pattern of war as the one that Ho Chi Minh fought against the French, except that at first the American government declared that it was only sending its troops out of generosity, to fulfill its obligations to an ally.

That is the outward appearance. But looking deeper, these two successive wars are essentially different in character: the United States, unlike France, has no economic interests in Vietnam. American firms have made some investments, but not so much that they couldn't be sacrificed, if necessary, without troubling the American nation as a whole or really hurting the monopolies. Moreover, since the U.S. government is not waging the war for reasons of a *directly* economic nature, there is nothing to stop it from ending the war by the ultimate tactic—in other words, by genocide. This is not to say that there is proof that the U.S. does in fact envision genocide, but simply that nothing prevents the U.S. from envisaging it.

In fact, according to the Americans themselves, the conflict has two objectives. Just recently, Dean Rusk stated: "We are defending ourselves." It is no longer Diem, the ally whom the Americans are generously helping out: it is the United States itself which is in danger in Saigon. Obviously, this means that the first objective is a military one: to encircle Communist China. Therefore, the United States will not let Southeast Asia escape. It has put its men in power in Thailand, it controls two-thirds of Laos and threatens to invade Cambodia. But these conquests will be hollow if it finds itself confronted by a free and unified Vietnam with 32 million inhabitants. That is why the military leaders like to talk in terms of "key positions." That is why Dean Rusk says, with unintentional humor, that the armed forces of the United States are fighting in Vietnam "in order to avoid a third world war." Either this phrase is meaningless, or else it must be taken to mean: "in order to *win* this third conflict." In short, the first objective is dictated by the necessity of establishing a Pacific line of defense, something which is necessary only in the context of the general policies of imperialism.

The second objective is an economic one. In October 1966, General Westmoreland defined it as follows: "We are fighting the war in Vietnam to show that guerrilla warfare does not pay." To show whom? The Vietnamese? That would be very surprising. Must so many human lives and so much money be wasted merely to teach a lesson to a nation of poor peasants thousands of miles from San Francisco? And, in particular, what need was there to attack them, provoke them into fighting and subsequently to go about crushing them, when the big American companies have only negligible interests in Vietnam? Westmoreland's statement, like Rusk's, has to be filled in. The Americans want to show others that guerrilla war does not pay: they want to show all the oppressed and exploited nations that might be tempted to shake off the American yoke by launching a people's war, at first against their own pseudo-governments, the compradors and the army, then against the U.S. "Special Forces," and finally against the GIs. In short, they want to show Latin America first of all, and more generally, all of the Third World. To Che Guevara who said, "We need several Vietnams," the American government answers, "They will all be crushed the way we are crushing the first."

In other words, this war has above all an admonitory value, as an example for three and perhaps four continents. (After all, Greece is a peasant nation too. A dictatorship has just been set up there; it is good to give the Greeks a warning: submit or face extermination.) This genocidal example is addressed to the whole of humanity. By means of this warning, 6 per cent of mankind hopes to succeed in controlling the other 94 per cent at a reasonably low cost in money and effort. Of course it would be preferable, for propaganda purposes, if the Vietnamese would submit before being exterminated. But it is not certain that the situation wouldn't be clearer if Vietnam *were* wiped off the map. Otherwise someone might think that Vietnam's submission had been attributable to some *avoidable* weakness. But if these peasants do not weaken for an instant, and if the price they pay for their heroism is *inevitable* death, the guerrillas of the future will be all the more discouraged.

At this point of our demonstration, three facts are established: (1) What the U.S. government wants is to have a base against China and to set an example. (2) The first objective *can* be achieved, without any difficulty (except, of course, for the resistance of the Vietnamese), by wiping out a whole people and imposing the Pax Americana on an uninhabited Vietnam. (3) To achieve the second, the U.S. *must* carry out, at least in part, this extermination.

The declarations of American statesmen are not as candid as Hitler's were in his day. But candor is not essential to us here. It is enough that the facts speak; the speeches which come with them are believed only by the American people. The rest of the world understands well enough: governments which are the friends of the United States keep silent; the others denounce this genocide. The Americans try to reply that these unproved accusations only show these governments' partiality. "In fact," the American government says, "all we have ever done is to offer the Vietnamese, North and South, the option of ceasing their aggression or being crushed." It is scarcely necessary to mention that this offer is absurd, since it is the Americans who commit the aggression and consequently they are the only ones who can put an end to it. But this absurdity is not undeliberate: the Americans are ingeniously formulating, without appearing to do so, a demand which the Vietnamese cannot satisfy. They do offer an alternative: Declare you are beaten or we will bomb you back to the stone age. But the fact remains that the second term of this alternative is genocide. They have said: "Genocide, yes, but *conditional* genocide." Is this juridically valid? Is it even conceivable?

If the proposition made any juridical sense at all, the U.S. government might narrowly escape the accusation of genocide. But the 1948 Convention leaves no such loopholes: an act of genocide, especially if it is carried out over a period of several years, is no less genocide for being blackmail. The perpetrator may declare he will stop if the victim gives in; this is still—without any juridical doubt whatsoever—a genocide. And this is all the more true when, as is the case here, a good part of the group has been annihilated to force the rest to give in.

But let us look at this more closely and examine the nature of the two terms of the alternative. In the South, the choice is the following: villages burned, the populace subjected to massive bombing, livestock shot, vegetation destroyed by defoliants, crops ruined by toxic aerosols, and everywhere indiscriminate shooting, murder, rape and looting. This is genocide in the strictest sense: massive extermination. The other option: what is *it?* What are the Vietnamese people supposed to do to escape this horrible death? Join the armed forces of Saigon or be enclosed in strategic or today's "New Life" hamlets, two names for the same concentration camps?

We know about these camps from numerous witnesses. They are fenced in by barbed wire. Even the most elementary needs are denied: there is malnutrition and a total lack of hygiene. The prisoners are heaped together in small tents or sheds. The social structure is destroyed. Husbands are separated from their wives, mothers from their children; family life, so important to the Vietnamese, no longer exists. As families are split up, the birth rate falls; any possibility of religious or cultural life is suppressed; even work—the work which might permit people to maintain themselves and their families— is refused them. These unfortunate people are not even slaves (slavery did not prevent the Negroes in the United States from developing a rich culture); they are reduced to a living heap of vegetable existence. When, sometimes, a fragmented family group is freed—children with an elder sister or a young mother—it goes to swell the ranks of the subproletariat in the big cities; the elder sister or the mother, with no job and mouths to feed, reaches the last stage of her degradation in prostituting herself to the GIs.

The camps I describe are but another kind of genocide, equally condemned by the 1948 Convention:

"Causing serious bodily or mental harm to members of the group.

"Deliberately inflicting on the group conditions of life calculated to bring about its physical destruction in whole or in part.

"Imposing measures intended to prevent births within the group.

"Forcibly transferring children of the group to another group."

In other words, it is not true that the choice is between death or submission. For submission, in those circumstances, is submission to genocide. Let us say that a choice must be made between a violent and immediate death and a slow death from mental and physical degradation. Or, if you prefer, *there is no choice at all.*

Is it any different for the North?

One choice is *extermination.* Not just the daily risk of death, but the systematic destruction of the economic base of the country: from the dikes to the factories, nothing will be left standing. Deliberate attacks against civilians and, in particular, the rural population. Systematic destruction of hospitals, schools and places of worship. An all-out campaign to destroy the achievements of 20 years of socialism. The purpose may be only to intimidate the populace. But this can only be achieved by the daily extermination of an ever larger part of the group. So this intimidation itself in its psycho-social consequence is a genocide. Among the children in particular it must be engendering psychological disorders which will for years, if not permanently, "cause serious . . . mental harm."

The other choice is *capitulation.* This means that the North Vietnamese must declare themselves ready to stand by and watch while their country is divided and the Americans impose a direct or indirect dictatorship on their compatriots, in fact on members of their own families from whom the war has separated them. And would this intolerable humiliation bring an end to the war? This is far from certain. The National Liberation Front and the Democratic Republic of Vietnam, although fraternally united, have different strategies and tactics because their war situations are different. If the NLF continued the struggle, American bombs would go on blasting the DRV whether it capitulated or not.

If the war were to cease, the United States—according to official statements—would feel very generously inclined to help in the reconstruction of the DRV, and we know exactly what this means. It means that the United States would destroy, through private investments and conditional loans, the whole economic base of socialism. And this too is genocide. They would be splitting a sovereign country in half, occupying one of the halves by a reign of terror and keeping the other half under control by economic pressure. The "national group" Vietnam would not be physically eliminated, yet it would no longer exist. Economically, politically and culturally it would be suppressed.

In the North as in the South, the choice is only between two types of liquidation: collective death or dismemberment. The American government has had ample opportunity to test the resistance of the NLF and the DRV: by now it knows that only total destruction will be effective. The Front is stronger than ever; North Vietnam is unshakable. For this very reason, the calculated extermination of the Vietnamese people cannot really be intended to make them capitulate. The Americans offer them a *paix des braves* knowing full well that they will not accept it. And this phony alternative hides the true goal of imperialism, which is to reach, step by step, the highest stage of escalation—total genocide.

Of course, the United States government *could have* tried to reach this stage in one jump and wipe out Vietnam in a *Blitzkrieg* against the whole country. But this extermination first required setting up complicated installations—for instance, creating and maintaining air bases in Thailand which would shorten the bombing runs by 3000 miles.

Meanwhile, the major *purpose* of "escalation" was, and still is, to prepare international opinion for genocide. From this point of view, Americans have succeeded only too well. The repeated and systematic bombings of populated areas of Haiphong and Hanoi, which two years ago would have raised violent protests in Europe, occur today in a climate of general indifference resulting perhaps more from catatonia than from apathy. The tactic has borne its fruit: public opinion now sees escalation as a slowly and continously increasing pressure to bargain, while in reality it is the preparation of minds for the final genocide. Is such a genocide possible? No. But that is due to the Vietnamese and the Vietnamese alone; to their courage, and to the remarkable efficiency of their organization. As for the United States government, it cannot be absolved of its crime just because its victim has enough intelligence and enough heroism to limit its effects.

We may conclude that in the face of a people's war (the characteristic product of our times, the answer to imperialism and the demand for sovereignty of a people conscious of its unity) there are two possible responses: either the aggressor withdraws, he acknowledges that a whole nation confronts him, and he makes peace; or else he recognizes the inefficacy of conventional strategy, and, if he can do so without jeopardizing his interests, he resorts to extermination pure and simple. There is no third alternative, but making peace is still at least *possible.*

But as the armed forces of the U.S.A. entrench themselves firmly in Vietnam, as they intensify the bombing and the massacres, as they try to bring Laos under their control, as they plan the invasion of Cambodia, there is less and less doubt that the government of the United States, despite its hypocritical denials, has chosen genocide.

The genocidal intent is implicit in the facts. It is necessarily premeditated. Perhaps in bygone times, in the midst of tribal wars, acts of genocide were perpetrated on the spur of the moment in fits of passion. But the anti-guerrilla genocide which our times have produced requires organization, military bases, a structure of accomplices, budget appropriations. Therefore, its authors must meditate and plan out their act. Does this mean that they are thoroughly conscious of their intentions? It is impossible to decide. We would have to plumb the depths of their consciences —and the Puritan bad faith of Americans works wonders.

There are probably people in the State Department who have become so used to fooling themselves that they still think they are working for the good of the Vietnamese people. However, we may only surmise that there are fewer and fewer of these hypocritical innocents after the recent statements of their spokesmen: "We are defending ourselves; even if the Saigon government begged us, we would not leave Vietnam, etc., etc." At any rate, we don't have to concern ourselves with this psychological hide-and-seek. The truth is apparent *on the battlefield* in the racism of the American soldiers.

This racism—anti-black, anti-Asiatic, anti-Mexican—is a basic American attitude with deep historical roots and which existed, latently and overtly, well before the Vietnamese conflict. One proof of this is that the United States government refused to ratify the Genocide Convention. This doesn't mean that in 1948 the U.S. intended to exterminate a people; what it does mean—according to the statements of the U.S. Senate—is that the Convention would conflict with the laws of several states; in other words, the current policymakers enjoy a free hand in Vietnam because their predecessors catered to the anti-black racism of Southern whites. In any case, since 1966, the racism of Yankee soldiers, from Saigon to the 17th parallel, has become more and more marked. Young American men use torture (even including the "field telephone treatment"*), they shoot unarmed women for nothing more than target practice, they kick wounded Vietnamese in the genitals, they cut ears off dead men to take home for trophies. Officers are the worst: a general boasted of hunting "VCs" from his helicopter and gunning them down in the rice paddies. Obviously, these were not NLF soldiers who knew how to defend themselves; they were peasants tending their rice. In the con-

---

*The portable generator for a field telephone is used as an instrument for interrogation by hitching the two lead wires to the victim's genitals and turning the handle. (Editor's note.)

fused minds of the American soldiers, "Viet Cong" and "Vietnamese" tend increasingly to blend into one another. They often say themselves, "The only good Vietnamese is a dead Vietnamese," or what amounts to the same thing, "A dead Vietnamese is a Viet Cong."

For example: south of the 17th parallel, peasants prepare to harvest their rice. American soldiers arrive on the scene, set fire to their houses and want to transfer them to a strategic hamlet. The peasants protest. What else can they do, barehanded against these Martians? They say: "The quality of the rice is good; we want to stay to eat our rice." Nothing more. But this is enough to irritate the young Yankees: "It's the Viet Cong who put that into your head; they are the ones who have taught you to resist." These soldiers are so misled that they take the feeble protests which their own violence has aroused for "subversive" resistance. At the outset, they were probably disappointed: they came to save Vietnam from "communist aggressors." But they soon had to realize that the Vietnamese did not want them. Their attractive role as liberators changed to that of occupation troops. For the soldiers it was the first glimmering of consciousness: "We are unwanted, we have no business here." But they go no further. They simply tell themselves that a Vietnamese is by definition suspect.

And from the neo-colonialists' point of view, this is true. They vaguely understand that in a people's war, civilians are the only visible enemies. Their frustration turns to hatred of the Vietnamese; racism takes it from there. The soldiers discover with a savage joy that they are there to kill the Vietnamese they had been pretending to save. All of them are potential communists, as proved by the fact that they hate Americans.

Now we can recognize in those dark and misled souls the truth of the Vietnam war: it meets all of Hitler's specifications. Hitler killed the Jews because they were Jews. The armed forces of the United States torture and kill men, women and children in Vietnam merely *because they are Vietnamese.* Whatever lies or euphemisms the government may think up, the spirit of genocide is in the minds of the soldiers. This is their way of living out the genocidal situation into which their government has thrown them. As Peter Martinson, a 23-year-old student who had "interrogated" prisoners for ten months and could scarcely live with his memories, said: "I am a middle-class American. I look like any other student, yet somehow I am a war criminal." And he was right when he added: "Anyone in my place would have acted as I did." His only mistake was to attribute his degrading crimes to the influence of war *in general.*

No, it is not war in the abstract: it is the greatest power on earth against a poor peasant people. Those who fight it are *living out* the only possible relationship between an overindustrialized country and an underdeveloped country, that is to say, a genocidal relationship implemented through racism—the only relationship, short of picking up and pulling out.

Total war presupposes a certain balance of forces, a certain reciprocity. Colonial wars were not reciprocal, but the interests of the colonialists limited the scope of genocide. The present genocide, the end result of the unequal development of societies, is total war waged to the limit by one side, without the slightest reciprocity.

The American government is not guilty of inventing modern genocide, or even of having chosen it from other possible and effective measures against guerrilla warfare. It is not guilty, for example, of having preferred genocide for strategic and economic reasons. Indeed, genocide presents itself as the *only possible reaction* to the rising of a whole people against its oppressors.

The American government is guilty of having preferred, and of still preferring, a policy of war and aggression aimed at total genocide to a policy of peace, the only policy which can really replace the former. A policy of peace would necessarily have required a reconsideration of the objectives imposed on that government by the large imperialist companies through the intermediary of their pressure groups. America is guilty of continuing and intensifying the war despite the fact that every day its leaders realize more acutely, from the reports of the military commanders, that the only way to win is "to free Vietnam of all the Vietnamese." The government is guilty—despite the lessons it has been taught by this unique, unbearable experience—of proceeding at every moment a little further along a path which leads it to the point of no return. And it is guilty—according to its own admissions—of consciously carrying out this admonitory war in order to use genocide as a challenge and a threat to all peoples of the world.

We have seen that one of the features of total war has been the growing scope and efficiency of communication. As early as 1914, war could no longer be "localized." It had to spread throughout the whole world. In 1967, this process is being intensified. The ties of the "One World," on which the United States wants to impose its hegemony, have grown tighter and tighter. For this reason, as the American government very well knows, the current genocide is conceived as an answer to people's war and perpetrated in Vietnam not against the Vietnamese alone, but against humanity.

When a peasant falls in his rice paddy, mowed down by a machine gun, every one of us is hit. The Vietnamese fight for all men and the American forces against all. Neither figuratively nor abstractly. And not only because genocide would be a crime universally condemned by international law, but because little by little the whole human race is being subjected to this genocidal blackmail piled on top of atomic blackmail, that is, to absolute, total war. This crime, carried out every day before the eyes of the world, renders all who do not denounce it accomplices of those who commit it, so that we are being degraded today for our future enslavement.

In this sense imperialist genocide can only become more complete. The group which the United States wants to intimidate and terrorize by way of the Vietnamese nation is the human group in its entirety.

"On Withdrawal"

Peter Dale Scott

It must be clearly understood that since 1950, the year of the Korean War and the China Lobby, there has never been a genuine US de-escalation in Southeast Asia. Every apparent de-escalation of the fighting, such as in Vietnam in 1954 and Laos in 1961-62, has been balanced by an escalation, either covert or structural, whose long-range result overshadowed America's previous war effort. In 1954, for example, America's direct involvement in the First Indochina War was limited to a few dozen USAF transport planes and pilots "on loan" to Chennault's airline CAT, plus 200 USAF technicians to service them. Though Dulles, Radford, and Nixon failed to implement their proposals for US air strikes and/or troop intervention, Dulles was able to substitute for the discarded plan for immediate intervention a "proposal for creating a Southeast Asia Treaty Organization."[1] SEATO soon became a cover for US "limited war" games in Southeast Asia, which in turn grew into the first covert US military involvement in Laos in 1959—the start of the Second Indochina War.

In early 1961 Kennedy resisted energetic pressures from his Joint Chiefs to invade Laos openly with up to 60,000 soldiers empowered, if necessary, to use tactical nuclear weapons (Nixon also conferred with Kennedy and again urged, at the least, "a commitment of American air power").[2] Unwilling with his limited reserves to initiate major operations simultaneously in both Laos and Cuba, Kennedy settled for a political solution in Laos, beginning with a cease-fire which went into effect on May 3, 1961. On May 4 and 5, 1961, Rusk and Kennedy announced the first of a series of measures to strengthen the US military commitment in South Vietnam. The timing suggests that the advocates of a showdown with China in one country had been placated by the *quid pro quo* of a build-up in another. In like manner the final conclusion of the 1962 Geneva Agreements on Laos came only after the United States had satisfied Asian and domestic hawks by its first commitment of US combat troops to the area, in Thailand.

In 1968, finally, we now know that the "de-escalation" announced by President Johnson in March and November, in the form of a cessation of the bombing of North Vietnam, was misleading. In fact the same planes were simply diverted from North Vietnam to Laos: the over-all level of bombing, far from decreasing, continued to increase.

One has, unhappily, to conclude that there is simply no precedent for a genuine US de-escalation in Southeast Asia, though there have been illusory appearances of de-escalation. This conclusion does not of itself prove that "Vietnamization" of the war is impossible, or a deception to delude the American electorate. It does however suggest that a twenty-year search for a successful war in Southeast Asia will not be easily converted into a search for the means to withdraw.

From "Cambodia—Why the Generals Won"
New York Review of Books
June 18, 1970

Map 1. Craterization and defoliation of Indochina.

From Ecological Effects of the Vietnam War*

E. W. Pfeiffer

The massive quantities of defoliant and high explosive being used in Vietnam are having an effect on the ecology of that country. How serious the effect is, or how long it will last, are not yet precisely known, but a careful investigation is urgently required. . . .

The physiographic core of Vietnam is the highland mass that accounts for 85 per cent of the total land mass. It extends southwards to the delta of the Mekong River and may reach altitudes of more than 2500 metres. These highlands step down gradually via sandstone and limestone tablelands to the Mekong Valley which is an alluvial lowland. Vietnam has a tropical monsoon climate characterized by dry winters and rainy summers. At Saigon the average temperature fluctuates less than 4° C throughout the year and about 200 cm of rainfall occurs annually, mostly between April and October. In highlands precipitation of more than 250 cm is common. About 30 percent of Southern Vietnam is forested. Where rainfall is sufficiently high there is a tropical rainforest. Where rainfall is markedly seasonal the forest becomes a mixed evergreen, deciduous type.

The major forest formations in Vietnam have been characterized as follows: evergreen, broad-leaf rain or moist forests (true rainforest is confined mainly to the lower and middle elevations on mountain slopes); dipterocarp forest, probably the most extensive type, covering about 50 percent of the total forested area; mixed deciduous forests, usually heavily cut over and quite open; dry evergreen forest, concentrated especially along the river streambanks; montane forests containing oak, frequently mixed with conifers at middle and upper elevations; coniferous forests, in which species of pine form rather extensive stands in the uplands; swamp forests, consisting of mangrove woodland (in coastal areas, in deltas and around river estuaries),

*Reprinted with permission from the author. Excerpted *from Science* Journal, Feb. 1969, pp. 33-38.

stands of Nipa palm (also in deltas and tidal reaches, growing with the mangroves) and fresh water swamps, generally in the interior; savannahs— open or sparsely wooded and dominated by a ground cover of coarse grasses; thorn woodland consisting of shrubs and small to medium sized trees often mixed with bamboo to form a very dense tangle difficult to penetrate; and bamboo breaks, frequently forming dense fringes along banks of streams and rivers, which develop rapidly in abandoned tilled land or when clearings are made in most types of forests.

According to French botanists, there are more than 1500 species of woody plants in Vietnam, so many of these forest associations are very complex. They have been greatly influenced for many centuries by human activities such as lumbering, burning and shifting agriculture. As a result, much of the vegetation that covers South Vietnam exists in the main as secondary growth interspersed with stands of primary forests.

The most extensive soil types found in southeast Asia are lateritic soils. The high temperature and abundant rainfall in this area produce almost continuous downward movement of water through the soil, resulting in heavy leaching. This leaves a typical red or yellow soil rich in iron oxide and

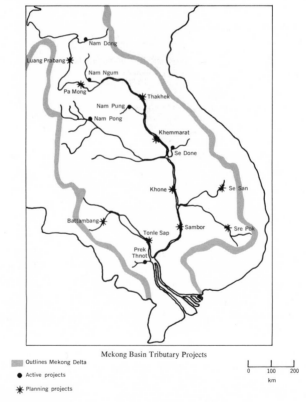

Mekong Basin Tributary Projects

Outlines Mekong Delta

● Active projects

✳ Planning projects

0   100   200
km

Map 2. Projects and planned projects for the Mekong River and its tributaries.

alumina that is subject to laterization, the process by which exposed soils become dried and turned to a hard red rock. Laterization does not occur under a cover of rainforest where the soils are always acidic and often deficient in plant nutrients. In the Mekong Delta of South Vietnam, the soils are primarily alluvial due to recurrent flooding, although some lateritic soils occur in this region. If denuded and dried, much of this soil could be irreversibly converted to laterite.

The biota of southeast Asia includes a great variety of rare and unique fauna. There are many large mammalian species including elephants, tigers, wild boar, deer, rhinoceros and primates, some unique, such as the Douc Langur and the Indo-Chinese Gibbon. There are also rare bovine species like the Kouprey, a cow that was not even discovered until 1936 and is limited to a few hundred individuals. The Gaur is another rare bovine of southeast Asia, one subspecies of which is down to only 300 individuals. As in all tropical regions, there is very rich bird life. In the marine waters there is a great variety of invertebrate life, some of which, such as cuttlefish, mollusks, shrimp and crabs, are important commercially.

California

Florida

Illinois

New York

Map 3. Four diagrams comparing South Viet Nam to various states.

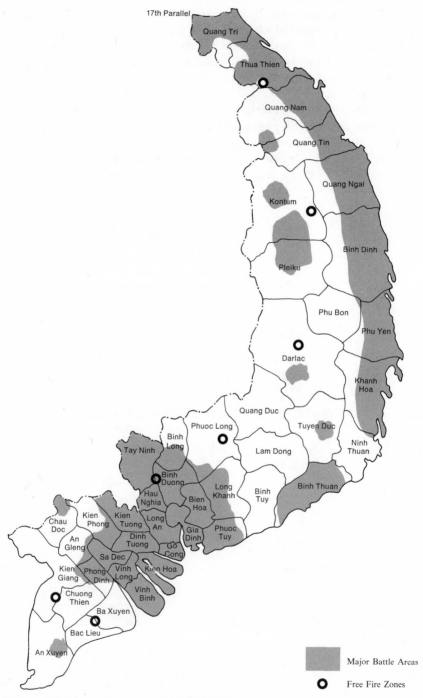

17th Parallel

Quang Tri

Thua Thien

Quang Nam

Quang Tin

Quang Ngai

Kontum

Binh Dinh

Pleiku

Phu Bon

Phu Yen

Darlac

Khanh Hoa

Quang Duc

Phuoc Long

Binh Long

Tay Ninh

Lam Dong

Tuyen Duc

Ninh Thuan

Binh Duong

Long Khanh

Binh Tuy

Binh Thuan

Hau Nghia

Bien Hoa

Chau Doc

Kien Phong

Kien Tuong

Long An

Gia Dinh

Phuoc Tuy

An Gleng

Dinh Tuong

Go Cong

Sa Dec

Kien Giang

Phong Dinh

Vinh Long

Kien Hoa

Chuong Thien

Vinh Binh

Ba Xuyen

Bac Lieu

An Xuyen

Major Battle Areas

Free Fire Zones

Map 4. This map shows areas of major battles and also depicts
free fire zones in South Viet Nam.

PART 3

The Earth Below: Destruction of The Living Landscape

Our peasants will remember their cratered rice fields and defoliated forests, devastated by an alien air force that seems at war with the very land of Vietnam.

S. Vietnam Minister of Information, 1968

Photo by Wide World photos

"Leaf Abscission?"*

Ngô Vinh Long

"Leaf abscission" is a term used by American military men to designate their chemical war in Viet Nam. The term, like its sister word "defoliation," is meant to suggest that the dumping of herbicides and other chemicals over a tiny piece of land that has also been the victim of the most intense bombing in world history[1] has helped to thin out a few troublesome trees and shrubs while causing no significant damage to anything else at all. On the contrary, the use of herbicides and other chemicals sprayed by the American military in Viet Nam has already caused untold misery to thousands of innocent civilians.

From late 1959 till early 1963 the author of this article was involved in making detailed military maps (scale 1/25,000) of the whole of South Viet Nam, and thus had occasion to be, at one time or another, in virtually every hamlet and village in the country. It was also in 1959 that the Diem regime began putting into effect its "pacification" program. As for the Vietnamese majority living in the plains, by February, 1959, "relocation of families within communities had begun and, in contrast to land development and refugee activities, these relocations were often forced."[2] The restructured villages, surrounded by moats and barbed wire, were euphemistically known as "agrovilles." (In Vietnamese they were called *khu trù mật*, a term coined from Chinese roots and which was presumably supposed to carry a graceful

---

*The Bulletin of Concerned Asian Scholars (CCAS), Vol. 2, No. 1 (Oct. 1969).
[1]According to an article entitled "Ravaging Vietnam," which appeared in *The Nation*, April 21, 1969, B-52 bombing had by 1968 produced an estimated 2.6 million craters of approximately 30 feet in depth and 45 feet in diameter. Filled with water, these are said to be ideal breeding grounds for malarial mosquitoes.
[2]W. A. Nighswonger, *Rural Pacification in Viet Nam*, Praeger, New York, 1966, p. 46.

connotation, although it literally means something like "compacted area" or "concentration zone.") People were taken from their plots of ground, where their houses, their rice-fields, their ancestral tombs, etc., were located, and moved to totally unsuitable areas where they could be "protected."[3] As for the ethnic minorities living in the mountains (often referred to in Western writings as "montagnards"), the Diem regime forced them down into the lowlands and into concentration-camp-like compounds where they were to call themselves by the new name of *Việt Nam Mới* (or "New Vietnamese") and were to dress like the Vietnamese majority—a "cultural revolution" of sorts! In both cases, the houses and fields of those who had been relocated were burnt, in order to deny their use to the Viet Cong. (As early as 1956, Diem was already making extravagant use of the term "Viet Cong," which literally means "Vietnamese Communists," meaning anybody who opposed him.)

By 1961, when the American defoliation program had begun against jungle growth along highways, railways, and in places considered to be Viet Cong areas, the Diem regime was not long in finding new uses for the chemicals: Seymour M. Hersh, in an article entitled "Our Chemical War" published in the *New York Review of Books* on April 25, 1968, quoted *Newsweek* in saying that by the end of November, 1961, American special warfare troops had begun teaching Vietnamese fliers how to spray "Communist-held areas with a chemical that turns the rice-fields yellow, killing *any crop* being grown in rebel strongholds." What *Newsweek* failed to say is that the Diem regime in fact began putting this training into practice before the end of the same year. The "rebel strongholds" referred to by *Newsweek* were more often than not, as the writer has witnessed personally, simply communities in sparsely populated areas isolated from effective government control. For this reason the Diem government felt it had to resort to killing their crops as a means of driving the population more quickly into the new and overly ambitious "strategic hamlets" (*ấp chiến lược*), which had replaced the abortive "agrovilles" early in the year. It was easier to order fliers to spray crops from the air than to send ground soldiers into the villages to force the people out by setting fire to their fields and houses. It had been discovered that government soldiers, on coming face to face with the misery and tearful entreaties of the dispossessed, were very often inclined to resist orders. The combined effects of regrouping the population in totally unsuitable areas and of killing their crops brought hunger and starvation to thousands of people.[4]

---

[3]Nguyễn Khắc Nhân, "Policy of Key Rural Agrovilles," in *Asian Culture*, Vol. 3, July December 1961, No. 3-4, p. 32; also Nighswonger, *loc. cit.*

[4]During my map surveying expedition, I witnessed countless heart-breaking incidents. Here are but a few: In a village of central Viet Nam one day I saw a group of children chasing after one another toward an open fire which the corvee laborers (who had been recruited to build the fence and the moats around the village) had made from uprooted grass. One boy threw a handful of something into the fire; the rest waited. As I was approaching them out of curiosity, one boy

The misery inflicted upon thousands of people through the killing of their crops to force them into the "strategic hamlets" and the repression of Buddhists and students, among other factors, led to the downfall of the Diem regime. In an attempt to stabilize the situation, the U.S. government began sending its troops into South Viet Nam. But even before the collapse of the Diem government, the U.S. military had already taken over the task of spraying crops in what they referred to as "Viet Cong territory."[5] In September, 1963, Rufus Philipps reported to the President of the United States, "giving [him] the estimates of USOM Rural Affairs that the Delta was falling under Viet Cong control in areas where pacification was supposedly complete."[6] The Delta is the whole land mass south and southwest of Saigon where most of the crops in the country were planted. "Viet Cong territory," as defined by the Americans, therefore comprised a very sizable part of the food-producing area of the country!

Beginning in 1965, the American military initiated still another version of "pacification" by sending the Marines to "secure villages" and to root out "Viet Cong infrastructures."[7] After two years of continuous effort, a *New York Times* report of August 7, 1967, cited official United States data on the loyalties of the hamlets, stating that the number of hamlets under total Saigon government control was a mere 168, while the number of those totally controlled by the Viet Cong was 3978. The rest of the hamlets were listed as "contested." To win the contest, or as the new name for the pacification program put it: to be successful in "The War to Win the Hearts and Minds of the People," the U.S. military was finding new ways to "pacify" the villages. One way was to send out American troops with bulldozers and bombers to raze the villages to the ground, and subsequently to transport the inhabitants to the so-called "camps for refugees fleeing from Communism" in and around the larger towns and cities where they could be "protected." (See two excellent books on this subject by Jonathan Schell: *The Village of Ben Suc,* and *The Military Half.*) Another way was the intensified use of chemicals,

---

used a stick to get the things out of the fire and the rest swarmed over hin, snatching them up. The "things" were baby rats! In near frenzy, the children began to pursue one another again, some tossed the hot rats between their two hands, others gulped them down whole. Another time, as I was approaching a village I saw a woman working in a rice-field with a small baby tied to her back by a piece of cloth, and a boy about four years old standing in the glaring sun at the border of the field and yelling out to her (his mother, I guessed). The baby cried. The woman switched the baby around to let it suck at her breast. The baby sucked as hard as it could but was not able to draw any milk and began crying again. The woman looked around as if to see whether I was watching. When I pretended that I was looking in the direction of the boy, she spat into the mouth of the child in an attempt to silence it.

Hunger struck most of the strategic hamlets I visited. In the village of Karom in central Viet Nam, 200 persons, mostly children, died in a single month. Many people had not eaten anything decent in months, and as a result, their anal muscles had become so dilated that every time they ate or drank something, it would pass right through them in not more than a few minutes.

[5]Seymour M. Hersh, "Our Chemical War," *The New York Review of Books*, April 25, 1968, pp. 1-2 of the article.
[6]Nighswonger, *op. cit.*, p. 64.
[7]*Ibid.*, pp. 114-115.

much in the same way Diem had used them before. In his article cited above, Seymour M. Hersh writes:

> But by early 1967, Presidential advisers had a different reason for using herbicides, one that wasn't directly linked to cutting off Viet Cong food supplies. The rationale was presented to a group of scientists who met in February with Donald Hornig, President Johnson's chief scientific adviser, to protest the use of anticrop chemicals. According to one scientist who attended the session, Hornig explained that the anticrop program was aimed chiefly at moving the people. The source quoted Hornig as explaining that when the United States found a Viet-Cong supporting area, it was faced with the alternatives of either bombing, bulldozing, and attacking it or dropping leaflets telling the people to move because the herbicides were coming. As Hornig expressed it, "it's all geared to moving people."

Mr. Hersh further states that the Pentagon used 60 million dollars' worth of defoliants and herbicides, or 12 million gallons, in Viet Nam in 1967, which was enough to cover "nearly half of the arable land in South Viet Nam." He also writes that, since Pentagon officials were arguing that the herbicides were more effective in killing crops than in stripping foliage,

> ...by the end of 1966 more than half of the C-123 missions were admittedly directed at crops, and it is probable that any effort at a trebling of capability in 1967 was aimed not at the jungles of South Viet Nam but at its arable crop land.

In a study of American anticrop and defoliation methods, Yōichi Fukushima, head of the Agronomy Section of the Japan Science Council, claims that American chemical attacks by 1967 had ruined more than 3.8 million acres (or one-half) of the arable land in South Viet Nam, and were a direct cause of death for nearly 1000 peasants and more than 13,000 head of livestock. The impact of the US anticrop program upon those peasants who escaped being taken to the "camps for refugees fleeing from Communism" is not known. As for the "refugees," their situation was (and is) so bad that the editorial staffs of Saigon newspapers, in spite of the harsh government censorship, felt compelled to run long articles on the misery endured by these people. For in Viet Nam people say that "you can't cover an elephant's mouth with a basket." Certain facts are so well known that they simply cannot be hidden from view. Thus, even *Sống* (a Saigon daily newspaper which was specifically created to justify the "pacification" program [of which the defoliation program is a part] and whose editor and staff were members and leaders of the Rural Development Cadre Teams sponsored by the joint cooperation of the CIA and the USOM) had this to say on December 10, 1967, in a long article entitled "Looking at the Faces of the Two Quảng Provinces in War, Hunger, Misery, and Corruption":

> This is a free area—free for depravity, corruption, irresponsibility, cowardice, obsequiousness, and loss of human dignity. What the devil is dignity when people sit there waiting to be thrown a few hundred piasters and allotted a few dozen kilos of rice a month? ... I believe that even if a certain Communist had in his

pockets several dozen "open-arms program" passes, after seeing the kind of humiliated life in a refugee camp he would run away without daring to look back.

But we seem to like this, and the Americans also like us to perform these kinds of activities so that they can have a lot of big statistics to present to both their houses of Congress. The Americans like to count, count people's heads, count square and cubic meters, and count the money they throw out. They think that the more they can count, the better is the proof of their success, the proof of their humanitarianism, and the proof of their legitimacy in this war.... How high a figure has the number of refugees who have to suffer and stay hungry reached? Many statistics proudly present the number two million. [Emphasis added]

If the number two million only referred to the situation in 1967, then how many more people have been victimized since then?

In an article entitled "Military Uses of Herbicides in Vietnam" published in the British journal *New Scientist* on June 13, 1968, Arthur Galston, Professor of Biology at Yale University and President of the Botanical Society of America, wrote:

The Air Force is preparing to spray about ten million gallons of herbicides over South Vietnam in the year beginning July 1968.... It is estimated that this will be enough to treat almost four million acres, of which about one-third will be crop land.

Professor Galston went on to say:

...With respect to the deliberate killing of crops in order to deprive the Viet Cong military of food, it can only be remarked that whenever starvation is used as a weapon against an entire civilian population, the main sufferers are inevitably the aged, the infirm, pregnant women, and children under five years old. The fighting man almost always gets enough food to sustain himself. Thus in using hunger as a weapon we are attacking the part of South Vietnamese society which is least involved in military operations and whom we would least wish to injure.

In the June 29, 1966 issue of *Christian Century*, two Harvard physicians, Dr. Jean Mayer, Professor of Nutrition, and Dr. Victor W. Sidel, warned that the U.S. anticrop program in Vietnam, like that of every food blockade or like some of the famines that they have witnessed, would create a process which begins with the death from starvation of small children first, then older children, and then the elderly. In the case of South Vietnam, as rightly noted in a report by the Boston-based Physicians for Social Responsibility, dated January 1967, *malnutrition, even before the anticrop program, was already a serious problem*, and beri-beri, night blindness, anemia, decayed or poor teeth, endemic goiter and other nutritional diseases were found to be widespread in the country. How high is the percentage of people affected by the above diseases now, after the U.S. military has effectively destroyed perhaps half or more of the arable land in South Vietnam? Nobody knows the exact figure.

Besides hunger and starvation and their accompanying effects, have the chemicals used by the American military in Vietnam caused any direct harm, immediate or eventual, either to animal or human life? At least three basic types of chemicals have been in use: 1) Agent Orange, a 50-50 mixture of two defoliants, 2,4,5-T (trichloro-phenoxyacetic acid) and 2,4-D (dichlo-rophen-oxyacetic acid); 2) Agent Blue, a neutralized cacodylic acid; and 3) Agent White, also known as Tordon 101, a weaker mixture of "unknown chemicals."[8]

First of all, according to a report of the National Institute of Environmental Health Science, September 1969, which contains data collected by the Bionetics Research Laboratory of Litton Industries (under contract for the National Cancer Institute) during the period 1965-1968 on the effects of pesticides, both 2,4,5-T and 2,4-D have been shown in tests on mice to produce significant increases in the incidence of malformation in fetuses and also in the incidence of cancer. The worst of the two is 2,4,5-T, which repeatedly produced test results of 100% in the proportion of abnormal litters.

In Vietnam there has for a long time been talk linking an apparent alarming rise in the incidence of birth deformities to the chemicals sprayed by the Americans there. The Americans and the Saigon regime have repeatedly denied that the chemicals they use could cause any harm whatever to animal or human life. Last summer, several Saigon newspapers, in defiance of the strict censorship and the possibility of having their offices closed down, printed stories and pictures of horribly deformed babies born in villages that had been "defoliated." For example, *Tin Sáng*, in its June 26, 1969 issue, printed an interview with an old woman who reported that her newly pregnant daughter was caught in a chemical strike, and fainted, with blood coming out of her mouth and nostrils, and later from the vulva. She was taken to a hospital where she was later delivered of a deformed fetus. *Dồng Nai*, another Saigon newspaper, printed on the same day a long article entitled "The Disease of Women Producing Stillborn Fetuses," which they said was a new phenomenon which was causing the "noisiest discussion" in the country. Next to the article is a photograph of a dead deformed baby with a face like that of a duck and the section around the stomach shrunken and twisted. The same newspaper, on the following day, reported a case of a woman giving birth, in Long An Hospital in Tan An District, to a deformed baby with two heads, three arms and 20 fingers. Just above the article, the paper carries a picture of another deformed baby with a head that resembles that of a poodle or a sheep. Still another Saigon newspaper, *Tia Sáng*, on June 26, 1969, printed a picture of a baby with three legs, a head squeezed in close to the legs, and two arms wrapped around a big bag that replaced the lower section of the face. Under the picture there is a separate report of the deformed baby mentioned above with two heads, three arms, and 20 fingers.

---

[8]Hersh, *loc. cit.*

The Saigon government's counter-argument was that the birth defects were caused by what it called "Okinawa bacteria." But many Vietnamese and American scientists who have seen the kinds of birth deformities in Viet Nam either in person or in pictures disagree with this argument. They say that venereal diseases can only cause warps in the bones and skin boils on newborn infants, and not such complete change in bodily structures. Even in an interview reported in the Saigon Army Newspaper, *Tiền Tuyến*, Dr. Phạm Tu Chính, director of the Hùng Vương Government Obstetrics Clinic, asserted that the cases of birth deformities that were causing concern in the country definitely could not have been caused by venereal diseases.[9]

In the rural areas, where most such known cases of deformed fetuses have occurred, there is an extreme shortage of trained medical personnel or of professional obstetric services, at least in those areas not held by the NLF. Thus it is difficult to compile accurate statistics concerning this phenomenon.

When the report of the National Institute of Environmental Health Sciences and the news of birth deformities in Viet Nam came to the attention of some American scientists, they went to Washington to try to persuade the U.S. Government to curb the use of the harmful chemicals. On October 31, 1969, the *Washington Post*, in an article entitled "New Curbs Won't Affect Defoliation in Viet Nam," reported:

> New White House restrictions on the use of a powerful herbicide will not affect its military usefulness in Vietnam, the Defense Department said yesterday.
> The Pentagon statement said no change would be made in policy governing military use of the defoliant 2,4,5-T because the Defense Department feels its present policy conforms to the new presidential directive.

Four days later, in an article entitled "Spray Earth Policy" in the *New York Post*, November 4, 1969, Frank Mankiewicz and Tom Braden had this to say:

> Those who are concerned over a possible massacre—even of women and children—in South Vietnam when U.S. troops depart might consider the fact that we now spray throughout South Vietnam enormous amounts of an anticrop chemical which has been known for three years to cause deformed births in test animals—at a rate of 100 per cent.
> At least four newspapers in South Vietnam printed stories—and pictures—last summer of deformed babies born in villages sprayed with the chemical (called 2,4,5-T), and the newspapers were promptly closed down by the Thieu government for "interfering with the war effort."
> Use of the chemical, described by our government as "probably dangerous," is now banned in "populated areas" and on or near food products in the United States, but the Pentagon announced last week that it would continue to use it in Vietnam, where Army Service Manuals set forth its appropriate use against food supplies.
> In addition, it is widely used in areas where the population captures its drinking water from rain, by the use of roof gutters and barrels, and where wells are sunk into soil saturated with the chemical.

[9]*Tiền Tuyến*, July 4, 1969.

Just how high an "offensive potential" this chemical warfare had was not really known until 1966 when, for the first time, the National Institute of Health commissioned tests on pregnant animals. The study showed that severe malformation of offspring occurred in rats at the rate of 39 per cent ... when they were given a small dose [of 2,4,5-T]. When this dose was increased to the level a Vietnamese woman might consume in a few days in her drinking water, the percentage of fetal malformation rose to 90 and beyond.

Whether the rate of human malformation from contact with this chemical is greater or less than with rats is, of course, unknown.

It was this that prompted the finding that 2,4,5-T was seriously hazardous and "probably dangerous" and caused its removal from the domestic market in the United States. The President's science adviser, Dr. Lee du Bridge, perhaps adumbrating the Pentagon's refusal to cut down its use against Asians, said only that the rate of fetal malformation was "greater than expected."

... Not since the Romans salted the land after destroying Carthage has a nation taken pains to visit the war on future generations.

As for Agent Blue, the *Merck Index of Chemicals and Drugs* says that it is an organic arsenical acid composed of 54.29 percent arsenic. Arthur W. Galston, the Yale biologist mentioned earlier, in an article in the August-September, 1967, issue of *Science and Citizen,* wrote that the lethal dose of the above compound in dogs is one gram per kilogram body weight, when administered beneath the skin. He added that if the same toxicity held for man, then about 70 grams, or slightly over two ounces, would kill the average 150-pound man. In the article already quoted, Seymour M. Hersh pointed out that in cases of "emergency," which he learned were not infrequent (especially when American pilots are exposed to heavy ground fire), the high-pressure spray nozzles of a plane on a spraying mission can eject the entire 1000-gallon cargo in just 30 seconds. In such cases, who knows what might happen to the people below!

In the already quoted study prepared by Yōichi Fukushima, there is a testimony by Cao Văn Nguyên, a doctor, which included a description of a chemical attack near Saigon on October 3, 1964, in which nearly 2500 acres of crop-producing land, a large number of livestock, and more than 1000 inhabitants were affected:

... They had only breathed in the polluted air or the poison had touched their skin. At first, they felt sick and had some diarrhea; then they began to feel it hard to breathe and they had low blood pressure; some serious cases had trouble with their optic nerves and went blind. Pregnant women gave birth to stillborn or premature children. Most of the affected cattle died from serious diarrhea, and river fish floated on the surface of the water belly up, soon after the chemicals were spread.

At a press conference in New York on April 3, 1969, E. W. Pfeiffer, Professor of Zoology at the University of Montana, and G. H. Orians, occupying the same position at the University of Washington, after returning from an official mission to Viet Nam to investigate the effects of the U.S. defoliation program, reported that while traveling in an armed naval vessel along a 65-mile strip of waterway linking Saigon with the sea, they observed that the mangroves on both sides had been denuded, that scarcely any living creatures were to be seen, and that bird life had apparently been greatly reduced.[10]

The dumping of herbicides and other chemicals in Viet Nam, besides causing harm to people, animals and crops, as we have seen, could also trigger changes in ecology that, according to the belief of many scientists, may permanently reduce the once-fertile fields in Viet Nam to dust bowls. Laterization, a process which occurs in tropical regions when the organic material and chemicals that normally enrich the soil are washed away because of lack of protective growth, thus resulting in a reddish soil which hardens irreversibly into a brick-like consistency upon exposure to sunlight, has begun in some areas in Viet Nam.

There is some evidence that even if the spraying were to be stopped now, the process of laterization would likely continue for some time in the future. Fred H. Tschirley, assistant chief of the Crops Protection Research Division of the U.S. Department of Agriculture and former adviser to the U.S. Department of State, in an article entitled "Defoliation in Vietnam" in the February 21 issue of *Science*, wrote:

> Strips of mangrove on both sides of the Ong Doc River, sprayed with Orange in 1962, were of particular interest. The treated strips were still plainly visible. Thus, one must assume that the trees were not simply defoliated, but were killed. . . 20 years may be a reasonable estimate of the time needed for this forest to return to its original condition.

Also, agent Blue (an arsenic compound) does not disintegrate or decompose in the soil but will keep on killing vegetation and soil microorganisms for a long time. Furthermore, as Representative McCarthy of New York pointed out in his book *The Ultimate Folly*, the herbicides used in Vietnam are made ten times more potent than their normal dose, while the spray nozzles used to administer them have not been altered, resulting in a heavy overdose for the trees and vegetation sprayed.

As if all the above were not enough, some in the American military would "escalate" the anticrop war to new proportions. Professor Arthur W. Galston, in his article "Military Uses of Herbicides in Viet Nam" already cited, reported that some U.S. military men and their advisers would very much like to spread an especially virulent strain of the rice-blast fungus developed at Fort Detrick, Maryland, "in the Vietnam theatre of war."

The U.S. government has again and again tried to tell the American people that it is in Viet Nam to protect freedom, democracy, and the right of self-determination for the Vietnamese. But the Vietnamese people understand very well what the U.S. government is in Viet Nam for.

---

[10]*The Nation*, April 21, 1969.

An open letter of September 23, 1967 to President Johnson from the Student Unions of Cần Thơ University, Vạn Hạnh University, Saigon University, and Dalat University (representing most of the university students in the country) begins with these words:

> The American intervention in the Vietnamese internal situation since after the Geneva Accord in 1954 has made the Vietnamese people regard the United States as replacing the French colonizers. The American policy, instead of helping the Vietnamese people, only pushes them into a destructive and bloody war. . .

At the beginning of this year, Professor Lý Chánh Trung of the University of Saigon, an ardent Catholic intellectual, was compelled to say the following words in a speech entitled "Why Do I Want Peace," delivered before the Saigon Student Union:

> Being a Vietnamese I can no longer stand the sight of foreigners arrogantly destroying my country through the use of the most modern and most terrible means, and through the use of the slogan "In protecting the Freedom" of the South Vietnamese population, a kind of freedom that the South Vietnamese population has had to throw up and vomit continuously during the last ten years or so without being able to swallow it successfully.

Apart from the "vocal minority," many other Vietnamese, perhaps finding it difficult to make public their views in so many words, choose to express themselves by continuing to fight.

Already, the war in Viet Nam has been the longest war in United States history, except perhaps, depending on just how one marks its duration, America's own War of Independence.

Star crater shown in foreground. *Photo by Orville Schell*

They Shall Inherit the Earth

Malcolm Somerville

The livelihood, both material and spiritual, of the Indochinese people has historically been their agriculture and their countryside. The destruction of much of the countryside, as well as devastating the morale of the people, has inevitably been accompanied by severe damage to the soils and fields which have sustained their societies through the centuries. The agricultural potential of Vietnam, as estimated for example by Moorman[1] in 1961, has probably been reduced drastically. The separation of the people from their countryside, caused by the war, may well continue long after the end of the struggle.

The extent of the damage, and the time required for recovery, where possible, cannot be accurately estimated in the absence of lengthy field studies. Some of the effects occur over a time span of years; for example, the permanent hardening of exposed soils to form the brick-like rock, laterite. The soils of the natural tropical forest are maintained by the forest itself, and are impoverished by the destruction of the forest. The time required for regeneration, if possible, of defoliated forests and mangroves, and the natural cycle of unwelcome bamboo and other pests, are measured in decades.

A consideration of the extent of the war's assault of the landscape and its danger to the soils suggests a drastic setback in the agricultural capability. Vagueness in the numerical and descriptive details of the soil damage indicates our general ignorance of the effects of the war technology.

Defoliating chemicals have been sprayed over at least 5 million acres, 12 percent of South Vietnam's area.[2] Orians and Pfeiffer[3] estimate that 20 to

---

[1]F. R. Moorman, "The Soils of the Republic of Vietnam," Republic of Vietnam, Ministry of Agriculture, Directorate of Studies and Research in Agronomy, etc., 1961,66 pp., Map, scale 1: 1,000,000.

[2]Stanford Biology Study Group, "The Destruction of Indochina," *California Tomorrow*, San Francisco, 1970, 9pp.

[3]Gordon H. Orians and E. W. Pfeiffer, "Ecological Effects of the War in Vietnam," *Science*, 168, May 1, 1970, pp. 544-554.

25 percent of the forest lands have been treated with defoliants two or more times; an estimate by the Provisional Revolutionary Government is much higher, 44 percent.[4] Perhaps half of the total acreage under intensive cultivation has been destroyed. More than 3 1/2 million 500- to 700-pound bombs dropped on Vietnam in 1967-1968 alone have excavated more than 2 1/2 billion cubic yards of earth,[2] ten times the excavation required for the Suez or Panama canals. The craters of these bombs occupy an area of almost 100,000 acres. Indochina contains enough bomb craters to occupy an area greater than the state of Connecticut's 5,000 square miles.

"According to Pentagon sources, aerial bombardment of Indochina from 1965 through 1969 reached 4 1/2 million tons, nine times the tonnage in the entire Pacific theater in World War II. This is about half of the total ordnance expended."[6]

Further hundreds of thousands of acres in South Vietnam have been completely stripped of vegetation by the Rome Plow.[7]

These assaults result in soil impoverishment, erosion, or hardening to form laterite rock, and critical damage to cropland and estuary.

In some instances there is evidence that devastation of the soils is included in the military strategy. Referring to Operations Sherwood Forest and Pink Rose, Thomas Whiteside wrote:[8]

> ... the ultimate folly in our defoliation operations in Vietnam was possibly achieved during 1965 and 1966, when the military made large-scale efforts in two defoliated areas to create fire storms—that is, fires so huge that all the oxygen in those areas would be exhausted. The apparent intention was to render the soil barren.... Neither of the projects, in which tons of napalm were thrown down on top of the residue of tons of sprayed 2, 4, 5-T, succeeded in creating the desired effect....

However, there is evidence that defoliation in itself is a disastrously effective weapon against the soils. The tropical forest is characterized by a complex interdependence of the soil, climate, plants and living creatures; the forest environment is unusually vulnerable to disturbances to any sector of the ecosystem. Most of the mineral nutrients of the humid tropical forest are carried in the standing crop or in the surface layers of the soil.[9] These nutrients include nitrates, phosphates, calcium, potassium, magnesium, sulphur, and other minor elements.[2] The heavy rainfall and high temperatures, among other minor factors, cause rapid washing away, or leaching, of

[4]Statement by Mme. Nguyen Thi Binhm, Chief of the Delegation of the Republic of Vietnam at the 55th Plenary Session of the Paris Conference on Vietnam, Feb. 19, 1970.
[5]S. M. Hersh, *Chemical and Biological Warfare*, Bobbs-Merrill, New York, 1968, 354 pp.
[6]Noam Chomsky, "Cambodia," *New York Review of Books*, June 4, 1970, footnote 53, p. 48.
[7]Midwest Research Institute, "Assessment of Ecological Effects of Extensive or Repeated Use of Herbicides," Final Report, Aug. 15 to Dec. 1, 1967, AD 824,314, pp. 281-284, 292.
[8]Thomas Whiteside, *Defoliation*, Ballantine Books, New York, 1970, 168 pp.
[9]G. Aubert, "Influence des divers types de vegetation sur les caracteres et l'evolution des sols en regions equitoriales et subequitoriales ainsi que leurs bordures tropicales semi-humides, in Symposium on Tropical Soils and Vegetation, Abidjan, UNESCO, 1959, pp. 41-58.

soil nutrients. Humus, the layer of decomposing vegetation on the forest floor, is not accumulated, but is just maintained at a level sufficient for the survival of the forest. Fungi provide the role of trapping nutrients released from decaying plants and making them available to the roots of living vegetation.[2] The nutrients cannot be retained by the vegetation in this manner when defoliation accelerates leaching of the soil. Defoliation is responsible for harsher conditions of rainfall, temperature and wind on the forest floor, and thereby causes rapid decomposition of the humus. The nutrients are quickly washed from the soil and lost altogether from the forest.

Living creatures play an important role in sustaining the tropical forest. The forest is pollinated by birds, bats and insects, rather than by the wind, and its seeds are dispersed to new clearings by animals and birds.

> These complex plant-animal relations have reached their greatest intricacy in tropical forests because of the mild and predictable climate. Animals can be active the year around because many flowering and fruiting trees provide food continuously. Massive defoliation means an end to this reliable food supply and death for those animals that are most important to the survival of the forest plants.[2]

> ... tropical forests hold the maximum number of individuals of most species that the resources will support. Reduction of forest habitats will decrease the populations of forest animals by an equivalent amount.[3]

Extinction of the fauna effectively prevents regrowth and spreading of the defoliated forest. Another factor inhibiting tropical forest regrowth, and hence retention of soil nutrients, is the tendency of pest species, such as grasses, shrubs and bamboo, to invade the forestland. This is a direct result of reduced soil fertility and the lack of seeds of the original forest plants. Giant bamboo is common in areas that have been cleared of trees for agricultural purposes, and other varieties are found as natural members of tropical forests in Vietnam.[10] The bamboo, growing in dense thickets, succeeds the natural tropical forest: consequently much of the fine hardwood forest now being destroyed by defoliation in Vietnam and Laos may be incapable of regeneraion.

Orians and Pfeiffer, reporting on a visit to South Vietnam in March, 1969, wrote:[3]

> Two or three spray applications may kill approximately 50 percent of commercially valuable timber in such (upland) forests ... possibly 20 to 25 percent of the forests of the country have been sprayed more than once.

As noted previously, this may be a conservative estimate of the extent of defoliation. The impoverishment of the tropical forest soil and the resulting succession by pest species make future agricultural use of the land very difficult. Defoliating, burning and cutting bamboo all fail to remove it once its hardy underground stems are established. The natural life cycle of bamboo is thought to be about thirty to fifty years.[10]

[10]Fred H. Tschirley, "Defoliation in Vietnam," *Science,* 163, Feb. 21, 1969, pp. 779-786.

The directness of the plant-soil interdependence has been summed up by Leitenberg:[11]

> If the soil is changed the forest will change. If the forest is changed the soil will change.

Angkor Wat, among other ancient shrines and monuments in Indochina, was constructed primarily of a durable, brick-like rock known as laterite. This rock actually forms from various soil types known as lateritic soils under certain tropical conditions. Lateritic soils develop in a strong rainy season alternating with a pronounced dry season of several months' duration.[12] [13] [14] These soils, characterized by a high iron oxide and aluminum content, occur over about half of Vietnam's terrain.[7] [13] The hardening of lateritic soils to form laterite rock is thought to occur under the following conditions:[15] ample drainage of the soil, gentle topography, and thorough drying (facilitated by increased exposure to sun and wind), possible over a period of several years. The climatic conditions which develop the lateritic soil also play a part in its conversion to laterite; there is alternate wetting and drying, and the water table fluctuates accordingly.

Millions of acres of bulldozed, bomb-cratered and defoliated land have been exposed to elevated temperatures and wind speeds, following the destruction of vegetation. The Mekong Delta area is susceptible to laterization because of its gentle topography and alluvial soils, which may be well drained in some areas. The dry season is especially pronounced in the Annamite mountain chain to the north of Saigon, and in much of the plain of Cambodia. In these regions the dry season is often a complete drought lasting three months, sometimes occurring for a few years in succession.[16] The Bolovens Plateau in southern Laos would be particularly susceptible to laterization.

Although laterization may be prevented by the steepness of the terrain in some areas, the war weapons are subjecting much of the land to the same conditions as have been responsible for the widespread occurrence of laterite in the tropics, for example in Thailand.[17] [18] Two types of laterite occur in South Vietnam.

[11]Milton Leitenberg, Draft of an unpublished mimeographed paper, Jan. 5, 1970, "The long-term effects of the use of chemical herbicides," Stockholm, Sweden.
[12]Mary McNeil, "Lateritic Soils," *Scientific American*, 211, May, 1964, pp. 96-102.
[13]R. Maignien, "Review of research on laterites," UNESCO, 1966, 148 pp.
[14]Lyle T. Alexander and John G. Cady, "Genesis and hardening of laterite in soils," U.S. Dept. of Agriculture Soil Conservation Service Technical Bulletin 1282, 1962.
[15]J. F. Taranik and E. J. Cording, "Laterite and its engineering properties," Mimeo Rep. 59th. Engin. Detachment (Terrain) (U.S. Army, A.P.O. 96491, 1967).
[16]Y. Henry, "Terres rouges et terres noires basaltiques d'Indochine," Hanoi, IDEO, 1931.
[17]Robert L. Pendleton, "Laterite and its structural uses in Thailand and Cambodia," *The Geographical Review*, 31, Feb., 1941, pp. 177-202.
[18]Robert L. Pendleton, "Laterite or Sila Laeng, a peculiar soil formation," *Thai Science Bulletin*, 3, Feb.-Mar., 1941, pp.61-77, pl. 1-24.

Wormhole laterite is generally consolidated and occurs as massive beds, commonly at the bottom of a 1- to 30-foot layer of well-drained soil. . . . Wormhole laterite occurs throughout most of the Mekong Terrace region, in soils of both forested and cultivated areas.

Pellet laterite is unconsolidated and occurs as small pellet-like concretions in an iron- or aluminum-rich soil. . . . Pellet laterite occurs on the iron-rich basalt plateau soils of the Mekong Terrace, the basalt plateau of Ban Me Thuot, the extreme western edge of the high plateau west of Pleiku, and in a small area around Quang Ngai. Pellet laterite has been observed forming on the metamorphic rocks near Bong Son and on some of the rocks near Qui Nhon. It is likely that wormhole and pellet laterite could occur in the northeastern coastlands, but this has not been substantiated by field studies.[10]

The Midwest Research Institute in its final report to the Department of Defense outlined the dangers of laterization:[7]

This end result (laterization) is never reached under a cover of rain forest. Lateritic soils may develop under grassland, savannah, or forest. Under the forest, however, the concentration of iron and aluminum compounds occurs at some depth from the surface, while under grassland it occurs at the surface. Clearcutting the forest and converting the area to grassland, though, may result in accelerating the hardening of lateritic soils into laterite rock, a process which greatly lowers the productive capacity of the site. . . . At Iata in the Amazon Basin, the land was deforested and bulldozed for an agricultural colony. What appeared to be a rich soil, with a promising cover of humus, disintegrated after the second planting. Under the equatorial sun, the iron rich soil began to bake into brick. In less than five years the cleared fields became virtually pavements of rocks.

Laterization of the soil would most likely occur in bombed and bulldozed areas along roadways, damaged cropland, cleared areas around base camps and in the vast forest areas which have been completely stripped of vegetation by the Rome Plow.

The Rome Plow has become one of the most surprisingly effective "weapons" of the Vietnamese war. This plow . . . is a sharpened 2,500-pound bulldozer blade long used commercially in ground-clearing operations. In Vietnam, Army engineers driving Caterpillar tractors with plows attached are cleaning hundreds of thousands of acres of jungle. . . . In the entire III Corps area about 102,000 acres were cleared between last July 1 (1967) and Dec. 3. Normally one plow, pushed by a Caterpillar tractor, can clear about 10,000 feet an hour of trees, up to 18 inches in diameter and of secondary growth. A heavy spike on one end of the blade, called a stinger, is used to split and weaken trees from 18 to 36 inches in diameter before they are cut off and pushed over. . . . For rubber trees, which grow on plantations in orderly rows, two tractors dragging a chain between them can fell whole rows quickly.[7]

A similar area of land has been totally devastated by bombing. As mentioned previously, in 1967-1968 alone, 3 1/2 million 500- to 750-pound bombs were dropped in Vietnam, leaving almost 100,000 acres occupied by bomb craters and excavating more than 2 1/2 billion cubic yards of earth.[2] The bombing of Indochina has amounted to perhaps the most massive excavation project in mankind's history. It dwarfs the Suez Canal and Panama Canal projects, both involving the excavation of about a quarter of a billion cubic yards of earth. The total cratered area in Indochina exceeds the area of the State of Connecticut, 5,000 square miles. This estimate is based on Pentagon figures[6] for the aerial bombardment from 1965 through 1969, and on Orians and Pfeiffer's report that a 500- to 750-pound bomb creates a crater as large as 45 feet across and 30 feet deep.[3]

In some areas the landscape has been altered almost beyond recognition. An aerial view of the section of Vietnam near the Parrot's Beak was reported by T. D. Allman:[19]

> ... the land is pitted by literally hundreds of thousands of bomb and shell craters. In some cases the years of day-and-night bombing have changed the contours of the land, and little streams form into lakes as they fill up mile after square mile of craters.

Much of the newly exposed terrain is subject to increased soil erosion. Large areas of the Annamite Mountains, now (or recently) covered by dense forest, possess clayey red and yellow soils characterized by a deep weathering profile, and sandier brown soils in the drier parts.[20] These soils on steep slopes would be highly susceptible to gullying and other forms of accelerated erosion following the destruction of vegetation or extensive bomb-cratering.[21] Rapid gullying and landsliding would lead to floods of silt and sand in valleys and on downstream watercourses. Large-scale exposure of unweathered bedrock would cause rapid rainwater runoff, causing higher floods and more prolonged droughts than previously.

As evidenced by the photographs, bombing has been used to destroy rice paddies and their irrigation systems. This can cause extensive erosion of paddy fields cut into steep or sloping country. The restoration of irrigation schemes and filling of bomb craters in the paddies which can be salvaged will be a monumental task. In flatter areas, dried-out paddy fields may well become pavements of laterite.

A 1967 report of the Agronomy section of the Japan Science Council claimed that:

> ... anti-crop attacks have ruined 3,800,000 acres of arable land in South Vietnam. ...[5]

This would amount to about half of the total acreage under intensive cultivation.[2]

In western Ca Mau Peninsula there is a large area of peat underlain by an acid and possibly saline soil. The area is not yet developed for cultivation but has considerable agricultural potential for rice production with a moderate amount of fertilization.[1] This potential could be greatly reduced if

[19]T. D. Allman, *Far Eastern Economic Review*, Feb. 26, 1970.
[20]R. Dudal and F. R. Moorman, "Major Soils of Southeast Asia," *Journal of Tropical Geography*, 18, Aug. 1964, pp. 54-80.
[21]Clyde Wahrhaftig, unpublished mimeographed paper, June 1970; "Some possible effects of military activity on soils of Southeast Asia," Berkeley, Calif.

deep bomb cratering destroys the protective peat cover and mixes the acid subsoil with the peaty surface soil.[21]

Destruction of mangrove forests bordering tidal estuaries permits bank erosion and salt-water intrusion of rice fields, with possible catastrophic reduction of rice yields. The Mekong Delta has suffered heavy bombing and defoliation. Tschirley, after visiting South Vietnam in March and April of 1968 to assess the ecological consequences of the defoliation at the request of the U.S. Department of State, reported that:[10]

> The mangrove species seem to be almost uniformly susceptible to Orange and White, the herbicides used for their control in Vietnam. . . . Strips of mangrove on both sides of the Ong Doc River, sprayed with Orange in 1962, were of par-ticular interest. The treated strips were still plainly visible. Thus, one must assume that the trees were not simply defoliated, but were killed.
> . . . 20 years may be a reasonable estimate of the time needed for this forest to return to its original condition. . . .

However, this time would be longer if there were removal of soil, which occurs more readily in a dead forest.

According to the Stanford Biology Study Group:[2]

> They (mangroves) also provide a special habitat for key stages in the life cycles of economically important fish and shell fish. . . . There will undoubtedly be a drastic and long-lasting effect upon river fishing and upon the natural processes of delta formation along Vietnamese rivers.

There is only one report of the use of soil sterilants in South Vietnam. The report,[22] in September 1967, referred to the Demilitarized Zone:

> Chemical soil killers will be used in South Vietnam warfare for the first time under the Pentagon's plan to create a barrier against infiltrating North Viet-namese troops. . . .

As far as is known, 2,4,5-T, Picloram, and 2,4-D, the most commonly used defoliation and herbicide agents, do not kill soil microorganisms. However, the effect of the decomposition products on microorganisms is not known. Nor do we know how long dangerous teratogenic residues will persist and threaten the lives of unborn children.

After more than a decade of highly technological warfare in Indochina, we have only preliminary evidence concerning the extent of the soil damage. However, current indications are of a disastrous reduction in agricultural capability. Desolate, inhospitable countryside awaits millions of refugee peasants. How many people can the land now sustain, and how many will return to attempt to revive their wasted land?

Acknowledgments

Clyde Wahrhaftig, Professor of Geology in the University of California, Berkeley, contributed much of the requisite research for this article. Andre Lehré, a doctoral student in Geology, assisted in the research.

[22]B. Horton, "Infiltration Barrier Planned, Soil Killer to Bare Viet Strip," (AP) *Minneapolis Star*, Sept. 8, 1967.

From Poisoning Plants For Peace*

by Arthur H. Westing

Americans have been killing vast areas of trees and crops in South Vietnam, North Vietnam, Cambodia, Thailand, and Laos.

The Department of Defense has admitted that four and a half million acres of forests and one-half million acres of cropland were sprayed through July 1969—about twelve percent of the land area of South Vietnam.

The spray program is carried out under the unofficial code name "Operation Ranchhand" (officially, "Operation Hades") by spraying or "putting in a burn" with one of several herbicidal mixtures from slow, low-flying aircraft. The Air Force unit assigned to the operation chose for its motto, "Only We Can Prevent Forests." Although originally categorized by the Department of Defense as biological warfare, herbicidal weapons in 1965 were redesignated as belonging to the arsenal of chemical warfare. Herbicides were not included in the President's rejection of biological and chemical weapons on November 25, 1969.

The chemicals currently in use seem to be limited to 2,4-D; 2,4,5-T; picloram ("Tordon"); and dimethyl arsenate (cacodylate; "Phytar"). Commonly used against forests is a mixture of 2, 4-D and 2, 4, 5-T (*agent Orange*). A mixture of 2, 4-D and picloram (*agent White*) also has been used. For the destruction of rice and other crops dimethyl arsenate (*agent Blue*) is employed.

Spray rates and sizes of contiguous areas treated far exceed the maxima recommended for roughly comparable herbicidal usage in this country (for example, to control vegetation on rights-of-way). Even dosages now considered safe in this country have been challenged by competent scientists having ecological or public health concerns totally unrelated to Vietnam.

The hazards and haphazards associated with military actions of any sort and the defensive need for jettisoning partial or entire thousand-gallon payloads during evasive maneuvers or because of engine trouble rather frequently lead to the application of phenomenal overdoses to relatively small

*Reprinted with permission from Friends Journal, *April 1, 1970*

areas. I also assume that the inadvertent sprayings of unintended areas must be rather common occurrences because of mistaken target identification, navigational errors, and wind-caused drifting of spray.

An instance of possibly unintended application was the dousing in April and May 1969, of some one hundred seventy-three thousand acres in Kompong Cham province, Cambodia. I recently returned from a study tour of the area, which includes about thirty-eight thousand acres planted to rubber and has a population of about thirty thousand inhabitants, whose lives thus were disrupted. Damages were set at more than twelve million dollars.

Forests are defoliated to deny the enemy cover or sanctuary. Trees are damaged or (particularly mangrove forests or after repeated spraying) killed. The result of spraying is by no means immediate. The leaves usually drop off only after several weeks.

The tactical benefits from such spraying have been questioned in several evaluations by military and civil authorities. My complaint is that we might well be altering drastically and detrimentally the ecology of vast acreages of South Vietnam. Vietnam is a small, impoverished, and ravaged country. Now we are adding even more to its burden without any reliable notion of the long-range consequences.

We have almost no knowledge of the effects of massive applications of herbicides under humid, tropical conditions. We have some indications, however, that there may be some serious long-term ecological (and associated economic) consequences.

One of the chemicals, picloram, does not decompose readily and may remain active in the environment for several years. The destroyed mangrove forests will take several decades to recover. The re-treated semideciduous forests are being converted to bamboo forests, which are economically inferior and foster increased populations of disease-carrying rats.

Among the more subtle changes that could contribute to the deterioration of ecosystems are the reduction in species diversity; the inhibition of nitrogen-fixing nodules in legumes (by 2,4-D); the induction of chromosomal aberrations in plants (by 2, 4-D and 2, 4, 5-T), leading to their lower environmental fitness; and the production of higher levels of nitrates in some plants (by 2,4-D) to the point where they become toxic to animals that depend upon them for food.

Our decimation of plants by herbicides must be added to the damage done to the environment by bombing (more than two and one-half million thirty-foot craters made in 1968 alone); extensive wildfires (particularly in herbicide-treated vegetation); and bulldozers (some five hundred thousand acres laid bare by giant plows through 1969).

Such insults to the environment accelerate soil erosion and in some locations perhaps even bring about the irreversible hardening of the topsoil (a process known as laterization, which is peculiar to one type of tropical soil found in South Vietnam).

In short, we may be altering drastically the vegetational composition—and with it the faunal composition—over a significant fraction of the country. This is the legacy we will leave the Vietnamese people, whose well-being we claim to be committed to preserve. . . .

. . .The United States is carrying on two methods of combat in Vietnam contradictory to stated Defense Department policy and presumably antithetical to basic American ideals.

On the one hand, we are employing weapons that are likely to upset for decades to come a significant fraction of the ecology of a small, destitute, friendly nation. On the other, we are employing weapons that have their most drastic impact on the civilians of that nation, not on the enemy combatants.

Our nation was the first and only one to unleash nuclear warfare. With our massive use of herbicides, we are chalking up yet another first, similarly unconfined in space and time and similarly unpredictable in its ultimate consequences.

The Chemically Poisonous Products' Effects on Particular Agricultural Products,

1. On corn and other cultivated foodstuffs:

Manioc: It has a very low resistance against poisonous chemicals and dies quickly. The manioc leaf withers from the poison, even if the plant is 6 kilometres from the place of attack. For example, during a chemical spraying in the small village of Binh Hoa which belongs to the An Lac village, the leaves on the manioc plants in the small village of Chau Binh Duc's orchards withered (the village of An Tin) 8 kilometres from there. When the attack occurs, and there are manioc plants in the way, the result is that they die three hours later. The leaves turn yellow and fall off, and the fruit dies. Generally, when a manioc fruit is ripe, it weighs 1,100 grams, but after exposure to 2,4-D or 2,4,5-T it does not weigh more than about 220 grams. For the most part, 75% of these 220 grams deteriorate, the fruit becomes hard as wood, the skin swells and the fruit is no longer edible.

Rice: If a rice plant is poisoned at the flowering stage, or when it is fully fertile, it falls and collapses onto the ground as if it had been hit by a storm, the leaves turn yellow, and shrink together. The bad plants at cultivation time rise to 68%.

Sweet potato: These die very quickly. Even if a chemical attack occurs far away, the leaves wither and fall off. If the chemical attack occurs at the same place they are growing, they die a few hours after the attack. The leaves roll themselves together, the fruit rots, and becomes totally unedible.

Maize: During a chemical attack—the plant becomes dwarfed, the roots swell and few roots grow. If the affected plant flowers, the corncob becomes dried out. If the maize plant, each of which bears 5-7 leaves, is attacked by

From Document Concerning the U. S. Chemical Warfare in South-Vietnam. Issued by The South Vietnamese Committee for the Revealing of the U. S. imperialists war crimes in South Vietnam. February 1970, pp. 6-8 ·

poisonous chemicals, it gives much less. Generally a maize cob weighs 126 grams, but if affected by chemicals it does not become larger than about 58 grams. Added to this, the cob becomes deformed, the kernels become very thin and dispersed and the quality of the plant is greatly reduced. Maize production therefore goes down to 68 grams per flower (126 grams-58 gr.) Every plant produces generally three fruits, this will then be a total reduction of 68 grams x 3 = 204 grams per plant. Plus this, the quality of the damaged maize plant is extremely bad.

2. Cultivated plants and fruit trees:

Coconut palms: The coconut palm has a long life. It is robust, it has no branches or forks, neither has it the ability to renew itself. Therefore it is very sensitive to a poisonous chemical. During an attack of a very concentrated chemical, the coconut tree dies immediately, the leaves dry out before they fall off, and the tops of the trees split. If it should rain after a chemical attack, a coconut palm would die even quicker, as the chemical poison which had fallen on the leaves then would run down the trunk and hasten the poisoning process. If the poison has a low concentration it splits up the higher part of the trunk (4-5 days later) into drawn-out pieces, sometimes 30-40 cm. Thereupon they crumble and fall even if the leaves have not completely withered. If the tree is only slightly damaged, the leaves become dark green, they grow properly but no fruit; or the coconuts are deformed, they mature too early, the shell dries too early, the flesh becomes soft, and the milk sour. A few coconuts fall off even if they are small, thereafter the remainder grow very fast. The remaining fruit that survives becomes square, the fibre-like shell thickens quickly, and the meat becomes very soft. Some of them become large and misshapen, but the insides of them are no larger than a nut and they have neither meat nor milk.

Jacquiers: (We cannot find an English name for this plant.) The life span of this fruit tree is generally very long. It is extremely sensitive to chemical agents. When a chemical attack occurs, the leaves dry and fall off, the trunk also dries and dies. If the chemical attack takes place at a distance of 4-5 km. the tree loses all its foliage, the young trees die, the older trees do not completely die, but after a while the trunk splits and the trees yield neither flowers nor fruit. (An Nghia and An Lao were large jacquiers producers, now there are practically no trees left.)

Banana trees: When a banana tree is affected by a chemical it splits easily and breaks. The banana swells and has no form, large and sponge like. It is no longer eatable. A poisoned banana is three times as large as an ordinary banana, and the fruit is ruined. Take for example a bunch of poisoned bananas:

The banana's length before the chemical effect	72,50 mm
The banana's length after the chemical effect	209,00 mm
The banana's circumference before the chemical effect	32,50 mm
The banana's circumference after the chemical effect	132,50 mm
The banana's skin thickness before the chemical effect	1,80 mm
The banana's skin thickness after the chemical effect	6,70 mm

Anganiers and letchiers: (Unfortunately we cannot find the English equivalent.) They die very quickly, their leaves dry and fall off, even if the spread of poison was very distant. (An Hoa.)

Hévéas: (We do not know the name of this in English either.) In October 1966, the Americans spread chemical poisonous agents over an hévéas plantation in Gia Lai, and through this, destroyed the hévéas in an area of 1,000 hectares. In central Nam Bo, 30,000 hectares of hévéas were damaged.

Ricin (Castor oil plant): When in an area of chemical attack, the leaves fall off and the plant dies.

Cotton: When under chemical attack, the leaves wither, the buds disappear and the young fruit falls off. The worst damage has been registered during the budding and fruition period. When poisoned, the fruit of the cotton bushes becomes elongated, soft and loses its resistance.

Tobacco: The leaves turn yellow, wither and fall. The plant dies. If it survives, the leaves are weak, and when one smokes the tobacco, it smells like burnt paper.

When one studies the effects of American poisonous chemicals on agricultural cultivation and other vegetation, one can conclude that the American imperialists all the time aim at damaging plants that are necessary for agriculture and industry and therefore are also necessary for the South Vietnamese people's daily existence.

Through the use of these chemical poisons, the Americans believe that they can starve the population from the free areas, and force them to live in an area which is temporarily occupied by them.

Rice disposal is part of the food denial program. *Photo by Paul Avery, Empire.*

Starvation as a Weapon*

Jean Mayer

Crop destroying agents are "good examples of strategic weapons." So said a 1960 report of the Senate Foreign Relations Committee, adding that the eventual result of their use "would be something of the same nature as a blockade cutting off vital foods and supplies."[1]

These strategic weapons are now being used on food crops in Vietnam. A U.S. Government spokesman explains that food is as important to the Viet Cong as weapons, and that herbicides are used "where significant denial of food supplies can be effected by such destruction."[2]

In the first nine months of 1966, the 12th Air Commando Squadron sprayed about 70,000 acres of crops, mostly rice. The acreage of croplands sprayed had by now risen to about 150,000.[3] These figures do not include accidental drifting of sprays onto agricultural land from the defoliation being carried out over a much larger portion of South Vietnam.

There is as yet little direct evidence from Vietnam of the effects of crop destruction on the Viet Cong: no data on starvation of persons who can be categorically defined as "Viet Cong"; no reports that Viet Cong prisoners have been found to be physically incapacitated by malnutrition; no clear evidence of lessening of the Viet Cong will to fight. Yet it is clear that malnutrition is common among Vietnamese civilians, whether due to diet deficiencies unrelated to the war, to food problems resulting from other war conditions—military and economic, to the conscious efforts of denying food to the Viet Cong, or to a combination of all three.

Information justifying the program has never been released by military or other U.S. Government sources. In the absence of such data, we must turn

*Reprinted with permission from *Scientist and Citizen*, Aug.-Sept., 1967.

to other, less direct information and to historical inferences. In spite of the paucity of information from Vietnam, the effects of food denial as a weapon are no mystery. We can turn to well documented sources for answers to the questions:

How does a food shortage affect a population?
Which elements of the population are most affected?
Is starvation an effective strategic weapon?

The answers to these questions can then be related to the situation in Vietnam.

The effects of starvation on the human body are well known and were described in detail in a number of publications immediately following World War II. Famine affects different elements of the population in different ways and to different degrees; this has been observed in famines occurring in peacetime as well as in war. The author has personally observed famines on three continents, one of them Asia.

Finally, although herbicides have not been used in previous wars, the creation of famine through blockade has been frequently used and there is historical evidence of its effects.

The first and most obvious effect of starvation on the human body is the wasting of its fat deposits. A nutrition survey of South Vietnam in 1959 found that the average weight of civilian males was 105 pounds,[4] suggesting that such body fat deposits would generally be meager in Vietnamese to start with.

The stomach and intestines, heart and lungs are affected next; the size of the liver is drastically diminished. The intestinal lining becomes thin and smooth, thereby losing some of its absorptive capacity, and diarrhea results. Thus starvation is a self-accelerating process, particularly in children; because of intestinal damage the food that is available is poorly absorbed and undernutrition increases correspondingly. The damaged lining of the stomach fails to secrete hydrochloric acid, which is important for digestion. Both blood pressure and pulse rate fall.

Early effects of starvation are cessation of menstruation in women and impotence and loss of libido in men. Hair is dull and bristling and in children abnormal hair grows on the forearms and back. The skin acquires the consistency of paper and not infrequently shows the irreversible dusty brown splotches which are permanent marks of starvation. In extreme cases, particularly among children, the lips and parts of the cheeks are destroyed.

The body becomes susceptible to infection and disease. The psychologic state deteriorates rapidly; the individual becomes obsessed with food, mentally restless, apathetic and self-centered.

A recent paper prepared by Physicians for Social Responsibility for Senate hearings on the refugee problem summarized the medical problems in South Vietnam.[5] It pointed out that malnutrition is widespread among South Vietnamese civilians; beri-beri, night blindness and anemia are found frequently; kwashiorkor, a form of protein malnutrition, occurs and is a major component of the problems of wound healing and resistance to infections; infant and child mortality is high. Kwashiorkor is a deadly disease affecting children after weaning. It causes degeneration of the liver, pancreas and intestines; edema, and eventually death. Diseases associated with malnutrition, such as tuberculosis, are rampant. Although it is impossible to know to what extent these problems stem from the crop destruction program, there can be no doubt that if the program is continued these problems will grow.

In many parts of Southeast Asia, there are food shortages in the best of times, and any strain on the food supply, whether from political factors or natural disasters, may result in famine. In East Pakistan, for example, when food production is as little as ten per cent below normal, disastrous famine ensues.[6]

Such a famine occurred in 1954 and 1955. For seven years prior to this time, beginning with the partition of India and Pakistan in 1947, large scale migrations of Moslems had created a tremendous refugee problem and placed heavy additional demands on the food supply. In 1954 and 1955, the Brahmaputra River and tributaries flooded, destroying homes and crops and disorganizing transport. This writer was in India in 1954 and observed some of the aspects of the famine which followed the flood and reached serious proportions in spite of the efforts of the Pakistan and Indian governments and outside help from the U.S. and other nations.

A recent nutrition survey of East Pakistan found that even under "normal" conditions adult males are better fed than other groups,[7] while 26 per cent of all liveborn children in that province die before their fifth birthday. This contrasts with 2.4 per cent of European children who die before age five.

This imbalance was aggravated in the Brahmaputra famine. As in all famines, small children were affected first and overwhelmingly. They were the first to die; older children and the elderly followed. Pregnant women not infrequently aborted, lactating mothers ceased to produce milk and the babies died. In addition to the food shortage itself, disruption and chaos typical of refugee populations were aggravated as people fled the flood areas and migrated in search of food. Thus social conditions also victimized the weaker elements of the population. The primary and secondary educational systems which the Pakistan government had been struggling to develop were brought to the verge of collapse.[8]

A general consequence of famine is the social disruption, including panic, which accompanies it. Starving people attempt to journey to other areas where they hope to find food, and chaos increases. Weakened by lack of food, they are susceptible to disease, and these factors interact with one another, disease adding to social disorganization which in turn makes disease more difficult to combat.

In Vietnam, migration has already been set in motion by military attacks on villages, or fear of such attacks, and by the destruction of agricultural lands already referred to. At Senate hearings on refugee problems in South Vietnam and Laos, Frank H. Weitzel, Acting Comptroller General of the United States, gave the number of refugees in South Vietnam in fiscal year 1965 as 600,000, six times what had been expected.[9] In November an additional statement from Mr. Weitzel gave a total of 719,000 but said 258,000 were classified as resettled. At the end of 1966, the *New York Times* put the figure at a million, growing at a rate of about 70,000 a month.[10] A July 3, 1967 news item states that almost two million refugees are now in government resettlement camps—one in every seven South Vietnamese.[11]* These recently uprooted people are a different population from the 1955 refugees from North Vietnam who, according to the South Vietnamese government, are now resettled.

In 1965, refugees were almost 100 per cent women, children and older men,[12] and this remains true.

Twenty-six years of almost uninterrupted war have placed strains on the food supply, especially severe in the last two years. South Vietnam, which exported forty-nine million metric tons of rice in 1964,[13] must now import it. Figures for 1966 are not yet available, but 240,000 tons were imported in 1965.[14]

The medical-nutritional picture in South Vietnam is typical of an underdeveloped country ravaged by war. Infant mortality is estimated at twenty-five to thirty per cent, more than ten times that of the U.S. Maternal death rate is twenty-five times that of the U.S. Life expectancy at birth is about thirty-five years. In an environment where sanitation is primitive and medical facilities are in short supply, a great additional hazard is the risk of epidemics which can grow like wildfire in a weakened, starving and migrating population.

Bubonic plague is endemic, and although only eight cases were reported in 1961, the number is said to have risen to 4500 in 1965.[5] Malaria is also endemic, and the appearance of a form of the disease which does not respond to traditionally effective drugs is a matter of grave concern. Cholera and smallpox have been habitual fellow travelers of Asian famines, with influenza and relapsing fever also frequent.

In 1965 alone the number of cases of cholera in Vietnam increased by 25,000 according to the World Health Organization.[15] In that same year Dr. Howard Rusk reported that among refugees "tuberculosis is highly prevalent, as are skin infections, intestinal parasites, trachoma and other diseases of the eyes, typhoid and leprosy."[16]

Starvation in Previous Wars

What has been the effect of food denial as a weapon in previous wars? Has it reduced the effectiveness of the fighting men in the blockaded nations?

*Officials of the Agency for International Development were quoted in the *St. Louis Post'Dispatch*, October 12, to the effect that the total number of refugees in South Vietnam in August, 1967 was 2,008,098.

Has it been decisive in bringing victory to the besiegers? What has been its effect on civilians? A study of three examples from wars fought within the past hundred years goes a long way toward answering these questions.

The siege of Paris. Paris was under siege by the Germans for 129 days in 1870-71, during the Franco-Prussian War. One of the reasons given by the government for surrender was the lack of food within the city. However there was a desperate military situation in the rest of the country. Prior to the siege, one of the main French forces was defeated at Sedan; during the siege, the other was defeated at Metz. Thirty-six new divisions were organized and equipped from Tours, but a number of them were driven into Switzerland, where they were disarmed and interned.

According to Baldick,[17] the death rate in Paris rose from 3,680 in the first week to 4,465 in the third—and presumably still higher as the siege dragged on for eighteen weeks. The winter was severe so that people suffered from cold as well as hunger; epidemics swept the city, with smallpox the biggest killer.

Melvin Kranzberg describes the effect of the food shortage on the people of Paris:

> With the exception of the dent made in their pocketbooks the rich did not suffer from famine during the siege. . . . As for the poor, the men were not badly off, but the women and children suffered. The men could get enough to eat and perhaps too much to drink merely by enlisting in the National Guard.[18]

Blockade of the Central Powers. In the early days of World War I, the western Allies were optimistic that the hunger engendered by the blockade of the Central Powers—Germany, Austria-Hungary and the smaller countries allied with them—would help win the war quickly. After the war, the importance of the blockade may have been exaggerated by German historians in order to play down military defeats; it may have been underestimated by British, French and American historians. The fact remains that it took four years of the combination of blockade and military action to defeat the Central Powers.

Famine edema, a relative increase in the water content of the body, was observed in civilians in Hamburg in the winter of 1916-17, in Berlin in January, 1917, in Vienna and the Rhineland later the same year. In 1918, it became common throughout Central Europe. Tuberculosis, which is closely related to malnutrition, had been decreasing, and reached its lowest point in 1913. It began to rise in 1914 and continued to rise throughout the war. In Vienna, the mortality rate from tuberculosis rose almost 100 per cent; in Germany, 44 per cent.[19]

The excess of deaths in the civilian population during each of the war years over the number of deaths for the year 1913 totaled 762,796.

These figures represent the number of deaths which under "normal circumstances" presumably would not have happened. They were probably due to a combination of the food shortage with other factors. Medical care of civilians suffered because of the army's drain on medical personnel and facilities. There was a shortage of fuel because importation of coal was reduced by the blockade and internal distribution was disrupted by the war. Although most of the war was fought on French and Russian soil, the Austro-Hungarian Empire was invaded, with some of its villages and countryside becoming a battleground.

If the figures above are compared with deaths in the army it can be seen that civilian deaths in excess of normal may have been about half as great as the army losses. However, it must also be said that the very war conditions which cause excess civilian deaths, make reliable statistics difficult to assemble.

	Deaths in the Army		Deaths in the Civil Population
	On the battle-field and through wounds	Through sickness	Due to the Blockade
1st War Year	451,506	24,394	88,235
2nd War Year	330,332	30,329	121,174
3rd War Year	294,743	30,190	259,627
4th War Year	317,954	38,167	293,760*
Postwar due to the War	62,417	10,902	
Total	1,456,952	133,982	762,796

*To end of 1918.

This table is taken from an article which appeared in the *Deutsche Medizinische Wochenschrift, Berlin,* April 10, 1919, Vol. 45, No. 15 entitled "Von der Blockade und Aehnlichem," by Dr. Ruth M. Rubner and are reprinted from "Blockade and Sea Power," by Maurice Parmalee, Thomas Y. Crowell, Co., N.Y. 1924. (Minor errors in totals corrected by S/C.)

George A. Schreiner, an Associated Press correspondent, spent the first three years of the war in Germany and the nations allied with it, including considerable time with the armies on both eastern and western fronts. He states that many men in the army received better food than they had as pre-war civilians. He says that the army "came first in all things" and that when it became necessary to reduce the bread ration, this was made good by increasing the meat and fat ration.[20] Schreiner quotes a "food dictator" as saying that thousands of the poor aged were going to a premature death.

The siege of Leningrad. The most recent, the most lethal, and yet the most completely ineffective use of starvation as a strategic weapon of war was the siege of Leningrad by the Nazis in World War II. It closed around the three million people of the city on September 8, 1941. For four months only 45,000 tons of food were brought in by water, air and finally by the road across the ice of Lake Ladoga, and this was expected to sustain the military as well as the civilian population. Late in January, 1942, a corridor was opened which permitted both the importation of food and the evacuation of large numbers of people, but the siege was not completely lifted until two years later. By this time almost a million people—about a third of the city's population—were dead from hunger, cold, and their attendant diseases, and from the bombing and shelling of the city.

As in the previous cases, the soldiers defending the city had better rations than the civilians, although their rations, too, had to be cut on November 20, 1941 when things were at the worst.[21] Hospital records for the starvation period show some of the effects on infants and pregnant mothers: an increase in stillbirth and premature birth and a rise in neonatal mortality.[22]

The early and worst parts of the siege were accompanied by German victories elsewhere in the nation; German armies came within a few miles of Leningrad homes and factories where people continued to live and work. Nevertheless, the troops besieged along with the city defended it successfully and eventually broke the blockade.

While historians differ in assigning significance to these blockades as effective military techniques it is clear from all three of these examples that food denial in war affects the fighting men least and last, if at all, and is therefore unsuccessful unless accompanied by military victories by the blockaders. It is hardest on civilians, particularly children and the elderly; where economic class divisions are sharp, it is particularly hard on the poor.

Destroying Food in Vietnam

The increasing use of herbicides in Vietnam referred to earlier suggests that the U.S. military plans to enlarge the area where food crops will be destroyed.

News stories have reported other methods being used in the food denial campaign. In areas under the political control of the Viet Cong, U.S. and South Vietnamese troops may establish temporary military control long enough for a "harvest protection" operation. This is carried out by entering the area at harvest time, holding off Viet Cong rice collectors while peasants are required to sell their surpluses to the government or to the commercial market and then withdrawing.[23]

The agricultural area in the demilitarized zone and just to the south of it has been rendered completely unproductive as have special areas in the immediate proximity of Saigon (operations Junction City and Cedar Falls in the "iron triangle"). As many as 600,000 Vietnamese have been removed from agricultural productive labor and are now residing in camps.[24]

Rice that has already been harvested may be destroyed. Sometimes it is dumped into large pits and covered with shark repellent or other obnoxious compounds; attempts have been made to burn or scatter it. Captured rice has been dumped into the Rachbenggo River by U.S. troops.

According to General William W. Berg, U.S. Air Force Deputy Assistant Secretary of Defense, "Our combat units are well aware of the food shortages in South Vietnam and are not wantonly destroying captured rice whenever it can be salvaged and put to local use. However, in a fluid combat situation, available time, manpower and transportation will not always permit removal of captured goods to a safe area."[25]

Charles Mohr has reported in the *New York Times* that the troops have found rice to be "one of the most maddeningly indestructible substances on earth. Even with thermite molten-metal grenades, it virtually will not burn. The scattering of rice does not prevent its collection by patient men."[23]

These practical difficulties suggest one reason for the use of chemical sprays. Another, and perhaps the most important reason, is that it entails a more efficient use of personnel.

"What's the difference between denying the Viet Cong rice by destroying it from the air or by sending in large numbers of ground forces to prevent the enemy from getting it?" a Pentagon spokesman asked. "The end result's the same; only the first method takes far less men."[26]

Whatever method is used, the examination of past wars and famines makes it clear that the food shortage will strike first and hardest at children, the elderly, and pregnant and lactating women; last and least at adult males and least of all at soldiers.

That these conclusions apply to Vietnam as well is suggested by the Vietnamese nutrition study carried out in 1959 by Americans and South Vietnamese under the latter's Committee on Nutrition for National Defense, in which an equal number of army and civilian Vietnamese were compared.[27]

"In the general sense, the nutritional status of the military is superior to that of the civilian population, without appreciable differences between Army, Navy, and Air Force," says the study. While the average civilian male weighs 104.3 pounds, his counterpart in the military weighs 113.0 pounds. And, for those who might suppose the difference results from military selection procedures favoring bigger men from the general population, the study reports:

> Inductees (Quang Trung) weighed 107 pounds on the average, the lowest weight among any of the military. A group of similar men completing their basic training (Quang Trung) has an average weight of 114 pounds, suggesting that the change from a civilian to a military diet resulted in a prompt weight gain, in spite of the strenuous activity of basic training. Considering the combined military services, continuation of such weight gain during the first year of military life was further evidenced by the weight gain from an average of 107 pounds for those in the service less than three months to an average of 118 pounds for those with six months to one year of service.

South Vietnamese army medical care is also superior to that available to civilians, as Dr. John Reed of the U.S. Public Health Service testified on his return from working with Vietnam refugees: "... there are only about 800 qualified physicians in the Republic of South Vietnam. Of this 800, 500 are in the military service. Of the remaining 300, approximately half, or 150, are in private practice in Saigon, so this leaves only about 150 doctors for the entire rural population in South Vietnam."[28]

This refers to the South Vietnamese government side, but on the other side, Viet Cong soldiers may likewise be expected to get the fighter's share of whatever food there is. Whether extra rations are enforced by an organized government structure or confiscated by armed bands of guerrillas, the end result is the same. Unless direct evidence to the contrary from U.S. observations in Vietnam is forthcoming, this conclusion seems unavoidable: from a military viewpoint, the attempt to starve the Viet Cong can be expected to have little or no effect. What it can be expected to do is to add to a flow of refugees already far beyond the capacity of the program designed to care for them.

This history of modern war has been one of increasing involvement of civilians. Starvation as a weapon is an aspect of such involvement, one which has the peculiar property of inflicting suffering on civilians while doing little damage to the military. To destroy crops—with herbicides or in any other way—is therefore to employ a weapon whose target is the weakest element of the civilian population.

References

1. Senate Committee on Foreign Relations, Subcommittee on Disarmament, "CBR Warfare and its Disarmament Aspects," Washington, D.C., 1960.
2. Donnelley, Dixon, Assistant Secretary, Dept. of State. Letter to Arthur Galston and other plant physiologists, September 28, 1966. Published in full in *BioScience*, January, 1967, p. 10.
3. Langer, Elinor. "Chemical and Biological Warfare (II): The Weapons and the Policies," *Science*, 155: 303. These numbers were supplied to *Science* in January by the Pentagon.
4. "Republic of Vietnam, Nutrition Survey, October-December, 1959," A Report by the Interdepartmental Committee on Nutrition for National Defense, July, 1960.
5. Collins, J. L., Frank Ervin, Vicki Levi, and David Savitz. "Medical Problems of South Vietnam," Physicians for Social Responsibility, Boston, January, 1967.
6. United Nations Commission for Asia and the Far East. "Multi-Purpose River Basin Development, Part 2B, Water Resources Development in Burma, India, and Pakistan," Bangkok, December, 1956.

7. Pakistan Ministry of Health (in collaboration with the University of Dacca and the U.S. Nutrition Section, Office of International Research, National Institutes of Health). "Nutrition Survey of East Pakistan, March, 1962-January, 1964," U.S. Department of Health, Education and Welfare, May, 1966.

8. "Pakistan 1955-1956," Pakistan Publications, Karachi, 1956.

9. Weitzel, Frank H. Testimony before Hearings of the Subcommittee to Investigate the Problems Connected with Refugees and Escapees of the Committee on the Judiciary, United States Senate, Eighty-Ninth Congress, July 13-September 30, 1965. U.S. Government Printing Office, 1965.

10. *New York Times*, October 9, 1966.

11. Arnett, Peter, and Horst Faas. "American Claims of Progress in Vietnam Disputed," *St. Louis Post-Dispatch* (AP), July 3, 1967.

12. Rusk, Howard. "Refugee Crisis in Vietnam," *New York Times*, September 12, 1965.

13. "Statistical Yearbook, 1966," U.N., 18th Issue, New York, 1967, p. 277.

14. Faltermayer, Edmund K. "South Vietnam's Economy," *Fortune*, March, 1966, p. 228.

15. World Health Organization. "Refugee Problems in South Vietnam," p.137.

16. *Ibid.*, Baldick, Robert, "The Siege of Paris," B.T. Batsofor,

17. Baldick, Robert. *The Siege of Paris*, B. T. Batsfor, Ltd., London, 1964.

18. Kranzberg, Melvin. "The Siege of Paris, 1870-71, A Political and Social History," Cornell University Press, Ithaca, New York, 1962.

19. Keyes, Ancel, et al. "The Biology of Human Starvation," 2 Vols., University of Minnesota Press, Minneapolis, 1950.

20. Schreiner, George A. "The Iron Ration," Harper and Bros., N.Y., 1918.

21. Werth, Alexander. "Russia at War," E. P. Dutton and Co., N.Y., 1964.

22. Antonov, A. N. "Children Born During the Siege of Leningrad," *J. Pediatrics*, 30:250-59, 1947, quoted by Keyes.

23. Mohr, Charles. "U.S. Spray Planes Destroy Rice in Viet Cong Territory," *New York Times*, December 21, 1965.

24. ABC Broadcast, July 2, 1967.

25. Berg, Gen. William W. Letter to Senator Jacob K. Javits, May 18, 1966.

26. Welles, Benjamin. "Pentagon Backs Use of Chemicals," *New York Times*, Sept. 21, 1966.

27. "Republic of Vietnam Nutrition Survey," pp. 1, 62, 85.

28. World Health Organization. "Refugee Problems in South Vietnam and Laos," p.134.

What Have We Done to Vietnam?*

by Robert E. Cook, William Haseltine and Arthur W. Galston[†]

President Nixon has proposed to call a halt to all biological warfare research and stockpiling operations in the United States, and to submit the Geneva Protocol to Congress for ratification. While these are commendable moves, the government is excluding from his ban the use of defoliants, herbicides, and antipersonnel gases in Vietnam. That is tragic, for these weapons respect neither the neutrality of the fertile farms nor the innocence of undefended civilians. The destruction in Vietnam is heightened because Allied forces, for the first time since World War I, have employed massive quantities of chemicals against the enemy: villages have been leveled with napalm; caves and bunkers have been saturated with tear gas to drive protected soldiers into open fire; crops have been destroyed and jungles defoliated to deny the enemy food and cover. It is the civilians who bear the major burden of this assault. Since there are no concrete enemy strongholds or fixed battlelines, battles arise whenever contact is made between US and South Vietnamese forces and the fluid enemy, whose primary tactic is mobility.

Since 1962 huge C-123 cargo planes, equipped with tanks and high pressure spray nozzles, have released more than 100 million pounds of chemical herbicides over more than 4 million acres, an area larger than the state of Massachusetts. This includes more than 500,000 acres of croplands growing

---

†ROBERT E. COOK is a graduate student in ecology at Yale, WILLIAM HASELTINE is a graduate student in biophysics at Harvard, and ARTHUR W. GALSTON is professor of biology at Yale.

Reprinted with permission from *New Republic*, Jan. 10, 1970.

Photo by Robert Scheu, Photon West

rice, manioc, beans and other vegetables. To decrease the number of flights necessary over enemy fire, the chemicals are sprayed in concentrations up to ten times those recommended for use in the United States. This spreads nearly 30 pounds of herbicide over each acre of land.

The Air Force has been spraying four different chemical compounds in varying combinations colorfully known as agents *Orange, Blue,* and *White. Orange* consists of equal parts of 2,4-D and 2,4,5-T, general weed killers used extensively in the United States. *Orange* usually persists for only one or two weeks in ground water or soil, but its disappearance depends upon microorganisms requiring specific conditions, including abundant oxygen. Thus, high concentrations could build up in stagnant water or poorly aerated ground. Agent *Blue* consists primarily of cacodylic acid which contains 54 percent arsenic. Its use against crops is forbidden in the United States, but it has been so used in Vietnam. Agent *White* is a blend of 2,4-D and picloram, the latter being an unusually persistent herbicide which is capable of killing vegetation and retarding regeneration for years.

These herbicides are a product of agricultural research done during the thirties and forties, when a number of hormone-like substances were identified in plants and brought to the attention of the Army for potential use in the control of plant cover and crop production. Research was undertaken at Fort Detrick, the home of chemical-biological warfare research, to develop the new compounds. After the war, direct toxicity levels for man and animals were investigated and determined to be low enough to make the chemicals acceptable for general use as weed killers. The US Department of Agriculture, the Federal Drug Administration, the National Institutes of Health, and the Fish and Wildlife Service all had a hand in sanctioning the widespread use of herbicides. By 1965, more than 120 million acres were being sprayed each year in the United States. Despite this wide usage, no studies had been conducted until very recently by any government agency on the possible carcinogenic, mutagenic, or teratogenic properties of herbicides, or on the ecological consequences of their use.

Many botanists and ecologists decried the ecological destruction which is an unavoidable consequence of the defoliation and crop denial program in Vietnam. They stressed repeatedly the extent of our ignorance concerning the consequences flowing from the introduction of massive amounts of chemicals into a complex tropical ecology. They warned of the possibility of soil erosion and laterization (an irreversible conversion to rock), the destruction of understory saplings and seedlings, the upheaval of insect, bird and small mammal populations, and of the effects these changes have on normal agriculture and the spread of disease. They deplored the use of herbicides to kill food crops because those who suffer the effects of starvation are mainly pregnant and lactating women, children under five, the sick and the aged.

With the publication of Rachel Carson's *Silent Spring* in 1962, the public became aware of the extent of chemical intrusion into the ecosystem and its possible adverse effect upon the flora and fauna of the world. It was in the same year that the massive use of herbicides in Vietnam began and expanded from an initial 4900 acres sprayed in 1962 to more than a million sprayed acres in 1967. The alarm of civilian scientists in the United States found some expression at the annual meetings of the American Association for the Advancement of Science. The council of this large, heterogeneous organization for long skirted the hot issue of the Vietnam war and adopted instead a resolution bearing on the relationship of herbicides to the environment. Until last week, attempts to broach the thorny issue of military herbicides proved fruitless because of the diffuse expression of views by the board of directors. Nonetheless, questions directed by the AAAS to the Department of Defense resulted in a study, sponsored by the Pentagon, of the literature dealing with the possible ecological effects of the massive use of herbicides. At about the same time, another government agency initiated long-delayed tests into the toxicity of some of the herbicides to laboratory animals, and by inference, to man.

In 1966 the National Cancer Institute commissioned a series of studies to evaluate the carcinogenic, teratogenic and mutagenic activity of selected insecticides, herbicides, fungicides and industrial chemicals. As part of this research, the chemicals were given to pregnant rats and mice at different dose levels and by subcutaneous and oral routes to study their potential interference with normal developmental processes, an action which has become known as teratogenesis. Late last month copies of the long classified study became available.

The Institute's tests revealed that two of the herbicides examined had caused gross abnormalities and birth defects in mice. 2,4-D was termed "potentially dangerous, but needing further study" while 2,4,5-T was labeled "probably dangerous." Further tests with 2,4,5,-T on rats confirmed its teratogenic effect; up to 100 percent of the litters fed varying doses of 2,4,5,-T in honey had excessive fetal mortality and a high incidence of serious developmental abnormalities in the survivors. Female rats that were fed doses as low as 4.6 milligrams per kilogram of body weight (equivalent to about 1/100 of an ounce for an average woman) bore three times as many abnormal fetuses as control rats. The study concluded that "it seems inescapable that 2,4,5-T is teratogenic."

The implications of these findings for Vietnam are obvious. In rural areas of the countryside where the spraying is most intense, drinking and cooking water is often taken directly from rain-fed cisterns and ponds, sources readily contaminated by chemicals sprayed from low flying aircraft. If 30 pounds of agent *Orange* are sprayed per acre, roughly 15 pounds of 2,4,5-T are released. If one assumes a one-inch rainfall after such a spraying, and the use of three liters of water a day for drinking and cooking by a Vietnamese woman, one can calculate that a dose of 2,4,5-T equivalent to 4.5 mg/kg body weight may be consumed. This is exactly the lowest dose which produced measurable effects in rats in the National Cancer Institute study. To make matters worse, it is not known whether humans are more sensitive to the teratogenic actions than rats.

Within the last year there have been a number of reports in Vietnamese newspapers about an increase in birth abnormalities. Viet Bang, a South Vietnamese journalist writing for the Buddhist newspaper *Chanh Dao*, has stated that the doctors in two main maternity hospitals (Tu Doc Hospital in Saigon and Hung Vuong Hospital in Cholon) are under orders to send all their files on miscarriages and malformed babies to the Ministry of Health, after which the files are no longer seen. The US response to these findings was conservative. The White House Science Advisor, Dr. Lee DuBridge, announced that "a coordinated series of actions are being taken by the agencies of government" to limit the use of 2,4,5-T. He stated that the Agriculture Department would cancel registration of 2,4,5 -T for use on food crops in the United States by January, 1970, unless the Food and Drug Administration found a basis for establishing a safe legal tolerance. Such caution at home was not paralleled by similar caution abroad. In the same statement, DuBridge announced that the Defense Department will not stop the use of 2,4,5-T in Vietnam but will restrict its use to areas remote from populations. The Pentagon has interpreted this as a sanction of its present policy; no change whatever will be made in the Army's policy governing the military use of 2,4,5 -T.

The possibility that teratogenic doses could have been ingested in this country is discounted by the government. DuBridge has said, "It seems improbable that any person could receive harmful amounts of this chemical from any of the existing uses of 2,4,5 -T, and while the relationships of these effects in laboratory animals to effects in man are not entirely clear at this time, the actions taken will assure safety of the public while further evidence is sought." Yet 2,4,5-T is sprayed primarily along powerlines and pipelines, and secondarily upon croplands. Biodegradation in the soil is very dependent upon the particular conditions at the site of spraying, and possibilities of accidental drift are high. Congressman Richard D. McCarthy (D, N. Y.) recently stated, "I find it difficult to understand how a complete ban on use of this defoliant in the United States can be postponed until January and how the Department of Defense can continue to use this defoliant after learning the results of the tests." Part of the answer to the congressman's difficulty may lie in the fact that 2,4-D and 2,4,5-T production contributes over $35 million annually to the herbicide industry.

The implications of the 2,4,5-T case, the government reaction and the entire defoliation program are profound. First, 2,4,5-T represents a chemical developed from scientific technology in the forties which has been massively applied to the human environment for 20 years before proper research into its potential harmfulness to humans was conducted; it may represent an ecological equivalent of thalidomide. How many more chemicals have been spawned by technology and spread throughout the human ecosystem without adequate testing? Neither picloram nor cacodylic acid were examined by the National Cancer Institute study; yet the recent Midwest Research Institute report on herbicides in Vietnam indicated a number of references in the literature that suggested some teratogenic activity in cacodylic acid.

Secondly, we have failed to consider the long-term hazards from the intrusion of chemicals into a system that has evolved its intricate arrangement for many millions of years. The complex ecology of a tropical region is much like the interdependence of a pyramid of toy blocks; the removal of one element upsets all the others. It has been assumed that if a chemical can be introduced without immediate detrimental effects, then its application can be doubled or tripled without worry. Yet very recently, in the case of DDT, we have seen how biological systems tend to accumulate chemicals over long periods of time. After 20 years of spraying, the hormonal effects of DDT are causing serious disruption in the reproductive cycles of many birds, and the end of its effects cannot be seen.

Finally, in Vietnam, we can detect the beginnings of a new military tactic in limited warfare. No longer is scientific technology used only to kill the enemy; chemicals are also employed to destroy the ecology that supports him. This environmental warfare has been conducted without any broad examination of the question whether any cause can legally or morally justify the deliberate destruction of the environment of one nation by another. The United States must begin to grasp the concept that belligerents in hostilities share a responsibility for preserving the potential productivity of the area of conflict. Otherwise, our technology may convert even the most fertile area to a desert, with lasting consequences to all mankind.

Approximate Amounts Aerially Sprayed

Year	Forest Land	Crop Land	Total Land	Forest Land	Crop Land	Total Land
	(in 1,000 acres)			(in 1,000 ha = 10 km²)		
1961	*	*	*	*	*	*
1962	*	*	10	*	*	*
1963	20	*	20	10	*	10
1964	80	10	90	30	*	40
1965	160	70	220	60	30	90
1966	740	100	850	300	40	340
1967	1,490	220	1,710	600	90	690
1968	1,270	60	1,330	510	30	540
1969 (1st half)	800	40	840	320	20	340
TOTAL	4,560	510	5,070	1,850	200	2,050

*Less than 10

NOTES:

Agents: Forest Land: Primarily Agent Orange; some Agent White between late 1966 and early 1970 (perhaps one-third). *Crop Land:* Primarily Agent Blue.

Basis: The above are released Defense Department estimates, based upon the amounts of herbicides expended (using the conversion of 3 gal. per acre). Repeat sprayings are included, which are estimated to be 15 — 20% of the sprayings.

Reliability: Total area covered during the years 1962-1968, as given above, is 4.2×10^6 acres [1.7×10^6 ha]. Elsewhere the Defense Department has published that more than 19,000 sorties were flown during this period, which calculates to more than 6.3×10^6 acres [2.6×10^6 ha]. Figures published by the "other side" for this period add up to 10.6×10^6 acres [4.3×10^6 ha].

Additional usage: The above table refers to amounts sprayed by the 12th Special Operations Squadron (Operation "Hades" or "Ranch Hand"), which accounts for roughly 80% of U.S. herbicide usage in South Vietnam.

Conversions: 1 mi.² = 640 acres
1 acre = 0.405 ha
1 km² = 100 ha
1 ha = 2.47 acres

Prof. Arthur H. Westing, Department of Biology, Windham College, Putney, Vermont 95346.

Major Herbicides Used

Agent ORANGE: 2,4-D and 2,4,5-T

Composition:	A 1:1 mixture of the n-butyl esters of 2,4-dichlorophenoxyacetic acid and 2,4,5-trichlorophenoxyacetic acid.
Active Ingredients:	4.1 and 4.4 lb./gal. [491 and 527 g/l]
Application:	Undiluted at 3 gal./acre [28 l/ha]
Major Use:	Against forest vegetation.

Agent WHITE: 2,4-D and Picloram

Composition:	A 4:1 mixture of the tri-iso-propanolamine salts of 2,4-D and 4-amino-3,5,6-trichloropicolinic acid in water. (Picloram is the the same as Dow Co. "Tordon"; the mixture used is the same as Dow Co. "Tordon-101")
Active Ingredients:	2.0 and 0.54 lb./gal. [240 and 65 g/l]
Application:	Undiluted at 3 gal./acre [28 l/ha]
Major use:	Same as for agent Orange (used beginning late 1966)

Agent BLUE: Cacodylic Acid

Composition:	A 6:1 mixture of sodium dimethyl arsenate and dimethyl arsenic acid in water. (Cacodylic acid is the same as Ansul Co. "Phytar-560G")
Active Ingredients:	3.1 lb./gal. [371 g/l]
Application:	Undiluted at 3 gal./acre [28 l/ha]
Major Use:	Against rice and other food crops.

Conversions:

1 lb./acre = 1.12 kg/ha
1 gal./acre = 9.35 l/ha
1 kg/ha = 0.892 lb./acre
1 l/ha = 0.107 lb./acre

Prof. Arthur H. Westing, Department of Biology, Windham College, Putney, Vermont 05346.

PART 4

The Spirit Within: The Destruction of a Culture

It became necessary to destroy the town to save it.

US Army Major, referring to the town of Ben Tre, reported by AP

To make progress in this country, it is necessary to level everything. The inhabitants must go back to zero, lose their traditional culture, for it blocks everything.

An American Diplomat in Vietnam and Laos, reported in the July 1968 issue of Le Monde by Jacques Decornoy

Photo by Paul Avery, Empire

The Children of Vietnam*

William F. Pepper[†]

For countless thousands of children in Vietnam, breathing is quickened by terror and pain, and tiny bodies learn more about death every day. These solemn, rarely smiling little ones have never known what it is to live without despair.

They indeed know death, for it walks with them by day and accompanies their sleep at night. It is as omnipresent as the napalm that falls from the skies with the frequency and impartiality of the monsoon rain.

The horror of what we are doing to the children of Vietnam—"we," because napalm and white phosphorus are the weapons of America—is staggering, whether we examine the overall figures or look at a particular case like that of Doan Minh Luan.

Luan, age eight, was one of two children brought to Britain last summer through private philanthropy, for extensive treatment at the McIndoe Burns Center. He came off the plane with a muslin bag over what had been his face. His parents had been burned alive. His chin had "melted" into his throat, so that he could not close his mouth. He had no eyelids. After the injury, he had had no treatment at all—none whatever—for four months.

It will take years for Luan to be given a new face ("We are taking special care," a hospital official told a Canadian reporter, "to make him look Vietnamese"). He needs at least 12 operations, which surgeons will perform for nothing; the wife of a grocery-chain millionaire is paying the hospital bill.

*Reprinted with permission from *Ramparts Magazine*.

†William F. Pepper is Executive Director of the Commission on Human Rights in New Rochelle, New York, a member of the faculty at Mercy College in Dobbs Ferry, New York, and Director of that college's Children's Institute for Advanced Study and Research. He spent six weeks in South Vietnam as an accredited journalist.

Luan has already been given eyelids, and he can close his mouth now. He and the nine-year-old girl who came to Britain with him, shy and sensitive Tran Thi Thong, are among the very few lucky ones.

There is no one to provide such care for most of the other horribly maimed children of Vietnam; and despite growing efforts by American and South Vietnamese authorities to conceal the fact, it's clear that there are hundreds of thousands of terribly injured children, with no hope for decent treatment on even a day-to-day basis, much less for the long months and years of restorative surgery needed to repair ten searing seconds of napalm.

When we hear about these burned children at all, they're simply called "civilians," and there's no real way to tell how many of them are killed and injured every day. By putting together some of the figures that are available, however, we can get some idea of the shocking story.

Nearly two years ago, for instance—before the major escalation that began in early 1965—Hugh Campbell, former Canadian member of the International Control Commission in Vietnam, said that from 1961 through 1963, 160,000 Vietnamese civilians died in the war. This figure was borne out by officials in Saigon. According to conservative estimates, another 55,000 died during 1964 and 100,000 in each of the two escalated years since, or at least 415,000 civilians have been killed since 1961. But just who *are* these civilians?

In 1964, according to a UNESCO population study, 47.5 per cent of the people of Vietnam were under 16. Today, the figure is certainly over 50 per cent. Other United Nations statistics for Southeast Asia generally bear out this figure. Since the males over 16 are away fighting—on one side or the other—it's clear that in the rural villages which bear the brunt of the napalm raids, at least 70 per cent and probably more of the residents are children.

In other words, at least a quarter of a million of the children of Vietnam have been killed in the war.

If there are that many dead, using the military rule-of-thumb, there must be three times that many wounded—or at least a million child casualties since 1961. A look at just one hospital provides grim figures supporting these statistics: A medical student, who served for some time during the summer at Da Nang Surgical Hospital, reported that approximately a quarter of the 800 patients a month were burn cases (there are two burn wards at the hospital, but burned patients rarely receive surgical treatment, because more immediate surgical emergencies crowd them out). The student, David McLanahan of Temple University, also reported that between 60 and 70 per cent of the patients at Da Nang were under 12 years old.

What we are doing to the children of Vietnam may become clearer if the same percentages are applied to the American population. They mean that one out of every two American families with four children would be struck with having at least one child killed or maimed. There is a good chance, too, that the father would be dead as well. At the very least, he is probably far from home.

When Wisconsin Congressman Clement Zablocki returned from Vietnam early in 1966, he reported that "some recent search and destroy operations have resulted in six civilian casualties to one Viet Cong." Though Secretary of Defense McNamara challenged the figure, Zablocki, relying on American sources in Saigon, stuck by them, and sticks by them today. What he didn't say is that in any six "civilian casualties," four are children.

McNamara, too, is sometimes more candid in private. A colleague of mine attended a private "defense seminar" at Harvard in mid-November, and heard the defense secretary admit, during a question period, that "we simply don't have any idea" about either the number or the nature of civilian casualties in Vietnam.

Perhaps because we see them only one at a time, Americans seem not to have felt the impact of our own news stories about these "civilian casualties." A UPI story in August, 1965, for instance, described an assault at An Hoa:

> "I got me a VC, man. I got at least two of them bastards." The exultant cry followed a ten-second burst of automatic weapon fire yesterday, and the dull crump of a grenade exploding underground. The Marines ordered a Vietnamese corporal to go down into the grenade-blasted hole to pull out their victims. The victims were three children between 11 and 14—two boys and a girl. Their bodies were riddled with bullets. . . . "Oh, my God," a young Marine exclaimed. "They're all kids . . ." Shortly before the Marines moved in, a helicopter had flown over the area warning the villagers to stay in their homes.

In a Delta province, New York Times correspondent Charles Mohr encountered a woman whose both arms had been burned off by napalm. Her eyelids were so badly burned that she could not close them, and when it was time to sleep, her family had to put a blanket over her head. Two of her children had been killed in the air strike that burned her. Five other children had also died.

"They're all kids," wrote Veteran Associated Press reporter Peter Arnett, describing in September a battle at Lin Hoc. There, in a deep earth bunker below the fury of a fierce battle, a child was born. Within 24 hours the sleeping infant awakened—and choked on smoke seeping down into the bunker. According to Arnett, the GI's had begun "systematically" to burn the houses to the ground, and were "amazed" as hundreds of women, children and old men "poured from the ground." For the baby, however, it was already too late.

Another Times correspondent, Neil Sheehan, described in June the hospital at Cantho, in the Delta region where fighting is relatively light. The civilians, he said, come through the gates into the hospital compound in ones, twos and threes. The serious cases are slung in hammocks or blankets. . . . About 300 of the 500 casualties each month require major surgery. The gravely wounded, who might be saved by rapid evacuation, apparently never reach the hospital but die along the way.

A few months before, Dr. Malcolm Phelps, field director of the American Medical Association Physician Volunteers for Vietnam, put the monthly figure for civilians treated at Cantho at about 800. That means at least 400 children, every month, in just that one hospital.

New Jersey doctor Wayne Hall, who worked at the Adventist Hospital in Saigon (he went at his own expense, as a substitute missionary surgeon), reported that overcrowding, even in this three-story Saigon institution, is a "chronic condition." No one was ever turned down: "When there were no more beds and cots, they were put on benches; when there were no more benches, they were put on the floor. Some were lying on a stone slab in the scrub room—delivery cases." Babies born on a stone slab. "Of course," Dr. Hall added, "this is the extreme—but it's a common extreme."

At the other end of the country, in Northern I Corps, David McLanahan reported that during last summer, the 350-bed Da Nang Surgical Hospital never had fewer than 700 patients. McLanahan, one of five medical students in Vietnam on an intern program sponsored by USAID, said that Vietnamese patients frequently would not talk freely to him, but that they told Vietnamese doctors and medical students enough about how they got hurt so that it was possible to estimate that at least 80 per cent of the injuries were inflicted by American or South Vietnamese action.

> My first patient [McLanahan said] was a lovely 28-year-old peasant woman who was lying on her back nursing a young child. The evening before, she had been sitting in her thatched hut when a piece of shrapnel tore through her back transecting the spinal cord. She was completely paralyzed below the nipple line. We could do nothing more for her than give antibiotics and find her a place to lie. A few mornings later she was dead, and was carried back to her hamlet by relatives. This was a particularly poignant case, but typical of the tragedy seen daily in our emergency room and, most likely, in all of the emergency rooms in Vietnam.

Most of McLanahan's patients, he said, were "peasants brought in from the countryside by military trucks. It was rare that we got these patients less than 16 hours after injury. All transportation ceases after dark. A small percentage of war casualties are lucky enough to make it to the hospital."

Cantho, Saigon, Da Nang, Quang Ngai—it is by putting together reports such as these that the reality of extrapolated figures becomes not only clear but plainly conservative. A quarter of a million children are dead; hundreds of thousands are seriously wounded. There must be tens of thousands of Doan Minh Luans.

Manufacturer Searle Spangler, American representative for the Swiss humanitarian agency Terre des Hommes, describes what his agency has found to be the pattern when children are injured in remote villages: "If he's badly ill or injured, of course, he simply won't survive. There is no medical care available. Adults are likely to run into the forest, and he sometimes may be left to die. If they do try to get him to a hospital, the trip is agony—overland on bad roads, flies, dirt, disease, and the constant threat of interdiction by armed forces." McLanahan says that virtually every injury that reaches the hospital at Da Nang is already complicated by serious infection—and describes doctors forced to stop during emergency surgical operations to kill flies with their hands.

Torn flesh, splintered bones, screaming agony are bad enough. But perhaps most heart-rending of all are the tiny faces and bodies scorched and seared by fire.

Napalm, and its more horrible companion, white phosphorus, liquidize young flesh and carve it into grotesque forms. The little figures are afterward often scarcely human in appearance, and one cannot be confronted with the monstrous effects of the burning without being totally shaken. Perhaps it was due to a previous lack of direct contact with war, but I never left the tiny victims without losing composure. The initial urge to reach out and soothe the hurt was restrained by the fear that the ash-like skin would crumble in my fingers.

In Qui Nhon two little children—introduced to me quietly by the interpreter as being probably "children of the Viet Cong"—told of how their hamlet was scorched by the "fire bombs." Their words were soft and sadly hesitant in coming, but their badly burned and scarred bodies screamed the message. I was told later that they evinced no interest in returning to their home and to whatever might be left of their family.

I visited a number of the existing medical institutions in South Vietnam, and there is no question that the problems of overcrowding, inadequate supplies and insufficient personnel are probably insurmountable. The Da Nang Surgical Hospital is probably as well off as any Vietnamese hospital outside Saigon—but it is for surgery only; there is also a Medical Hospital not so well equipped.

Even in the Surgical Hospital, there are a number of tests that can't be done with the inadequate laboratory and X-ray equipment. Frequent power failure is a major problem (suction pumps are vital in surgery rooms; one child died in Da Nang, for instance, because during an operation he vomited and—with no suction pump to withdraw the stomach contents from his mouth—breathed them into his lungs). Though 100 burn patients every month reach Da Nang Surgical Hospital, McLanahan reported that while he was there, the hospital had only one half-pint jar of antibiotic cream— brought in privately by a surgeon—which was saved for "children who had a chance of recovery." In Sancta Maria Orphanage, I frequently became involved in trying, with a small amount of soap and a jar of Noxzema, to alleviate the festering infections that grew around every minor bite and cut.

In the nearby Medical Hospital, there are frequent shortages of antibiotics, digitalis and other equipment. While the Surgical Hospital makes use of outdated blood from military hospitals, most Vietnamese hospitals are chronically short of blood. According to another medical student, Jeffrey Mast, a hospital at Quang Ngai (60 miles south of Da Nang) occasionally "solved" a shortage of intravenous fluids by sticking a tube into a coconut— a common practice in outlying areas and, reportedly, among the Viet Cong.

The Swiss organization Terre des Hommes, which is attempting to provide adequate medical care for Vietnamese children (they were responsible for transporting Doan Minh Luan and Tran Thi Thong to England, and a few other children to other European countries), issued a report last spring which said in part that in Vietnam,

> hospitals ... show the frightening spectacle of an immense distress. To the extent that one finds children burned from head to foot who are treated only with vaseline, because of lack of a) ointment for burns, b) cotton, c) gauze, d) personnel. In places with the atmosphere of slaughter houses for people, where flies circulate freely on children who have been skinned alive, there are no facilities for hygiene, no fans, and no air conditioning ...

In South Vietnam, approximately 100 hospitals provide approximately 25,000 beds to serve the ever growing needs of the civilian population. Bed occupancy by two or three patients is not uncommon (two to a bed is the rule at Da Nang). I can testify personally to the accuracy of Manchester Guardian writer Martha Gellhorn's description of the typical conditions at Qui Nhon.

> In some wards the wounded also lie in stretchers on the floor and outside the operating room, and in the recovery room the floor is covered with them. Everything smells of dirt, the mattresses and pillows are old and stained; there are no sheets, of course, no hospital pajamas or gowns, no towels, no soap, nothing to eat on or drink from.

Searle Spangler, of Terre des Hommes, says that there are only about 250 Vietnamese doctors available to treat all the civilians in South Vietnam. My own information is that there are even fewer; Howard Rusk of the New York Times gave a figure of 200 in September, and I have been told that there are now about 160. Obviously the difference hardly matters when at least five times that many children die every week. Dr. Ba Kha, former Minister of Health, told me that there are about nine nurses, practical and otherwise, and about five midwives for every 100,000 persons. He also told me that his ministry, charged with administering the entire public health program for South Vietnam, is allocated an unbelievable two per cent of the national budget.

There are, of course, American and "free world" medical teams at work, and USAID is increasingly supplying the surgical hospitals (a new X-ray machine has been installed at Da Nang, which AID hopes to turn into a model training hospital), but while their contribution is vital and welcome, it is like a drop in the ocean of civilian pain and misery. To speak of any of this as medical care for the thousands of children seared by napalm and phosphorus is ridiculous; there is simply no time, nor are there facilities, for the months and possibly years of careful restorative surgery that such injuries require. Burn patients receive quick first aid treatment and are turned out to make room for other emergency cases.

Although of course no one can talk about it openly, there are known to be cases in which pain is so great, and condition so hopeless, that the treatment consists of a merciful overdose. In an alarmingly large number of other cases, amputations—which can be performed relatively quickly—take the place of more complex or protracted treatment so that more patients can be reached in the fantastic rush that is taking place in every hospital. Any visitor to a hospital, an orphanage, a refugee camp, can plainly see the evidence of this reliance on amputation as a surgical shortcut. Dr. Hall has reported that hospitals allow terminal cases to be taken away by their families to die elsewhere, so that room can be made for more patients.

Then there are politics. A leading doctor and administrator in the I Corps area has found it difficult to get supplies for his hospital because he is suspected in Saigon of having been sympathetic to the Buddhist movement. In Hue, a 1500-bed hospital shockingly is allowed to operate under capacity because some of the faculty and students at the associated medical school expressed similar sympathies; apparently in punishment, the school and hospital receive absolutely no medical supplies from Saigon; only aid from the West German government keeps it operating at all. The dean of the medical school and some of his students were arrested last summer; a shipment of microscopes donated by West Germany was heavily taxed by Saigon. The harassment goes on.

At the present time, two groups are trying to do something about the horror of burned and maimed Vietnamese children. They are the Swiss-based international group, Terre des Hommes, a nonpolitical humanitarian organization founded in 1960 to aid child victims of war; and a newly-formed American association with nationwide representation called the Committee of Responsibility. Their approaches are somewhat different, but they are cooperating with each other wherever it seems helpful.

In the autumn of 1965, Terre des Hommes arranged for about 400 hospital beds in Europe—like the two in England paid for by Lady Sainsbury—and for surgeons to donate their services. They contacted North Vietnam, the NLF representative in Algiers and the government of South Vietnam. The first two turned down the offer, but the South Vietnamese government seemed willing to cooperate. Air fare from Saigon to Europe is about $1500, so Terre des Hommes asked for help from the United States government.

American soldiers in Vietnam who accidentally suffer serious burn injuries from napalm are rushed aboard special hospital planes—equipped to give immediate first aid treatment—and flown directly to Brook Army Hospital in Texas, one of the world's leading centers for burn treatment and for the extensive plastic surgery that must follow. Burnt Vietnamese children must fare for themselves.

It was the use of such special hospital aircraft that Terre des Hommes was hoping for, though any air transportation would have been welcome. Although American authorities in Saigon at first seemed enthusiastic, the decision was referred to the White House. In January 1966, Chester L. Cooper—now in the State Department "working," he says, "on peace"—wrote on White House stationery to issue a resounding NO.

> ... the most effective way of extending assistance [Cooper wrote] is on the scene in South Vietnam where children and others can be treated near their families and in familiar surroundings.... U.S. aircraft are definitely not available for this purpose.

Terre des Hommes wrote back to Cooper to argue the absurdity of the American position—there are, of course, no "familiar surroundings" in napalm-torn Vietnam, thousands of the children are displaced orphans, and in any case there are no medical facilities for the long and difficult rehabilitation of burned children. In November of this year, asked directly about the request, Cooper said:

> A doctor in Switzerland, of apparently good intentions but somewhat fuzzy judgment, wanted planes to take these innocent Vietnamese kids to Switzerland for treatment. [Edmond Kaiser, founder of Terre des Hommes, is not a doctor.] ... The problem, basically, is that Terre des Hommes—and the chap involved, I want to emphasize, is a well meaning man—when we looked into it—and I worry just as much about the injured kids as the next fellow, maybe more so—what they want to do, they want to be taking these frightened little kids halfway across the world and dump them there in a strange, alien society ...
>
> However much better a Swiss home or hospital might be, it cannot compensate for having their own families around them in familiar surroundings in their own country. Experienced social workers and hospital workers have described what happens when you take a child suddenly out of his environment: culture shock and trauma. ...

Either Cooper is grotesquely misinformed about medical facilities and family coherence in South Vietnam, or he would genuinely rather keep these horribly maimed children in the bosom of frequently nonexistent families, in the "familiar surroundings" of dirty fly-ridden hospitals or jammed refugee camps or burned-out villages, rather than subject them to the culture shock and trauma of clean hospital beds, relief from pain, and a chance for the kind of surgery that will give a Tran Thi Thong back her eyelids and enable a Doan Minh Luan to close his mouth.

In any case, while the argument was going on, Terre des Hommes turned to commercial airlines and asked them to donate whatever empty space they might have on flights from Saigon to Europe; they refused, possibly feeling that the experience might be psychologically difficult for their other passengers. Finally, in May, Terre des Hommes brought 32 children (including Luan and Thong) out of Vietnam at its own expense; they were both sick and wounded, and eight were burn victims. The tiny victims were brought out by arrangement with Dr. Ba Kha, the Saigon Minister of Health; when I visited Saigon, the doctor was extremely cooperative and seemed eager to implement any program that could benefit even a few of the people who, he acknowledged, are suffering terribly.

In September, Terre des Hommes arranged for another 26 children to be flown to Europe, and one of their representatives in South Vietnam chose the children. But when the planeload arrived in Geneva, the people waiting received a terrible shock. It contained no war-wounded children at all. All 26 were polio, cardiac and cerebral spastic victims, chronically ill children. Dr. Paul Lowinger of Wayne State University's medical school was on hand when Terre des Hommes officials learned what had happened, and described them to me as "disappointed and frustrated" over the violation of the terms of the agreement.

So far, no one has been able to determine what happened to the burned and other war-wounded children who were chosen by Terre des Hommes but somehow didn't arrive on the plane in Geneva. They have, seemingly, disappeared—or died. I have letters in my possession indicating that physicians who have been to Vietnam since my return fear that wounded and burned children are being hidden or kept out of sight of visiting doctors.

In the meantime, Dr. Ba Kha had been replaced, apparently for his actions in attempting to get the burned children out of the country, and his successor has demonstrated much less concern for the Terre des Hommes project. Most officials of the Swiss organization are convinced, though they cannot of course say so publicly, that the firing of Ba Kha and the substitution of the children was directly related to the fact that in England and elsewhere in Europe, the arrival of the first group of children had caused a tremendous stir about the cruel effect of the bombing. The arrival of Luan and Thong in Great Britain stimulated a large, spontaneous flow of gifts and contributions—and not a small amount of indignation about their condition.

Incidentally, Canadian reporter Jane Armstrong, who visited the Sussex hospital where the two children are being treated, wrote that "the hospital staff have been astonished by their happy dispositions," and notes that "no one can say what will happen to Luan," who has no known relatives. The culture shock and unfamiliar surroundings don't seem to be bothering the children.

In any case, Searle Spangler, Terre des Hommes representative in New York, seems firmly to believe in "spylike hanky panky" by the South Vietnamese government, including the secreting of badly injured children in order to play down the problem. He also said that "some of our Vietnamese workers have been mistreated, and we have reason to fear for them." On the adequacy of medical care in Vietnam, Spangler notes that Terre des Hommes operates the only children's hospital in the country—600 patients for 220 beds, with many of the children lying on newspapers—and that in other hospitals, some newspapers and wrapping paper are commonly used as dressings for burns, being the only material available.

The American group, the Committee of Responsibility, has only recently been formed. Its concern is specifically with children burned by American napalm and white phosphorus.

Its national coordinator and moving spirit, Helen Frumin, a housewife from Scarsdale, New York, became interested in the problem last spring when she encountered some Terre des Hommes material. Later, in Lausanne, she met Kaiser and learned more about the problem. She became convinced that Americans have a special responsibility toward the burned children of Vietnam.

"Napalm is an American product," Mrs. Frumin says. "The tragedy that is befalling children in Vietnam is all the more our responsibility where children burned by napalm are concerned; only the United States is using this weapon, and it is fitting that we should provide the care for the mutilated children."

The Committee backs up its position by citing such sources as a story in Chemical and Engineering News, last March, about a government contract for 100 million pounds of Napalm B, an "improved" product. The older forms of napalm, the article goes on to say, left "much to be desired, particularly in adhesion."

This, of course, refers to the ability of the hateful substance to cling to the flesh of the hamlet dwellers on whom it is usually dropped, insuring a near perfect job of human destruction after prolonged agony. It is because American tax dollars are behind every phase of the process, from manufacture to delivery and use, that the citizens of the Committee of Responsibility (who include prominent doctors throughout the country) feel that American dollars might best be spent in relieving the suffering they buy.

The Committee hopes at first to bring 100 napalmed children to America for extensive treatment. Hospital beds are being arranged, 300 physicians are ready to donate their services, homes have been found. But the cost for treating each child is still between $15,000 and $20,000, not including transportation from Vietnam to the United States.

The fantasy of the position that "adequate" care can be provided within South Vietnam and that "culture shock" might result from displacing a child, was pointed up in a report prepared for the Committee by Dr. Robert Goldwyn, a noted Boston plastic surgeon. He said in part:

The children of Vietnam are the hardest struck by malnutrition, by infectious disease, and by the impact of terror and social chaos. They begin with the disadvantages implicit in a colonial society after nearly 25 years of continuing war, economic backwardness, inadequate food and medical facilities. Particularly helpless under such conditions is the burned child . . .

A burn is especially critical in a child because the area of destruction relative to total body surface is proportionately greater than that of an adult. And in the present real world of Vietnam, his nutritional status and resistance to infection is lower than that of an adult.

The acute phase of burn demands immediate and complex attention involving physicians, nurses, dressings, intravenous foods, plasma, often blood, antibiotics, and after the first week, wound debridement and skin grafting. Unless evacuation is simple and immediate and well-supervised, these early burns are best treated at or near the scene of injury.

. . . However, the child who has survived the initial stages of a burn would be a highly suitable candidate for treatment elsewhere. Since most of the burns are the result of napalm or white phosphorus, they are deep, and subsequent deformities and contractures are usual. These deformities, which interfere with function and offer extreme psychological obstacles for social readjustment, can be relieved by well-known and standardized plastic surgical procedures. These operations can ideally be done in a country such as the United States where facilities are adequate and where the environment is conducive to total rehabilitation.

The child would not have to lie in a bed with two or three others; he would not be exposed to parasitic infestation or sepsis or diarrhea or epidemics which are now prevalent in most of the Vietnamese civilian hospitals. He would be out of a war-torn country and could heal his psychological wounds as well.

. . . While one is instinctively reluctant to think of taking a child away from familiar surroundings, family and friends, for medical treatment and rehabilitation, these phrases are empty in the present context; we are talking of children whose homes are destroyed, who may be orphaned, whose "familiar surroundings" are the hell of disease, famine and flame attendant on modern warfare. . . . Further, the choice is not between care at home and better care in the United States, but in realistic terms, between token care or often, no care at all, and adequate care.

To Dr. Goldwyn's analysis can be added that of Dr. Richard Stark, past president of the American Society of Plastic and Reconstructive Surgery, who agreed in a speech on October 3 that plastic surgical facilities in Vietnam are "presently inadequate."

There is, of course, an official United States position on the use of napalm in Vietnam. The Department of the Air Force set it forth on September 1, 1966, in a letter to Senator Robert Kennedy: Napalm is used against selected targets, such as caves and reinforced supply areas. Casualties in attacks against targets of this type are predominantly persons involved in Communist military operations.

I am compelled to wonder what military functions were being performed by the thousands of infants and small children, many of whom I saw sharing hospital beds in Vietnam, and a few of whom appear in photographs accompanying this article.

In the brutal inventory of maimed and killed South Vietnamese children one must also include those who are the helpless victims of American defoliants and gases. The defoliants used to deprive the Viet Cong of brush and trees that might afford cover are often the common weed-killers 2, 4-D and 2,4,5-T. Yet the pilots spraying from the air cannot see if women and children are hiding in the affected foliage. These chemicals "can be toxic if used in excessive amounts," says John Edsall, M.D., Professor of Biology at Harvard.

The U.S. has admitted it is using "non-toxic" gas in Vietnam. The weapon is a "humane" one, says the government, because it creates only temporary nausea and diarrhea in adult victims. Yet a New York Times editorial on March 24, 1965 noted that these gases "can be fatal to the very young, the very old, and those ill with heart and lung ailments. . . . No other country has employed such a weapon in recent warfare." A letter to the Times several days later from Dr. David Hilding of the Yale Medical School backed up this point: "The weakest, young and old, will be the ones unable to withstand the shock of this supposedly humane weapon. They will writhe in horrible cramps until their babies' strength is unequal to the stress and they turn blue and black and die . . ." Once again, the children of Vietnam are the losers.

About eight per cent of Vietnam's population live in refugee shelters or camps; about three quarters of the shelter population, or over 750,000 persons, are children under 16. In shelters like that of Qui Nhon, which I visited, there is unimaginable squalor and close confinement. There were 23,000 in that camp when I was there, and I have been told that the figure has since tripled.

Father So, unquestioned leader of these thousands of refugees in Qui Nhon and in the rest of Binh Dinh province, works for 20 hours a day to provide what relief he can, particularly for the orphaned children. These usually live in a hovel-like appendage to the main camp, frequently without beds. Food and clothing are scarce.

As So's guest, I attended with him a meeting with Dr. Que, the South Vietnamese High Commissioner of Refugees, and with the USAID Regional and Provincial Representatives and the Coordinator of Refugees. So reminded the AID officials of their promise to supply badly needed food; the province representative replied that 500 pounds of bulgar had been given to the district chief with instructions that it was to be delivered to So for distribution in the camp.

So said nothing in reply. Later, he laughed softly and said to me that neither he nor the children would ever see that bulgar. The district chief had more lucrative connections.

The shelter child receives little if any education. Crossed strands of barbed wire form the perimeter of his living world. There are no sanitary facilities—those in camps near a river are lucky. Even shelters with cement floors have no privies for as many as 160 families. Plague and cholera increasingly threaten the health of the children (and of course the adults, though to a lesser degree), and I noticed an amazing amount of body infection on the youngsters, ranging from minor to extremely serious in nature. Their level of resistance is quite low, and the filth, combined with the absence of hygienic knowledge, is so universal that mosquito and ant bites quickly become infected. There is not usually medical help for the children of these camps. Tuberculosis and typhoid are evident, with periodic local epidemics; about one per cent of all Vietnamese children will have TB before reaching the age of 20.

Many of the shelter children show traces of the war. I particularly remember a tiny girl whose arm had been amputated just below the elbow, and who followed me from one end to the other. The children also display a reaching out, not in a happy but in a sort of mournful way. The shy ones frequently huddle together against the side of a hut and one can always feel their eyes upon him as he moves about. No one ever intended for them to live like this—but there they are. One small child provided for me their symbol. He sat on the ground, away from the others. He was in that position when I entered and still there several hours later when I left. When I approached, he nervously fingered the sand and looked away, only finally to confront me as I knelt in front of him. Soon I left and he remained as before—alone.

Another 10,000 children—probably more by now—live in the 77 orphanages in South Vietnam. I lived for a time in Sancta Maria orphanage (in an area officially described as influenced by Viet Cong, and off limits to American military personnel). I arrived there during a rest hour, to find the children in a second floor dormitory, two to a bed, others stretched out on the floor. Their clothing consisted of only the barest necessities, though Sancta Maria was better off than other institutions I visited.

Here, too, food was scarce and there was a shortage or a complete absence of basic supplies such as soap, gauze, towels and linen. I devoted some evenings to teaching elementary English vocabulary, and I was impressed by the amount of motivation displayed by some of these children despite the horrors that frequently characterized their past—and present. Their solemnity was very real, however, as was their seeming general inability to play group games.

In most orphanages, as in the refugee shelters, there is no schooling at all, but despite this and the shortages of food and other supplies there is a growing tendency in Vietnam for parents to turn children over to the camps or to abandon them. Mme. LaMer, UNICEF representative to the Ministry of Social Welfare, expressed alarm over this tendency while I was in Vietnam; it seems to be one more example of the rapid deterioration of family structure because of the war. Officials told me that infant abandonment has become so common that many hospitals are now also struggling to provide facilities for orphan care.

Finally, there is the forgotten legion of Vietnamese children in the cities and provincial towns—clinging together desperately in small packs, trying to survive. Usually they have at best threadbare clothing, and sometimes they are naked; they go unwashed for months—perhaps forever; almost none have shoes. They live and sleep on the filthy streets, in doorways and alcoves. Despite the gradual process of animalization, in their striving to maintain a semblance of dignity, they are beautiful.

On a few occasions I took an interpreter into the streets with me and spent hours sifting histories (often, feeling that my presence might inhibit the response, I stayed away and let the Vietnamese carry out the interview).

Some had come to the cities with their mothers, who turned to prostitution and forced the children into the streets. Others, abandoned in hospitals or orphanages or placed there while ill, had merely run away. Still others had struggled in on their own from beleaguered hamlets and villages. Once on the streets, their activities range from cab flagging, newspaper peddling and shoe shining to begging, selling their sisters and soliciting for their mothers. I saw five- and six-year-old boys trying to sell their sisters to GI's; in one case the girl could not have been more than 11 years old.

With misery comes despair, and one of its most shocking forms was called to my attention by Lawson Mooney, the competent and dedicated director of the Catholic Relief Services program in Vietnam. Mooney said he had noticed, between the autumn of 1965 and the spring of 1966, a fantastic increase in the rate of adolescent suicide.

I began to check the newspapers every day—and indeed, there was usually one, frequently more than one suicide reported among the city's children. In several cases, group suicides were reported: a band of young people, unable to face the bleakness and misery of their existence, will congregate by agreement with a supply of the rat poison readily available in Vietnam, divide it, take it, and die.

"Many of these suicides," Lt. Col. Nguyen Van Luan, Saigon Director of Police, told Eric Pace of the New York Times, "are young people whose psychology has been deformed, somehow, by the war." Van Luan went on to say that in the Saigon-Cholon area alone, 544 people attempted suicide during the first seven months of 1966—many of them, of course, successfully. In that one section of the country—with about 18 per cent of the total population—that is an average of 78 a month. Last year, Luan noted, the monthly average had been about 53, so the increase was about 50 per cent. "You must remember," Luan went on, "that these are young people who have never known peace. They were more or less born under bombs."

These are the "familiar surroundings" away from which American policy will not transport the horribly burned children of Vietnam, the "frightened little kids" whom White House aide Chester Cooper says that humanitarians want to take "halfway around the world and dump them there in a strange, alien society." One must agree with his further comment that "it is a very ghastly thing." Clearly, the destruction of a beautiful setting is exceeded only by the atrocity that we daily perpetrate upon those who carry within them the seeds of their culture's survival. In doing this to them we have denied our own humanity, and descended more deeply than ever before as a nation, into the depths of barbarism.

It is a ghastly situation. And triply compounded is the ghastliness of napalm and phosphorus. Surely, if ever a group of children in the history of man, anywhere in the world, had a moral claim for their childhood, here they are. Every sickening, frightening scar is a silent cry to Americans to begin to restore that childhood for those whom we are compelled to call our own because of what has been done in our name.

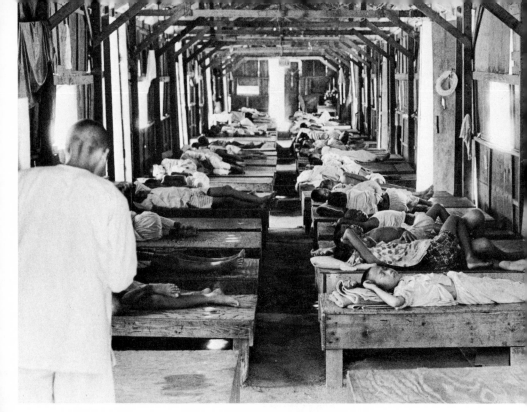

"The children are automated to robot status. But how else could you run an orphanage of 2500 children?" Orphanage Administrator for Bien Hoa Province. *Photos by Robert Scheu, Photon West.*

Photo Study

Many people think it is impossible for guerrillas to exist for long in the enemy's rear. Such a belief reveals a lack of comprehension of the relationship that should exist between the people and the troops. The former may be likened to water and the latter to the fish that inhabit it. How may it be said that these two cannot exist together?

We can learn to prevent the emergence of the famous sea in which Mao Tse-Tung taught his men to swim.

if the direct application of mechanical and conventional power takes place on such a massive scale as to produce a massive migration from countryside to the city, the basic assumptions underlying the Maoist doctrine of revolutionary war no longer operate.

This photo essay illustrates America's response to Mao's famous dictum of the fish and the sea, "separating the fish from the water by draining off the water." Thus the net effect of ecological warfare is to force the rural peasant population into urban slums and a growing consumer economy in order to separate the guerrilla forces from their popular base.

These pictures depict this process, beginning with the destruction of villages, saturation bombing, defoliation, refugee camps and into the slums of Saigon. Perhaps as many as half the sixteen million people of South Vietnam alone have taken this journey designed to "win the hearts and minds of the people."

Photo by Wide World photos

Photo by Orville Schell

Photo by Orville Schell

Photo by Philip Jones Griffiths, Magnum

*Photo by
Paul Avery*

VILLAGE BURNING
"The world of a Vietnamese is ordered to an extent unknown in the Western World. Each person is part of a larger, completely ordered environment, in which man and nature exist symbiotically. The natural laws of harmony and equilibrium dictate the social patterns of life."

CRATERIZATION
"The bombing of Indochina has amounted to perhaps the most massive excavation project in mankind's history, ten times the excavation of the Suez and Panama Canals combined. The total cratered area in Indochina exceeds the area of the state of Connecticut, 5,000 square miles."

Photo by Gordon Orians

Photo by Orville Schell

DEFOLIATION

"It has been calculated that, taking into account the average amount of 2,4,5-T in Agent Orange sprayed per acre in Vietnam by the military, and assuming 1 inch rainfall after a spray, a 40 kilo (about 88 pounds) Vietnamese woman drinking two liters (about 1.8 quarts) of contaminated water a day could very well be absorbing into her system a 120 milligrams of 2,4,5-T a day. Thus, if a Vietnamese woman who is exposed to Agent Orange were pregnant, she might very well be absorbing into her system a percentage of 2,4,5-T only slightly less than the percentage that deformed 1 out of every 3 fetuses of pregnant experimental rats."

Photo by Gordon Orians

Leaves, three years after defoliation.

REFUGEE CAMP

"Such camps are usually placed in the baking sun on bulldozed earth lots surrounded by barbed wire. Small houses with tin roofs, which cause them to heat up like ovens under the tropical sun, are lined up like cars on a parking lot. Foreign food is brought in to replace their native rice."

Photo by Orville Schell

Photo by Van Bucher

SAIGON
"Just fifteen years ago all but 15 percent of the South Vietnamese people lived in rural areas. Now 60 percent live in urban areas. Saigon has grown from a city of 300,000, which it was designed to be, to more than 3 million. It is the most highly congested city in the world."

Photo by Philip Jones Griffiths, Magnum

Cage
for the Innocents*

by Orville Schell†

Scores of GI's in combat fatigues who had been sprawled out on the benches in the Danang Air Base passenger shed started getting up and moving outside. Once outside they gathered in small knots on the rain-soaked aprons, watching. Some half-heartedly fumbled with cameras. Over-head, jets screamed off the runways into the fluffy early-morning clouds to their targets. A large army truck had just pulled up a short distance from the shed and disgorged about sixty barefoot Vietnamese dressed in ragged shorts and faded dirty shirts. Each had a gray sandbag pulled down over his head. They clung to each other in a disjointed human chain as they were herded by shotgun-toting GI's into an awaiting C-130 transport plane. Moving over closer to this faceless procession, I noticed that several captives had long hair flowing out from under their gray sacks. At the end of the groping line two people were limping and were being helped along by anonymous friends. A Japanese correspondent tried to take a picture and was waved off. He was told that it was against regulations. No one was quite sure what regulation it was against, so he took it anyway.

I walked over to the officer in charge and asked who these people were and where they were being taken.

"These here are hard-core V.C.," he drawled. "You can tell just by lookin' at 'em."

An assistant corrected him and said that he thought that they were CD's (Civil Defendants). I asked what that meant.

*Reprinted with permission from *The Atlantic Monthly*, January, 1968.

Orville Schell is co-director of The Bay Area Institute and has traveled extensively in South Vietnam. He is co-editor of a three-volume work, *The China Reader*.

"We don't deal in the meanings of all these names," he said, "but we know they're Charlie—maybe saboteurs, collaborators, and like that."

Meanwhile the Vietnamese were slowly being loaded through the rear door of the tadpole-shaped C-130. Since they could not see, they were moving very cautiously, feeling their way slowly up on the hanging tail gate. A GI who was jabbing them along with the barrel of his shotgun said playfully, "If one of these slopes takes off his bag, I'll blow his fuckin' head off."

The officer in charge, who was not accompanying the flight, handed over the manifest of passengers to the pilot. "Well, Chief," he said, "here are the Mexicans. They're all yours."

Inside the aircraft the "sacked" Vietnamese sat utterly silent on the cabin floor. Four GI guards sat on the fold-down seats on both sides of the aircraft. In the dim light of the interior the Vietnamese looked like some sort of strange hooded religious order. Except for one or two pathetic parcels wrapped in brown paper, these people carried no personal possessions. As the engines started, they shrank back against one another in terror. Sensing their fear, one of the GI's poked the Vietnamese nearest to him in the foot with his rifle barrel. The man lunged back away from his unseen tormentor. Another guard commenced breaking his shotgun and cocking his pistol. The noise sent a wave of cringing down the line of huddling figures.

Finally the plane was cleared and started down the runway on its take-off. As it got airborne the hydraulic system to retract the landing gear went on making a high-pitched scream. The Vietnamese clutched each other in fear.

One of the guards hooted above the noise of the engines, "Hang on, sweethearts!" Then he leaned over to me and said, "Hope none of 'em barfs."

I asked if they would be allowed to remove their sacks if they became sick.

"Hell, no!" he replied. "They're so dirty they don't give a shit, and neither do we because we're getting rid of 'em."

As we gained altitude, the Vietnamese began shaking their heads and hitting their ears. They apparently did not understand how to pop their ears. Several became quite frantic. One of the guards looked toward them and then at me in feigned amazement that anyone could be so stupid.

In a half hour we landed at Chulai Air Base in Quangtin Province. The Vietnamese were herded off the plane and led into a small barbed-wire enclosure, about twenty-five feet by twenty-five feet, out under the blazing hot sun. Here they squatted on the sandy ground and waited. Within a half hour a large pickup truck arrived. The Vietnamese were then divided into two groups and thirty were jammed into the back of the truck. The fact that the vehicle was really too small to transport the whole group in two trips seemed to disturb no one. None of the captors spoke Vietnamese, and obviously none of the captives spoke English. When a guard's command was not immediately understood and obeyed, he would start swearing and shoving the Vietnamese as though they were some dumb stubborn animals refusing to leave the barn.

After some hesitation the driver agreed to let me accompany him to camp, and we set off across the Chulai Air Base, headquarters for Task Force Oregon. The giant runways stretched endlessly away, finally disappearing into mirages in the heat. Sandbag bunkers, gun emplacements, barracks, and hundreds of miles of barbed-wire fence were all that broke the monotony of the dry, sandy dunes upon which the base is built.

The truck finally pulled up in front of a large sign emblazoned with two crossed pirate pistols which read CHULAI POWC (Prisoner of War Camp). As the Vietnamese were being unloaded, I was ushered into the camp headquarters and introduced to the temporary commanding officer, a morose-looking sergeant from Cincinnati who had eyes like Robert Mitchum's. I explained that I was a journalist and that I had accompanied the newly arrived Vietnamese from Danang. I said that I was interested in finding out just who these people were, what they had done, and where they were being taken. The sergeant said that until he had had a chance to look at their papers he couuld not be certain. Five minutes later he returned and announced that the Vietnamese who had just flown down from Danang were what is known as IC's (Innocent Civilians). He said that this meant that they had been interrogated and found to be innocent of aiding or cooperating with the enemy. He proudly informed me, "These people will be returned to their villages just as soon as we get a chance to ship them out. And if their villages have been destroyed or lie in V.C. areas, well, then we'll turn them over to the Vietnamese refugee authorities and let them take care of them."

The Chulai camp lies on a sand dune bluff overlooking the blue ocean and a beautiful beach, where GI's can be seen riding on air mattresses in the surf and cooking barbecues. All day, low-flying jets, transports, gun ships (helicopters), and small Cessna spotters circle noisily overhead. The prisoners' compound itself consists of four barbed-wire enclosures known as "cages." In each cage the prisoners have built a small thatched roof structure faced on three sides by rattan matting to protect themselves from the sun and rain. Besides the prisoners, a latrine, and the sandy ground, there is nothing else inside the cages. At night the prisoners are given army cots on which to sleep. In the daytime these are stacked neatly outside the cages near the cooking area, into which the prisoners are brought three times a day in two shifts to cook their own meals over an open fire. The army provides dried meat, onion soup, tomato juice, and Texas long grain rice. The reasoning behind this bizarre bill of fare is unclear. The fact that it was not Vietnamese left the sergeant undisturbed.

"Since these people like American chow," he said, "there is no sweat. We treat these people like human beings, not animals."

The camp medic hastened to add, "You know, some of these folks really cry when they have to leave here. [This was said to me on numerous occasions during the next two days.] We give them four squares a day and all the pills they can eat. And we try and show them the American way of life so that when they go back to their villages : . ."

He trailed off, not knowing exactly how to finish his sentence. Outside the office the new arrivals were squatting in the sand up against a barbed-wire fence. They had removed their sandbag hoods. There were six women and several extremely young looking males. They sat listlessly looking up at the bare-chested Americans towering over them. No one talked. Their faces showed no trace of any kind of feeling.

Inside, the briefing continued: There were 141 people imprisoned at the camp. Chulai POWC is the collection point for Vietnamese "detained" in the area of operations of Task Force Oregon. In some areas and on some military operations only people with weapons are picked up and brought in. In other areas where there are known or suspected hostile forces, everyone is picked up and brought in. This includes the aged, women, and children. There are no systematic rules for determining who will be a "detainee." The decision is left up to the field commander's judgment. I asked several people to explain the difference between a "refugee" and a "detainee." Most of those asked assumed that the words were somehow self-explanatory. But none of them could systematically articulate the difference.

Like so many other terms in the Vietnam War lexicon, these words are adopted out of administrative necessity, although they may have very little relation to reality. In Vietnam the situation is very different from any previous war situation in which there have been "detainees" and "refugees": every Vietnamese in the field is potentially hostile. Yet the army needs categories to handle and process these people efficiently even if the categories do not accurately describe the people involved. Every Vietnamese encountered by U.S. forces must fit into one of the previously determined categories. The words "refugee" and "detainee" are really words without meaning. They bring with them old meanings which are irrelevant as designation for the people they are describing. For instance, both "detainees" and "refugees" are "generated" by U.S. and ARVN forces as they move through the countryside on operations destroying villages. These people are not fleeing Communism. They are forced to leave by an invading army. Their designation usually depends on a hasty battlefield decision. It is this decision which makes a person a "refugee" or "detainee." Often a suspect is questioned briefly in the field by a team of ARVN interrogators. But under combat conditions this intelligence-gathering can become extremely indiscriminate and brutal. The emphasis is on getting quick information which may save American lives as the operation moves on. Torture and intimidation are common. After this field interrogation, any villager who is still suspect is bound, blind-folded, and taken back to Chulai to be questioned at greater length and then finally classified. Until this time he is treated just like a prisoner, since there is no way to ascertain whether a "detainee" is hostile or friendly. He is guilty until proven innocent; then if found innocent he suddenly becomes a "refugee." As one colonel in J2 (intelligence) at the Saigon Pentagon put it, "Our job concerns us with the intelligence we can get so that we can take a hill or save a life—this is our interest. But we do respect the dignity of others and treat them in a humane Christian manner. But you mustn't forget that there is a war going on out here."

At Chulai, 52 out of the 127 prisoners (not including the 59 new arrivals) were designated as IC's. Throughout all of Vietnam 65 percent of all detainees finally prove to be IC's. In other words, two out of three suspects brought in from the field are innocent. There are only two other possible designations besides IC; PW (Prisoner of War) and CD (Civil Defendant). North Vietnamese regulars, Viet Cong, or any other person who has committed an act against a "friendly force" is designated as a PW. But an average of only 7 percent of all detainees prove to be PW's. These prisoners are turned over to Vietnamese Army-run PW camps, of which there are now six with a capacity of over 10,000. One camp which is under construction on Phuquoc Island on the Cambodian border will have a capacity of 20,000 when finished. These camps are technically built according to Geneva Convention specifications, and the inmates are theoretically under the jurisdiction of the Treatment of Prisoners of War section of that convention. But because it is extremely difficult to gain access to these camps on anything more than a short formal tour, it is impossible to be certain of what conditions in them are really like.

The third possible designation for a detainee is CD. This is the vaguest and most poorly defined of the three categories. Officially, someone who is suspected of being a "spy, saboteur, or terrorist" comes under this category. But actually it is a convenient designation for anyone about whom the interrogation teams cannot make up their minds. These unfortunates fall into a limbo category. Since they have not committed a belligerent act against a friendly army they cannot be classified as PW's and therefore do not fall under the protection of the Geneva Convention. They are treated as criminal or political prisoners and thrown into local provincial jails, which are under the jurisdiction of the national police. Treatment is rough, and conditions are indescribably squalid. Such prisons are prime targets for raiding Viet Cong units. For instance, on August 29 the Viet Cong hit the capital city of Quangngai Province and sprang the local jail, freeing 1200 prisoners, many of whom were CD's. A national average of 28 percent of all detainees are finally designated as CD. During the time I was at the Chulai camp 30 out of 141 fell into this category.

In a situation where every Vietnamese is potentially hostile, the United States, as the figures suggest, is forced to the desperate tactic of picking up vast numbers of questionable cases. A large number of civilians are simply shot in the field by scared trigger-happy GI's who have learned that it is risky business to trust any Vietnamese, especially any Vietnamese near or in a combat area. Of course, any dead Vietnamese is conveniently considered V.C., thereby raising the unit's enemy KIA (Killed in Action) body count, the summa of progress in Vietnam. As one enlisted man in Ducpho District, Quangngai Province, said, "Anything dead that's not white is V.C."

For instance, on an operation a unit may take sniper fire from the direction of a village. This is sufficient justification for calling in an air strike and wiping out part or all of the village. (The casualness with which Americans put air strikes on "suspected enemy positions" is disturbing.) The Vietnamese have learned to build bunkers under their huts for just such an eventuality. But when the ground forces finally do move into what is left of the village, anyone who is caught hiding in a bunker is automatically treated with great suspicion. He or she is usually detained.

In the month of June 10,000 Vietnamese were detained. In July the figure rose to 15,000. Only 2.5 percent of the July detainees were finally designated as PW's. This is a very small return and a very large catch. In the last six months in I Corps, where combat had been most intense, this mass detention of tens of thousands of people and the attendant disruption of rural life have created a critical but largely ignored social problem. These people are taken forcibly from their farms (which are usually burned), separated from their families, and taken to collection centers like Chulai to await interrogation and designation. Frequently they are moved again because of overcrowded facilities. It often takes weeks before a detainee is finally declared innocent and released. Then he is usually released into one of the badly overcrowded refugee camps. A military police spokesman in Saigon from the Plans and Policy branch, when asked what effect he thought this mass detention was having on "winning the hearts and minds of the people," merely said, "Bringing in so many people is just a problem which is necessarily inherent in this type of war. But it has not yet been presented as a problem area."

For the detainee it *is* a "problem area." At Chulai, no one had told any of the prisoners or detainees with whom I talked why they had been picked up. I talked to several Innocent Civilians who had no idea why they were being held, and had not even been told that in fact they had already been designated as IC's and were only waiting to be transported to refugee centers. The Americans seemed totally oblivious of this piteous information gap. It was blandly assumed that somehow these small unintelligible yellow-skinned people were different, that they could live anywhere, eat anything, and not be disturbed by common American emotions and concerns for one's family, oneself, and the future. None of the Americans I met spoke Vietnamese. They were totally dependent on the seven ARVN interpreters who had been assigned to them for communication with their captives. The only real communication took place during the interrogations. At this time the Americans asked all the questions, never the other way around.

Behind the "cages" at the Chulai camp, four small open interrogation huts have been constructed out of plywood. The head of Interrogation assigned one of them to me for interviewing some of the inmates. Then, accompanied by an interpreter and a Press Information Officer, we walked down to the cages to select some subjects.

Most of the prisoners were lying on the sand in the shade of the thatched roof shelter when we arrived. As we entered the cages they all stood up. One old man jumped to his feet and saluted .in a pathetic attempt to please. He wore the black pajama-like garb which is the traditional peasant mode of dressing. Like all the other inmates, he had a large white cardboard tag fastened to his shirt which identified him not by name but by number. The prisoners stood uneasily as we walked between them checking their tags.

Two IC's were finally chosen and let out of the compound.

Nguyen Mê, the first of the group of prisoners whom I interviewed, is forty-six years old and comes from Phuongdong village in Quangtin Province. He has been told that he has been designated an Innocent Civilian, but he does not know what that means. He is a slight man, under five feet tall. He wore a dirty pair of black cotton shorts and a black cotton shirt, which was fastened in the front by the large safety pin which secured his white numbered identity card. His feet were bare, archless, and splayed out from years of working in the fields. His skin had been burned a dark brown by the sun. During the whole interview he sat very upright. He smiled only once, when the PIO major offered him a **Life-Saver** (which at first he did not know what to do with). The rest of the time he listened intently and spoke simply and directly. He betrayed no hostility or any sense of having been wronged. His whole tone was so matter-of-fact that if it had not been for the brief moments when a mixture of pain and bewilderment would cross his face, one might have assumed that he was narrating the story of another person.

Q. How long has it been since you were detained?

A. I don't know. I can't exactly remember how many days. Each day is the same, so they are hard to count.

Q. How were you captured?

A. I was captured in the morning time when everyone was still in the village. We began to hear some shooting and then bombs started to fall [probably mortars]. So we all ran into the shelters under our houses.

Q. Did everyone in your village have a shelter?

A. Yes, every house has one. We dug them two years ago when the bombing and artillery fire first started coming. We really need our shelters.

Q. What happened after you went into your shelters?

A. We couldn't see much or hear much. It was difficult to tell what was happening outside. I was with my wife and children. After a while we heard someone yelling into our house with a voice that we did not understand saying something about Chieu Hoi [the official name for defectors from the Viet Cong]. They fired some shots. I was very scared, but I came out anyway. I thought that it must be the Americans because we had seen helicopters flying over our village earlier. When I came out they pointed guns at me and grabbed me. I was afraid because I could not understand them and didn't know what would happen to me. The Americans are very kind, but these Americans were very rough and hit me. They pushed me back into my house and gestured for me to call my family out of the shelter. I had no choice but to call them.

Q. What did they do after you were all out?

A. They ran off to get a Vietnamese soldier who asked us where the V.C. were and where the V.C. kept their rice. I told them that the V.C. came through our village every four days or so to get rice. But the soldiers were in a big hurry. They tied our hands and put sacks over our heads and led us away someplace. I couldn't see where we were going.

Q. Where was your family?

A. We got separated. We were led away someplace where there were lots of other people. I couldn't see and didn't dare call out to them. They never came to the camp. Now I don't know where they are.

Q. Was your rice already planted when you were picked up?

A. Yes, but now I don't know who will harvest it.

Q. What happened to everything that you owned, like your house, buffalo, et cetera?

A. I am not sure. We were not allowed to bring anything with us at all. Our hands were tied. How could we?

Q. Do you have an extra change of clothes with you?

A. No. I haven't been able to wash my clothes since I have been here.

Q. Did the soldiers destroy many houses?

A. They were burning many when they caught me. Do you know if they burned my house down? [Inmates constantly assumed that since I was American I must have some sort of authority and could help them.]

Q. How many houses had been destroyed before the day you were captured?

A. Six.

Q. How many houses were there in the village?

A. Twenty-seven.

Q. Why were the six houses destroyed?

A. They were near the mountain and the airplanes bombed them.

Q. Were many people killed?

A. Yes, quite a few because they didn't have time to get into their shelters.

Q. Where are they going to take you from here?

A. I don't know. Someone said to the Hoiduc refugee center. But I don't know if my family is there. I want to see them very badly. But that is up to the higher people.

Nguyen Luc, who is seventy-seven years old, came from Phuctien village, in Tienphuc District, Quangtin Province. He had also been designated an Innocent Civilian and was waiting to be shipped out. He was probably the oldest inmate in the Chulai camp. Although his hair was not completely gray, he was hunched over from years of bending down working in the rice paddies. He walked extremely slowly and finally had to be helped up the steps of the interrogation hut. I reached down to give him a hand. His wiry body could not have weighed more than eighty pounds. A major from the Press Information Office thrust out a glad hand in welcome. But Nguyen did not know the significance of shaking hands. Instead he placed both hands together in front of him in a prayer-like motion, which is the traditional form of Vietnamese greeting. The major gave a nervous laugh and then tried to clasp him around the back like a public relations man squiring a big client into his office. But Luc had already begun to sit down. His eyes were riveted to the ground the whole time. He wore an oversize pair of sawed-off army fatigues, and sat quietly on a small wood stool. He seemed neither nervous nor scared, just weary. I had the feeling that even if I had wished to, I could have done nothing which would have elicited any emotional response from him.

Q. How long have you been here?

A. Six days.

Q. How were you captured?

A. I was captured in the morning while out in the rice fields working. The Americans and the ARVN's came and ordered me to go with them.

Q. Did they allow you to return home and talk to your family or bring any possessions?

A. No, they were in a big hurry. They pointed guns at me and I just went.

Q. Had your fields been planted?

A. Yes.

Q. What will happen to them now?

A. I don't know who will harvest the rice. I would like to go back because now there are very few people in the village. They all live underground. All our houses have been bombed and destroyed. The bombs have made big holes in our rice fields.

Q. When did the bombing start?

A. [He paused.] It started three years ago—but then not as much as now.

Q. Did the people fear the V.C. or the bombing more in your village?

A. We don't like the Viet Cong because they take our rice and some-times make us work.

Q. But which do you fear the most?

A. We fear the bombing because we don't know when it will come and we can't see it. [At this point Luc began fidgeting with his pants. I asked why, but he did not respond.]

Q. Who are the Americans?

A. [Pause.] The Americans are like the French. The French were very cruel.

Q. Are the Americans cruel?

A. The French beat the people.

Q. Do the Americans beat the people?

A. [Luc glanced over at the agitated but silent PIO officer.] Sometimes the Americans give candy. [Again he started tugging at his baggy fatigue shorts, which I noticed were missing most of the buttons on the fly.]

Q. Why are you fidgeting? Are you hurt?

A. [A long pause during which time Luc stared at his feet.] I want some underwear. I am embarrassed because my pants will not fasten.

Q. Have you asked the Americans for some new clothes? You know that they give clothes to inmates, don't you?

A. Yes.

Q. Have you asked them? [The PIO major interrupted here to assure me that all prisoners received all the clothing and medical attention that they needed.]

A. Yes, once.

Q. What happened?

A. I asked the Americans, but they did not understand me. They just laughed at me, and one struck me. He slapped me on my face. I was very scared. I didn't dare ask again.

Q. Why don't you ask now? I have explained that I am not in the army.

A. The atmosphere is good. [The PIO major acted shocked and assured me that this "oversight" would be corrected. After the interview he hurried to the office to launch his protest.]

Q. Do you know why your village was bombed?

A. The people said that it was because of the Communists.

Q. What is a Communist? Who are they?

A. [Long pause.] They are . . . I don't know.

Q. Have you ever heard of Nguyen Cao Ky or Nguyen Van Thieu?

A. No, I do not know them.

Q. Have you ever heard of Ho Chi Minh?

A. Yes, he sent troops from the North. He is well known.

Q. Why were you detained?

A. I don't know why. They just brought me in.

Q. But has anyone explained to you the reason for detaining you?

A. No. They do not speak Vietnamese. We cannot understand one another.

Q. What did they tell you in the interrogation?

A. They asked me questions. They asked me if I was a Viet Cong and if I knew where the Viet Cong were hiding. They just asked me questions.

Q. Do you know that you have been designated an Innocent Civilian?

A. What is that? [The PIO major moved forward on his chair ready to give an explanation.]

Q. Where are you going when you leave here?

A. I don't know what they are going to do with us. Will I be able to go back to my village? I am very worried because no one is there to look after our ancestral tombs.

Q. Do you have a family?

A. Yes, a wife, two sons, and some grandchildren.

Q. Where are they now?

A. I don't know. I am very sad because I don't know what has happened to them. Maybe they are worrying about me also.

Q. Perhaps they are in refugee camps. Do you know anything about the resettlement program?

A. No.

Q. Have the Americans ever dropped leaflets on your village explaining the refugee program and warning you to leave your village because it will be bombed?

A. Yes, sometimes they drop leaflets. But I can't read. Many people can't read. Now there are no schools in the countryside. They are all destroyed.

Q. Do you know what is going to happen to you?

A. No, I don't know. I need someone to help me. I am very scared here all alone.

From After Pinkville*

Noam Chomsky

As to the bombing of North Vietnam, this had always been a side-show, in large measure a propaganda cover for the American invasion of the South. The US government could not admit that it was invading South Vietnam to protect from its own population a government that we had installed. Therefore it was rescuing the South Vietnamese from "aggression." But then surely it must strike at the "source of aggression." Hence the bombing of North Vietnam. This, at least, seems the most rational explanation for the bombing of North Vietnam in February 1965, at a time when no North Vietnamese troops were in the South, so far as was known, and there was a bare trickle of supplies.

To be sure, those who are "in the know" have different explanations for the bombing of North Vietnam. Consider, for example, the explanation offered by Sir Robert Thompson, the British counter-insurgency expert who has been for many years a close adviser of the American army in South Vietnam—a man who is, incidentally, much admired by American social scientists who like to consider themselves "tough minded, hard-nosed realists," no doubt because of his utter contempt for democracy and his relatively pure colonialist attitudes. In the British newspaper *The Guardian*, May 19, 1969, his views are explained as follows:

> He also condemns the bombing of the North. The US Air Force in 1965 was having great budgetary problems, because the army was the only one that had a war on its hands and was thus getting all the money. "So the Air Force had to get in, and you had the bombing of North Vietnam . . . the budgetary problems of the Air Force were then solved."

In his *No Exit from Vietnam* (1969), he explains more graphically the attractiveness of air power:

---

*Reprinted with permission from The New York Review of Books, Jan. 1, 1970.

One can so easily imagine the Commander of the Strategic Air Command striding up and down his operations room wondering how he could get in on the act. With all that power available and an enormous investment doing nothing, it is not surprising that reasons and means had to be found for their engagement. The war was therefore waged in a manner which enabled this massive air armada to be used round the clock. . . . In this way the war could be fought as an American war without the previous frustrations of cooperating with the Vietnamese.

Or consider the explanation for the bombing of the North offered by Adam Yarmolinsky, Principal Deputy Assistant Secretary of Defense for International Security Affairs, 1965-66, previous Special Assistant to the Secretary of Defense. According to his analysis, the strategic bombing of North Vietnam "produced no military advantages except for its putative favorable impact on morale in the south. But [this step] was taken, at least in part, because it was one of the things that the US military forces were best prepared to do."[2]

So North Vietnam was flattened and impelled to send troops to the South, as it did a few months after the bombing began, if the Department of Defense can be believed.

Since the bombing of North Vietnam "produced no military advantages" and was extremely costly, it could be stopped with little difficulty and little effect on the American war in South Vietnam. And so it was, in two steps: on April 1, 1968, when the regular bombing was restricted to the southern part of North Vietnam, and on November 1, when it was halted. At the same time, the total American bombing, now restricted to Laos and South Vietnam, was increased in April and increased again in November. By March 1969 the total level of bombardment had reached 130,000 tons a month—nearly two Hiroshimas a week in South Vietnam and Laos, defenseless countries. And Melvin Laird's projection for the next twelve to eighteen months was the same.[3] The redistribution (and intensification) of bombing and the largely empty negotiations stilled domestic protest for a time and permitted the war to go on as before.

We can now look back over the failure of the "peace movement" to sustain and intensify its protest over the past four years. By now, defoliation has been carried out over an area the size of Massachusetts, with what effect no one has any real idea. The bombardment of Vietnam far exceeds the bombardment of Korea or anything in World War II. The number of Vietnamese killed or driven from their homes cannot be seriously estimated.

It is important to understand that the massacre of the rural population of Vietnam and their forced evacuation is not an accidental by-product of the

---

[2]*No More Vietnams?*, R. Pfeffer, ed., Harper & Row, 1968.

[3]For detailed analysis based largely on Defense Department sources, see Gabriel Kolko, *London Bulletin*, August, 1969.

war. Rather it is of the very essence of American strategy. The theory behind it has been explained with great clarity and explicitness, for example by Professor Samuel Huntington, Chairman of the Government Department at Harvard and at the time (1968) Chairman of the Council on Vietnamese Studies of the Southeast Asia Development Advisory Group, in effect the State Department task force on Vietnam. Writing in *Foreign Affairs*, he explains that the Viet Cong is "a powerful force which cannot be dislodged from its constituency so long as the constituency continues to exist." The conclusion is obvious, and he does not shrink from it. We can ensure that the constituency ceases to exist by "direct application of mechanical and conventional power ... on such a massive scale as to produce a massive migration from countryside to city," where the Viet Cong constituency—the rural population—can, it is hoped, be controlled in refugee camps and suburban slums around Saigon.

Technically, the process is known as "urbanization" or "modernization." It is described, with the proper contempt, by Daniel Ellsberg, a Department of Defense consultant on pacification in South Vietnam, who concludes, from his extensive on-the-spot observations, that "we have, of course, demolished the society of Vietnam," that "the bombing of the South has gone on long enough to disrupt the society of South Vietnam enormously and probably permanently"; he speaks of the "people who have been driven to Saigon by what Huntington regards as our 'modernizing instruments' in Vietnam, bombs and artillery."[4] Reporters have long been aware of the nature of these tactics, aware that "by now the sheer weight of years of firepower, massive sweeps, and grand forced population shifts have reduced the population base of the NLF . . ."[5] so that conceivably, by brute force, we may still hope to "win."

One thing is clear: so long as an organized social life can be maintained in South Vietnam, the NLF will be a powerful, probably dominant, force. This is the dilemma which has always plagued American policy, and which has made it impossible for us to permit even the most rudimentary democratic institutions in South Vietnam. For these reasons we have been forced to the solution outlined by Professor Huntington: to crush the people's war, we must eliminate the people.

A second thing is tolerably clear: there has been no modification in this policy. Once again, as two years ago, there is mounting popular protest against the war. Once again, a tactical adjustment is being devised that will permit Washington to pursue its dual goal, to pacify the people of South

[4]*No More Vietnams?* For further discussion, see my article in *The New York Review*, Jan. 2, 1969.
[5]Elizabeth Pond, *Christian Science Monitor*, Nov. 8, 1969.

Vietnam while pacifying the American people also. The first of these tasks has not been accomplished too well. The second, to our shame, has been managed quite successfully, for the most part. Now we hear that the burden of fighting the war is to be shifted away from the American infantry to the B-52s and fighter-bombers and a mercenary force of Vietnamese. Only a token force of between 200,000 and 300,000 men, backed by the Pacific Naval and Air command, will be retained, indefinitely, to ensure that the Vietnamese have the right of self-determination.

At a recent press conference, Averell Harriman explained that the North Vietnamese cannot believe that we really intend to abandon the huge military bases we have constructed in Vietnam, such as the one at Cam Ranh Bay (*Village Voice*, Nov. 27). Knowledgeable American observers have found it equally difficult to believe this. For example, as long ago as August 27, 1965, James Reston wrote in the *Times*:

> US bases and supply areas are being constructed on a scale far larger than is necessary to care for the present level of American forces . . . in fact, the US base at Cam Ranh . . . is being developed into another Okinawa, not merely for the purposes of this war, but as a major power complex from which American officials hope a wider alliance of Asian nations, with the help of the US, will eventually be able to contain the expansion of China.

The phrase "contain the expansion of China" must be understood as code for the unpronounceable expression: "repress movements for national independence and social reconstruction in Southeast Asia."

Premier Eisaku Sato, in a speech described by American officials as part of a joint Japanese-American policy statement, announced that we are entering a "new Pacific age" in which "a new order will be created by Japan and the United States" (*New York Times*, Nov. 22, 1969). His words, one must assume, were chosen advisedly. To perpetuate this new order we will need military bases such as that at Cam Ranh Bay, which can play the role of the Canal Zone in the Western Hemisphere. There we can base our own forces and train those of our loyal dependencies.

We will no doubt soon proceed to construct an "Inter-Asian" army that can protect helpless governments from their own populations, much as the Brazilians were called in to legitimize our Dominican intervention. Where popular rebellion is in progress, these forces can gain valuable experience. Thus a senior American officer at Camp Bearcat in South Vietnam, where Thai units are based, explains that "they are infusing their army with experience they could never get in their own homeland. . . . They are coordinating their own piece of real estate." And a Thai Colonel adds: "If my country ever has the same subversion, I'll have to fight there. I want to practice here" (*New York Times*, December 3). Surely Reston was right in 1965 in speculating about our long-range plans for the South Vietnamese bases, from which our "token force" of a quarter of a million men will operate in the Seventies.*

Who can complain about a quarter of a million men, a force that can be compared, let us say, with the Japanese army of 160,000 which invaded North China in 1937, in an act of aggression that scandalized the civilized world and set the stage for the Pacific phase of World War II? In fact, counter-insurgency experts like Sir Robert Thompson have long argued that the American forces were far too large to be effective, and have advocated a "low-cost, long-haul strategy" of a sort which will now very likely be adopted by the Nixon administration, if, once again, the American people will trust their leaders and settle into passivity.

As American combat troops are withdrawn, their place, it is hoped, will be taken by a more effective force of Vietnamese—just as Czechoslovakia is controlled, it is reported, by fewer than 100,000 Russian troops. Meanwhile, the war will no doubt be escalated technologically. It will become more "capital intensive."[6] Some of the prospects were revealed in a speech by Chief of Staff William Westmoreland, reported in the *Christian Science Monitor* (October 25-27) under the heading: "Technologically the Vietnam war has been a great success." General Westmoreland "sees machines carrying more and more of the burden." He says:

> I see an army built into and around an integrated area control system that exploits the advanced technology of communications, sensors, fire direction, and the required automatic data processing—a system that is sensitive to the dynamics of the ever-changing battlefield—a system that materially assists the tactical commander in making sound and timely decisions.

Further details are presented by Leonard Sullivan, Deputy Director of Research and Development for South East Asian Matters:[7]

> These developments open up some very exciting horizons as to what we can do five or ten years from now: When one realizes that we can detect anything that perspires, moves, carries metal, makes a noise, or is hotter or colder than its

*On December 10, after this article was written, Reston returned to the question of Cam Ranh Bay, stating that it was now "an air and naval base which is the best in Asia," and that it has been a "fundamental question throughout the Paris negotiations" whether the US is willing to abandon it "and many other modern military bases." He raises the question whether the US would withdraw all troops or only all "combat forces," a plan which "could leave a couple of hundred thousand Americans in Vietnam to maintain and fly the planes and helicopter gunships and continue to train and supply and help direct the Vietnamese."
There is no indication of any serious intention to withdraw all forces or to abandon the bases. As Joseph Kraft has reported, the American refusal to commit itself to the principle of complete withdrawal is one of the factors blocking progress in Paris.

[6]In the apt phrase of E. Herman and R. Duboff, "How to coo like a dove while fighting to win," pamphlet of Philadelphia SANE, 20 S. 12th St., Phila. 19107.
[7]*Congressional Record*, Aug. 11, 1969. Cited in the *Bulletin of Concerned Asian Scholars*, Oct., 1969 (1737 Cambridge St., Cambridge, Mass.—an important journal for those concerned with Asian affairs).

surroundings, one begins to see the potential. This is the beginning of instrumentation of the entire battlefield. Eventually, we will be able to tell when anybody shoots, what he is shooting at, and where he was shooting from. You begin to get a "Year 2000" vision of an electronic map with little lights that flash for different kinds of activity. This is what we require for this "porous" war, where the friendly and the enemy are all mixed together.

Note the time scale that is projected for Vietnam. News reports reveal some of the early stages of these exciting developments. The *Times*, November 22, reports a plan to use remote-controlled unmanned aircraft as supply transports for combat areas. On October 1, the *Times* explains that:

> The landscape of Vietnam and the border regions are studded with electronic sensors that beep information into the banks of computers. Radar, cameras, infrared detectors and a growing array of more exotic devices contribute to the mass of information. Not long ago reconnaissance planes began carrying television cameras.

The data go into the Combined Intelligence Center near Tansonnhut Air Base: "Day and night in its antiseptic interior a family of blinking, whirring computers devours, digests and spews out a Gargantuan diet of information about the enemy," the better to serve the "conglomerate of allied civil and military organizations that work together to destroy the Vietcong's underground government"—freely admitted to have been the most authentic popular social structure in South Vietnam prior to the American effort to demolish the society of Vietnam. One can understand the gloating of Douglas Pike: "The tactics that delivered victory in the Viet Minh war, however impressive once, had been relegated by science to the military history textbook."[8]

What this means is, to put it simply, that we intend to turn the land of Vietnam into an automated murder machine. The techniques of which Westmoreland, Sullivan, and Pike are so proud are, of course, designed for use against a special kind of enemy: one who is too weak to retaliate, whose land can be occupied. These "Year 2000" devices, which Westmoreland describes as a quantum jump in warfare, are fit only for colonial wars. There is surely an element of lunacy in this technocratic nightmare. And if we are still at all capable of honesty, we will, with little difficulty, identify its antecedents.

Our science may yet succeed in bringing to reality the fears of Bernard Fall—no alarmist, and fundamentally in favor of the war during its early

---

[8] *War, Peace, and the Viet Cong*, MIT, 1969. He estimates that in 1963 "perhaps half the population of South Vietnam at least tacitly supported the NLF." The same estimate was given by the US Mission in 1962. Elsewhere, he has explained that in late 1964 it was impossible to consider an apparently genuine offer of a coalition government, because there was no force that could compete politically with the Viet Cong, with the possible exception of the Buddhists, who were, not long after, suppressed as a political force by Marshal Ky's American-backed storm troopers. The same difficulty has been noted, repeatedly, by spokesmen for the American and Saigon governments and reporters. For some examples, see Herman and Duboff, *op. cit.* or my *American Power and the New Mandarins*, Pantheon, 1969, chapter 3.

years—who wrote in one of his last essays that "Vietnam as a cultural and historic entity ... is threatened with extinction as the country literally dies under the blows of the largest military machine ever unleashed on an area of this size." The South Vietnamese minister of information wrote in 1968 that ordinary Vietnamese would continue "to be horrified and embittered at the way the Americans fight their war .... Our peasants will remember their cratered rice fields and defoliated forests, devastated by an alien air force that seems at war with the very land of Vietnam."[9]

American reporters have told us the same thing so often that it is almost superfluous to quote. Tom Buckley—to mention only the most recent describes the delta and the central lowlands:

> ... bomb craters beyond counting, the dead gray and black fields, forests that have been defoliated and scorched by napalm, land that has been plowed flat to destroy Vietcong hiding places. And everywhere can be seen the piles of ashes forming the outlines of huts and houses, to show where hamlets once stood.[10]

The truth about defoliants is only beginning to emerge, with the discovery that one of the two primary agents used is "potentially dangerous, but needing further study" while the other causes cancer and birth defects, and probably mental retardation. Both will continue to be used in Vietnam against enemy "training and regroupment centers"—i.e., anywhere we please, throughout the countryside.[11]

Of course it may be argued that the American government did not know, in 1961, that these agents were so dangerous. That is true. It was merely an experiment. Virtually nothing was known about what the effects might be. Perhaps there would be no ill effects, or perhaps—at the other extreme—Vietnam would become unfit for human life, or a race of mutants and mental retardates would be created. How could we know, without trying? In such ways "the tactics that delivered victory in the Viet Minh war, however impressive once, had been relegated by science to the military history textbook."

[9]*New York Times*, June 11, 1968

[10]*New York Times Magazine*, November 23, 1969.

[11]See Washington *Post*, Oct. 31; Los Angeles *Times*, Oct. 31; New York *Post*, Nov. 4; *Science*, Nov. 7. A Vietnamese student in the United States, Ngo Vinh Long, has summarized much of what is known, including his personal experience from 1959-1963 when he visited "virtually every hamlet and village in the country" as a military map maker, in *Thoi-Bao Ga*, Nov., 1969, 76a Pleasant St., Cambridge, Mass., a monthly publication of Vietnamese students in the United States. He describes how defoliation has been used since 1961 to drive peasants into government controlled camps, and from his own experience and published records in Vietnam, he records some of the effects: starvation, death, hideously deformed babies. He quotes the head of the Agronomy Section of the Japan Science Council who claims that by 1967 about half the arable land had been seriously affected. For American estimates, see the report of the Daddario subcommittee of the House committee on Science and Astronautics, Aug. 8, 1969. They estimate the total area sprayed through 1968 as 6,600 square miles (extrapolating through 1969 the figure would reach about 8,600 square miles, about 60 percent of this respraying—over 10 percent of it crop destruction).

To see what may lie ahead, I'd like to turn away from Vietnam to a less familiar case. It has been claimed that Vietnam is the second most heavily bombarded country in history. The most intensively bombarded, so it seems, is Laos. According to *Le Monde*, "North Vietnam was more heavily bombed than Korea; Laos is now being bombed even more than North Vietnam. And this battering has been going on for over five years . . . . The US Air Force carries out more than 12,500 raids a month."[12] On the same day, October 1, *The New York Times* announced its discovery that in Laos, "the rebel economy and social fabric" are now the main target of the American bombardment, which is claimed to be a success:

> Refugees from the Plaine des Jarres area say that during recent months most open spaces have been evacuated. Both civilians and soldiers have retreated into the forests or hills and frequently spend most of the daylight hours in caves or tunnels. Refugees said they could only plow their fields at night because they were unsafe during the day. "So long as the US bombing continues at its new level," a European diplomat said here this week, "so-called Communist territory is little but a shooting range . . . ." The bombing, by creating refugees, deprives the Communists of their chief source of food and transport. The population of the Pathet Lao zone find it increasingly difficult to fight a "people's war" with fewer and fewer people.

The world's most advanced society has found the answer to people's war: eliminate the people.

It is, incidentally, remarkable that the *Times* can so blandly announce that the rebel economy and social fabric are the main target of the American bombardment. It is remarkable that this claim, which, if correct, sets American policy at the moral level of Nazi Germany, can be merely noted in a casual comment, with—so far as I know—no public reaction of horror and indignation.

Still, it is good that the American press has discovered that the rebel economy and social fabric are the target of the American bombardment of Laos. Perhaps we will be spared the pretense that our targets are steel and concrete, or that the bombing is "the most restrained in modern warfare" (as McGeorge Bundy so elegantly put it at the time when virtually every structure in North Vietnam, outside of the centers of Hanoi and Haiphong, was being demolished).

The discovery has been mysteriously delayed. For example, in July, 1968 the Southeast Asia expert of *Le Monde*, Jacques Decornoy, published detailed reports of his visits to the liberated areas of Laos: "a world without noise, for the surrounding villages have disappeared, the inhabitants themselves living hidden in the mountains . . . it is dangerous to lean out at any time of the night or day" because of the ceaseless bombardment which leads to "the scientific destruction of the areas held by the enemy." "The Ameri-

---

[12]Weekly selection, October 1.

cans are trying to 'break' the Laotian Left, both psychologically and, if possible, physically." The nature of their relentless attack "can only be explained if the target is the central administration of the Neo Lao Haksat"—the political organization that won handily in 1958 in the only unrigged election in Laos. This electoral victory inspired the American effort at subversion that led to the Laotian crisis of the early sixties, which still persists.

Decornoy describes "the motionless ruins and deserted houses" of the central town of Sam-Neua district:

> The first real raid against the population center itself was launched on February 19, 1965. Very serious attacks were made on it quite recently on March 17 and 19, 1968 .... The two ends of the town were razed to the ground. The old ruins of 1965 have disappeared, those of March 1968 were still "smoking" when we visited them. Branches of trees lay all along the length of the river, houses were totally burned out (phosphorus had been used). At the other end of San-Neua, the sight was even more painful. Everywhere enormous craters, the church and many houses were demolished. In order to reach the people who might be living there, the Americans dropped their all-too-famous fragmentation bombs. Here lay a "mother bomb" disembowelled, by the side of the road. All round, over a dozen metres, the earth was covered with "daughter bombs," little machines that the Vietnamese know well, unexploded and hiding hundreds of stèel splinters .... One of the officials of Sam-Neua district told us that between February, 1965 and March, 1968, 65 villages had been destroyed. A number impossible to verify in a short report, but it is a fact that between Sam-Neua and a place about 30 kilometres away where we stayed, no house in the villages and hamlets had been spared. Bridges had been destroyed, fields up to the rivers were holed with bomb craters.

Decornoy reports that "American raids on 'liberated Laos' began in May 1964, therefore well before the Gulf of Tonkin incident (August, 1964) and the policy of escalation to North Vietnam (Spring, 1965). For this reason, Laos has, in some ways, served as a testing ground or experimental site." He describes the amazing persistence of the Laotians in maintaining and advancing the social revolution in the face of this attack, their "virulent nationalism" and refusal to follow foreign models, the schools and factories in caves, the prosperity of the rare villages that have still, for unknown reasons, escaped destruction. Finally he quotes an American diplomat in Vientiane who says: "To make progress in this country, it is necessary to level everything. The inhabitants must go back to zero, lose their traditional culture, for it blocks everything." And Decornoy comments: "The Americans accuse the North Vietnamese of intervening militarily in the country, but it is they who talk of reducing Laos to zero, while the Pathet Lao exalts the national culture and national independence."

No doubt Laos is still serving as a testing ground or experimental site, for our new long-haul, low-cost policy. If the American people will only trust their leaders, perhaps there is still a chance to crush the people's war in South Vietnam in ways that will be as well concealed as have been those of the Laotian war.

The secret can be kept. Americans know virtually nothing about the bombing of South Vietnam. To my knowledge, there has been only one pro-Western correspondent who has spent time in the liberated zones of South Vietnam, Katsuichi Honda—and I am sure that his reports in *Asahi* in the fall of 1967 are known to very few Americans.[13] He describes, for example, the incessant attacks on undefended villages by gunboats in the Mekong river and by helicopter gunships "firing away at random at farmhouses":

> They seemed to fire whimsically and in passing even though they were not being shot at from the ground nor could they identify the people as NLF. They did it impulsively for fun, using the farmers for targets as if in a hunting mood. They are hunting Asians . . . . This whimsical firing would explain the reason why the surgical wards in every hospital in the towns of the Mekong delta were full of wounded.

He is speaking, notice, of the Mekong Delta, where few North Vietnamese soldiers were identified until several months after the Tet offensive; where, according to American intelligence, there were 800 North Vietnamese troops before last summer;[14] and, which contained some 40 percent of the population of South Vietnam prior to the American assault.

Occasionally such material finds its way to the American press. Consider again the Mekong Delta. "In March [1969] alone, the United States Ninth Infantry Division reported that it killed 3,504 Vietcong troops and sympathizers in the northern delta [and] senior officers confidently forecast that they will continue to kill at least 100 a day well into the summer." The "conflagration . . . is tearing the social fabric apart." In "free-fire zones, the Americans could bring to bear at any time the enormous firepower available from helicopter gunships, bombers and artillery . . . fighter-bombers and artillery pound the enemy positions into the gray porridge that the green delta land becomes when pulverized by high explosives."[15]

Apparently the performance of the Ninth Division was not entirely satisfactory, however. ". . . in the Mekong Delta, US military advisers at My Tho told a UPI correspondent, Robert Kaylor, that the government's pacification program was still being hampered by the effects of indiscriminate killing of civilians by US Ninth Infantry Division troops recently withdrawn from the area. 'You can't exactly expect people who have had parts of their

[13]They have appeared in English, and can be obtained from the Committee for the English publication of "Vietnam—a voice from the villages," c/o Mrs. Reiko Ishida, 2-13-7, Nishikata, Bunyo-ku, Tokyo.

[14]"Before this summer, the enemy in the delta consisted mostly of indigenous Vietcong units and guerrillas, many of whom worked during the day in the rice fields and fought at night. The only North Vietnamese were troops and officers who led some of the guerrilla units. They numbered about 800 as against an estimated total of 49,000 Vietcong soldiers and support troops." *New York Times*, September 15, 1969. On Sept. 16, the *Times* reports that "for the first time in the war, a regular North Vietnamese army unit, the 18B Regiment, had attacked in the delta."

[15]*New York Times*, Peter Arnett, April 15, 1969. Arnett claims that only 90 percent of the enemy forces of 40,000 are recruited locally, giving a far higher estimate of North Vietnamese than the intelligence reports cited above, or others: e.g., *Monitor*, Sept. 16, which reports that in the early fall of 1969 "North Vietnamese troops in the delta doubled in number, to between 2,000 and 3,000 men."

family blown away by the Ninth to be wholeheartedly on our side,' said the US source, a member of a pacification team."[16]

In the *Monitor*, October 14, there is a front page story reviewing such efforts. It explains that "the proportion of the country 'pacified' has risen with the flow of peasants to resettlement and refugee areas," although the Viet Cong "currently are intensifying their campaign to drive peasants back to their home areas where [they] have a better chance of controlling them." The picture is clear. We, in our magnanimity, are using our modernizing instruments, bombs and artillery, to lead the suffering peasants to the promised land of resettlement and refugee areas, while the ferocious Viet Cong— mere "village thugs," as the MIT political scientist, Ithiel Pool, explains in the journal of the Gandhi Peace Foundation—cruelly drive them back to their homes. The *Monitor* article also notes that "Despite years of thought and effort, officials here are still not agreed on how best to pacify a troubled land. In those years, pacification has advanced from being a theoretical ideal —though inconvenient—to the more important but second-class status of being 'the other war' "—and a proper theoretical exercise for American scientists and scholars.

The New York Times, September 24, presents an example of how pacification proceeds. Northwest of Saigon, 700 soldiers encircled a village, killing twenty-two and arresting fifty-three. It was the fourth such operation in this village in fifteen months. As for the villagers: "The Vietcong are everywhere, they say, and will be back when the Americans leave." An American junior officer, looking at the deserted central market, had this to say: "They say this village is 80 per cent VC supporters. By the time we finish this it will be 95 per cent." Such reports are hardly more newsworthy than a small item of September 27 which notes "that United States Army helicopter gunships mistakenly attacked a group of Vietnamese civilians 25 miles west of Tamky Tuesday, killing 14 civilians . . . United States helicopter gunships killed 7 unarmed civilians and wounded 17 others in a similar incident Sept. 16 in the Mekong delta." It is not easy to avoid such accidents as we try to ensure that the Viet Cong constituency ceases to exist.

In *Look* magazine, November 18, Foreign Editor Robert Moskin describes his visit to a refugee camp, which "tells part of the story of Vietnam's hopelessness." Its 3,125 refugees (240 men) were transfered to this "desolate sand-dune camp" in a military sweep last summer from an island that was regarded as a VC stronghold: "The rest of the men are still hiding with the VC in the tall grass." This is in Quang Nam province, where even the American officials in charge admit that the battle was lost "to Viet-Cong forces recruited for the most part from within the province."[17] With an honesty that others would do well to emulate, Moskin states that in Vietnam "America's historic westward-driving wave has crested."

[16]Boston *Globe*, Dec. 1.
[17]William Nighswonger, *Rural Pacification in Vietnam*, Praeger, 1967.

With justice, "a staff major [of the America Division in Chulai] said: "We are at war with the 10-year-old children. It may not be humanitarian, but that's what it's like."[18]

And now there is Song My—"Pinkville." More than two decades of indoctrination and counter-revolutionary interventions have created the possibility of a name like "Pinkville"—and the acts that may be done in a place so named. Orville and Jonathan Schell have pointed out[19] what any literate person should realize, that this was no isolated atrocity, but the logical consequence of a virtual war of extermination directed against helpless peasants: "enemies," "reds," "dinks." But there are, perhaps, still deeper roots. Some time ago, I read with a slight shock the statement by Eqbal Ahmad that "America has institutionalized even its genocide," referring to the fact that the extermination of the Indians "has become the object of public entertainment and children's games."[20] Shortly after, I was thumbing through my daughter's fourth-grade social science reader.[21] The protagonist, Robert, is told the story of the extermination of the Pequot tribe by Captain John Mason:

> His little army attacked in the morning before it was light and took the Pequots by surprise. The soldiers broke down the stockade with their axes, rushed inside, and set fire to the wigwams. They killed nearly all the braves, squaws, and children, and burned their corn and other food. There were no Pequots left to make more trouble. When the other Indian tribes saw what good fighters the white men were, they kept the peace for many years.
> "I wish I were a man and had been there," thought Robert.

Nowhere does Robert express, or hear, second thoughts about the matter. The text omits some other pertinent remarks: for example, by Cotton Mather, who said that "It was supposed that no less than six hundred Pequot souls were brought down to hell that day."[22] Is it an exaggeration to suggest that our history of extermination and racism is reaching its climax in Vietnam today? It is not a question that Americans can easily put aside.

The revelation of the Song My atrocity to a wide public appears to have been a by-product of the November mobilization. As Richard L. Strout wrote in the *Monitor*:

> American press self-censorship thwarted Mr. Ridenhour's disclosures for a year. "No one wanted to go into it," his agent said of telegrams sent to Life, Look, and Newsweek magazines outlining allegations . . . . Except for the recent antiwar march in Washington the event might not have been publicized. In connection with the march a news offshoot (Dispatch News Service) of the left-wing Institute of Policy Studies of this city aggressively told and marketed the story to approximately 30 US and Canadian newspapers.[23]

[18]Henry Kamm, *New York Times*, Dec. 1.
[19]*New York Times*, Nov. 26.
[20]In *No More Vietnams?* On the widely noted analogy between Vietnam and the Indian wars see my *American Power and the New Mandarins*, chapter 3, note 42.
[21]Harold B. Clifford, *Exploring New England*, New Unified Social Studies, Chicago: Follett Publishing Co., 1961.
[22]See Howard Zinn, "Violence and social change," Boston University *Graduate Journal*, Fall, 1968. When disease decimated the Indians, Mather said: "The woods were almost cleared of those pernicious creatures, to make room for a better growth."
[23]On Nov. 24. Attention, Mr. Agnew.

Apart from this, it probably would have disappeared from history, along with who knows what else.

The first investigation by the Pentagon "reported that the carnage was due to artillery fire. Civilian casualties by artillery fire among hostile villages are so common that this explanation ended the inquiry."[24] But the murdered Vietnamese were not the victims of artillery fire. Since the soldiers looked into the faces of their victims, the inquiry must continue, despite the difficulties. Henry Kamm reported in *The New York Times* that:

> The task of the investigators is complicated by the fact that last January, most of the inhabitants of the peninsula were forcibly evacuated by American and South Vietnamese troops in the course of a drive to clear the area of Vietcong. More than 12,000 persons were removed from Bantangan Peninsula by helicopters and taken to a processing camp near this provincial capital. Heavy American bombing and artillery and naval shelling had destroyed many of the houses and forced them to live in caves and bunkers for many months before the evacuation.... An elaborate interrogation and screening procedure, in which American intelligence agents were said to have taken an important part, yielded only a hundred or so active Vietcong suspects. Most of the people were sent to a newly established refugee camp .... Despite the extensive movement of the population and the military operation, the Vietcong remain active in the area.[25]

On November 22, Kamm adds the further information that "the number of refugees 'generated'—the term for the people forcibly dislocated in this process—exceeded intelligence estimates four-fold." "The 12,000, instead of being scattered in many hamlets where it would be difficult to keep out the Vietcong, are now concentrated in six guarded, camp-like settlements."

It is perhaps remarkable that none of this appears to occasion much concern. It is only the acts of a company of half-crazed GI's that are regarded as a scandal, a disgrace to America. It will, indeed, be a still greater national scandal—if we assume that to be possible—if they alone are subjected to criminal prosecution, but not those who have created and accepted the long-term atrocity to which they contributed one detail—merely a few hundred more murdered Vietnamese.

Recently, a study of American public opinion about Vietnam concluded with this speculation: ". . . little reaction to the war is based on humanitarian or moral considerations. Americans are not now rejecting 'war,' they merely wish to see this current conflict ended. To achieve this goal, most Americans would pursue a more militant policy and ignore resultant atrocities."[26] We

[24]*Ibid.*, Nov. 29.

[25]Henry Kamm, *New York Times*, Nov. 15.

[26]J. Robinson and S. G. Jacobson, in *Vietnam: Issues and Alternatives*, Shenkman, 1968, a symposium of the Peace Research Society (International). This organization, following a script by Orwell, is concerned with a special kind of peace research: the question of "how pacification can be achieved in turbulent village societies," along lines that we have been pioneering in Vietnam, for example. The editor explains that the United States is one "participant in the game of world domination." It might be asked why scholars should assist the Government in this game. The answer is that the foreign policy of the US has been characterized "by good-intentioned leaders and policy makers," so the problem, presumably, does not arise. But even the Peace Research Society (International) is not monolithic. It would be unfair to assume that the conclusion of the cited study is mere wishful thinking. It has to be taken seriously.

may soon discover whether this speculation is correct. Of course, there is sure to be a segment of American society that will not "ignore resultant atrocities"—namely, the irresponsible, loudmouth vocal minority, or those who are described so nicely by Colonel Joseph Bellas, commanding officer of a hospital in Vietnam where soldiers boycotted Thanksgiving dinner in protest against the war: "They're young, they're idealistic and don't like man's inhumanity to man. As they get older they will become wiser and more tolerant."[27] If a majority of the American people will, indeed, ignore resultant atrocities and support Nixon's policy of pursuing a war without discernible end, then this segment of American society may be subjected to domestic repression of a sort that is not without precedent in American history; we seem to be seeing the early signs today with the savage repression of the Panthers, the conspiracy trial in Chicago, and other incidents.

The fact that repression may be attempted does not imply that it must succeed. Surely the possibility exists, today, of creating a broad-based movement of opposition to war and repression that might stave off such an attack. It is now even imaginable, as a few years ago it was not, that a significant American left may emerge that will be a voice in national affairs, and even, perhaps, a potential force for radical social change. There has been a remarkable shift in popular attitudes over the past months, an openness to radical political thinking of a sort that I do not recall for many years. To let these opportunities pass is to condemn many others to the fate of Vietnam.

---

[27]Reuters, Boston *Globe*, Nov. 27.

Photos by Paul Avery, Empire

Editor's Note

During the French domination of Indochina the cities of Saigon, Hanoi and Pnom Penh were noted for their picturesque beauty. Saigon was known as the "Paris of the East." But with the massive saturation bombing of the countryside, peasants soon began to swell the limited service capacities of Saigon built by the French. The city grew tenfold in the same number of years. This is now happening to Pnom Penh, Vientiane and all major cities of Southeast Asia. The forced evacuation of the rural population into cities "is not an accidental by-product of the war. Rather it is the very essence of American strategy." Noam Chomsky clearly identifies what has become the primary objective of American warfare, "massive migration from country-side to city."

The result, massive congestion, squalor, disease and turmoil is described in "The Tragedy of Saigon." Although written four years ago, it previews what is now well documented. "Ecocide in Indochina," included in the Overview, supplies a recent description.

The recent defoliation of the Delta area will no doubt force countless tens of thousands more peasants into an already unbearable urban slum in Saigon. With four million peasants in the Delta, the added strain of their forced migration may well force the breaking point of the Saigon regime. Writing in the *New Republic* of June 27, 1970, D. E. Ronk describes present-day Saigon in an article entitled "Can Thieu Hold On?"

Rich folk get rich, the poor and middle class struggle with an inflation best described as just short of runaway. Even the traditional middle class of Vietnam, the civil servants, curse their employer, the state, and its American paymaster. There is no redress. On every side are the police. Tens of thousands (perhaps hundreds of thousands—those who care can't find out and those who know don't care) are already in prison, or worse, for objecting. Vietnam is at the mercy, both literally and figuratively, of foreigners.

Distrust has replaced old friendships of a more hopeful time, and personal accusations of general responsibility for Vietnam's humiliation have replaced discussion. Long-time foreign residents who took long walks through the city now ride to avoid thrown rocks and garbage. The Vietnamese wife of an American journalist tells of the anti-American and government obscenities shouted at her as she and friends, an American and an Indian, helped wounded people from a Pagoda attacked by government agents. "It's everywhere and all the time now," she says. "The Vietnamese are even refusing to speak Vietnamese to strange foreigners who can speak the language. All the Americans I know are becoming afraid and their Vietnamese friends are afraid for them. . . ."

Mr. Ronk, after further narrating present conditions in Saigon concludes:

Is this then the revolt within a revolt against the government that will topple it?

The Tragedy of Saigon*

by Frances FitzGerald

The United States had been "in the war" for five years when we published the article with which this chronicle begins. The feud about reporting the war between officials and journalists on the scene was an old story. So was the "credibility gap" at home. A few months earlier we had noted in a report from Saigon that the best that U.S. officials could say was: "Although the war is no longer in danger of being lost, it is sobering in these sometimes excessively optimistic days to reflect on how long it may take to win." What was beginning to turn in the public mind was the improbability of "victory" for anybody. We had more than 360,000 Americans in Vietnam, and the number was to swell by 10,000 that month. What had we to show for five years of involvement in the lives of the South Vietnamese?

We knew that doubts about the course of American policy and about the Administration's devotion to its own rhetoric demanded answers to the question—and that these answers could come only through tough, knowledgeable, thorough reportage. The sort of reportage we had in mind was hard to find; then we saw the work of Frances FitzGerald. Her observations were jolting: the war and the American presence were seen to be so injurious to the social, political, and economic structure of South Vietnam as to render dubious our claims that we were protecting the country from the tyranny of the Communist North. This was what we wanted the Atlantic to be doing: showing the reality in unfettered three-dimensional form, in contrast to the two-dimensional reporting of the "news" in newspapers and newsmagazines and on television. Personal opinion would naturally show through, but it would justify itself—and, we hoped, win a hearing in Washington—because of the author's reportorial precision and sophistication.

*Reprinted with permission from the *Atlantic Monthly*, Dec. 1966.

Frances FitzGerald went out to Vietnam early in 1966, leaving off a promising sequence of reports for New York Magazine *about the culture and society of the city.*

"I don't know what you feel about footnotes," she wrote from Saigon as she dispatched this article, "but a few more of them might be useful. For instance, (a) no statistic in this country is ever accurate—all are a mix of various wishful thoughts; (b) the AID budget for Vietnam is $760 million or 20% of the total aid budget, yet as $400 million goes into the commodity import program and $100 million into food for peace, only $170 million can be used on actual programs—things like that.

"The piece has no name."

We called it "The Tragedy of Saigon" and presented it together with a report on mushrooming American military activities in Thailand by Maynard Parker, then a Life *correspondent.*

Before entering Saigon, the military traffic from Tansonnhut airfield slows in a choking blanket of its own exhaust. Where it crawls along to the narrow bridge in a frenzy of bicycles, pedicabs, and tri-Lambrettas, two piles of garbage mark the entrance to a new quarter of the city. Every evening a girl on spindle heels picks her way over the barrier of rotting fruit and onto the sidewalk. Triumphant, she smiles at the boys who lounge at the soft-drink stand, and with a toss of her long earrings, climbs into a waiting Buick.

Behind her the alleyway carpeted with mud winds back past the facade of new houses into a maze of thatched huts and tin-roofed shacks called Bui Phat. One of the oldest of the refugee quarters, Bui Phat lies just across the river from the generous villas and tree-lined streets of French Saigon. On its tangle of footpaths, white-shirted boys push their Vespas past laborers in black pajamas and women carrying water on coolie poles. After twelve years and a flood of new refugees, Bui Phat is less an urban quarter than a compost of villages where peasants live with their city children. The children run thick underfoot. The police, it is said, rarely enter the quarter for fear of a gang of teen-age boys whose leader, a young army deserter, reigns over Bui Phat.

Though most of Bui Phat lives beyond the law, the electricity lines, and the water system, it is changing, growing rich. Here and there amid the chaos of shacks and alleyways, new concrete buildings rear up in a splendor of pastel-faced walls, neon lights, and plastic garden furniture. In one of them there is an American who suns himself half naked on a porch under a clothesline draped with military uniforms. He does not know, and probably never will, that the house just down the alleyway is owned and inhabited by an agent of the Viet Cong.

Except for Bui Phat and its likenesses, Vietnam shows few signs of its twenty-one-year-old war. Weeds grow quickly in the charred earth of a village, and the jungle sweeps back over the cleared land; where a 500-pound bomb has exploded, a hole several feet wide fills slowly with paddy silt; people no longer build the grand stone tombs that their ancestors lie in. But Bui Phat is the new face of Vietnam. From Danang in the north to Rachgia, the slow port at the base of the Delta, the new slums, these crushed villages, spread over all the cities and garrisoned towns. Plastered against sandbag forts, piled up under the guns of provincial capitals, huddled behind the straight streets of Saigon, Nhatrang, Quinhon, they are everywhere—everywhere that the refugees can find a piece of land sheltered from the war.

In the past year [1966] of the American buildup half a million people have left their villages to be counted as refugees—officially. How many more people have left their homes, no one knows, but for a single year the estimate is a million.* By any estimate (and none is more than an educated guess), the last two years [1965-1966] of war have changed the demography of Vietnam. People wash across the country as if the very land had been tilted to drain, primarily into the cities and towns, the real "strategic hamlets" of the war. Sometimes traveling but a thumbspan on the map, these refugees lose their lands, their families, their ancestral homes, and the structure of their lives. Today, more than a quarter of the whole population and over half of the people under government control live in the six big coastal cities, or rather, in the urban complexes, for there is only one "city" in South Vietnam.

Saigon is *the* city. Once a medium-sized commercial town and the capital of Cochin China, it has over the last two decades grown into one of the major capitals of the Far East, the center of a country which had no center and the headquarters of several armies. The two million people who live within its twenty-one square miles and the million inhabitants of urban Giadinh Province make Saigon ten times more populous than Danang, its largest rival. Since the beginning of World War II, its population has quadrupled within the old city limits, filling in the space between the two formerly independent nuclei of Saigon and Cholon, spreading across the rivers, then imploding back into itself. Closed in on three sides by the marshes and by the war, confined on the fourth by its own army, Saigon now outrivals Tokyo for the greatest density of population in the world. Yet nearly all of its inhabitants live in one- and two-story houses, by habit, because Saigon rests on a low mudbank, half-flooded during the monsoon season, in a lacework of rivers and canals.

The public services installed by the French before the war have all but disintegrated under the pressure of the new population, amid which the 30,000 Americans count for more than their numerical weight. Having lost much of the Indochinese trade and gained but a handful of light industries, Saigon could not under normal conditions support a third of its present population. Without the American troops and their construction projects, unemployment, serious when the French left in 1954, would rise to unimaginable dimensions.

---

*By bureaucratic definition the word "refugee" means an individual to whom local officials have granted temporary relief. How many people who have fled war zones and have not applied for or not been granted relief remains a matter of speculation.

After twenty-one years of war and political crisis, Saigon resembles a single lifeboat thrown into the sea for all the passengers of a sinking ocean liner. It lives on a gamble, a small percentage of probability. In a year the prices of all basic commodities have risen 100 to 200 percent—with the exception of the price of rice, which, because of the U.S. import program, has risen only 60 percent. While in some sectors, wages have soared almost in parallel, the continual adjustments, exaggerated by the blockages of the port as well as the Viet Cong roadblocks, create continual social frictions. In Saigon a man has one out of ten chances to contract tuberculosis; his children, if they reach the age of four (two out of three actually do), have a somewhat better chance to join a gang of juvenile delinquents than to go to a public secondary school.

Though no accurate estimates of their numbers exist, Viet Cong political and paramilitary networks crisscross the city, their agents spreading propaganda, collecting supplies and intelligence. Not surprisingly, the most effective and resistant of the political cells lodge in the miserable quarters. In downtown Saigon Americans are advised for their own safety to avoid a patch of execrable slums between the United States Agency for International Development (USAID) and a U.S. Army complex.

Although the Viet Cong can no longer hope to take Saigon militarily, the conditions of life in Saigon—and to a lesser extent in other cities— present them with a number of political possibilities. In the three years [1963- 1966] since the fall of the Diem regime, labor strikes, urban demonstrations, and military shuffles in Saigon have made and unmade the successive governments. In addition to the successful coups, numerous coups manqués, demi- coups, and semipopular uprisings, threats, and rumors have so preoccupied military commanders in the field that the government war effort has been seriously retarded. While the demonstrations have not specifically protested against urban conditions, all of them have fueled themselves on the discontent of the dispossessed city people. During the political crisis last spring, the streets of Saigon were filled each night with crowds waiting for the slightest pretext to attack anything that lay in their path; riots were the evening's pastime—since there was little other entertainment in the city.

Having once stirred up the mobs in Danang and Saigon, the Buddhists lost control, and politics waited on gangs of teen-agers. For weeks the government hesitated to call out the riot police, afraid not so much of the demonstrators as the void of popular support. In the period of confusion, the Viet Cong drew from the reservoirs of violence, but never fully exploited them. The fact that they did not, and that they have never actively campaigned for organized urban support, owes, perhaps, less to the bias of Maoist doctrine than to their own emotional ties with the Vietnamese village. But they may learn better. Faced with a military stalemate, as one analyst points out, they can only hope for a major breakthrough by exploiting urban unrest. Already in Cholon, Chinese Communist agents are rumored to be filling the gap of leadership that opened after the fall of the

Diem regime. If the Ky government cannot win a solid base of support in its cities, its hold on the nation will remain as tenuous as it seemed at the height of the crisis.

Despite Saigon's importance to the national government and despite the whirlwind of money passing through it, the city collects very little to spend on its residents. In a war of staggering figures, the city budget at a total of 8.7 million (771 million piasters) roughly equals that of Lynchburg, Virginia, or Allentown, Pennsylvania. When two thirds of it is deducted for the police and for official salaries, the remainder for all other city programs comes to slightly more than one dollar per person per year.

Although Saigon receives some additional money from the ministries of Youth, Social Welfare, and other departments, the amount, apart from the officials' salaries, is so small and so enmeshed in the national budget that it would yield itself up only to a determined systems analyst with an IBM machine. Unlike every other region of the country, Saigon gets nothing from the special wartime funds distributed by the Revolutionary Development Ministry—of which even Anxuyen, a province only 4 percent controlled by the government, receives over a million dollars for its agriculturally rich population. Because of their relative freedom from red tape, these funds are more important than their size would indicate; they are virtually the only resources available for new programs, for building rather than maintenance. As for the direct USAID contributions to Saigon, their total, unknown for 1965, unreleased for 1966, does not exceed by much the sum for the water and electricity development projects.

But it is not just a question of money. There is no effective administration. Thick as a morning smog, the bureaucracy hangs over Saigon, wisping, whorling, drifting directionless, going nowhere. Theoretically responsible for the "autonomous city" (autonomous, that is, from the provincial administration), the mayor of Saigon cannot so much as replace a spigot on a city water line on his own authority. Below him a vast network of officials reaches down into the district, subdistrict, ward, and family groupings of the city. Created by the Diem regime as a political control system, the network now has grown so brittle that impulses from the top never reach the bottom —or indeed, many of the intermediary levels—if they demand more than the filling out of forms. Since the system was never designed to work in the opposite direction, by "government" the people of Saigon understand the police, the tax collector, and the generals.

As for the mayor, his power rests on his persuasiveness, his relations with the ministers and the ruling junta. Each year he must make his way to all of the relevant national ministries to have each program authorized before he can spend a piaster of the city budget. Under this system, inevitable in a centralized government with no elected officials, he can spend only three quarters of the remaining budget, or about two million dollars, for such programs as street repairs, school building, sanitation, and social welfare.

The rest just vanishes into the books. The books, those heavy yellowing ledgers that lie in quadruplicate around the offices of the ministries—where not a typewriter clatters and all that can be heard is the peeling of the paint and the fall of the plaster, where clerks form letters in their painstakingly elegant script and the functionaries sit at empty desks, staring into space. The mayor, who is a paratrooper colonel at heart as well as by rank, grows restive occasionally. Before the Vietnamese New Year in 1966, when the price of pork was soaring unimpeded by any effort of the commodity import controllers, he rushed over to the Ministry of Economics in desperation and threatened the minister with a gun. After a few days had passed and no action had been taken, he returned with a hand grenade from which he had pulled the pin. Cautiously the officials evicted him—and went back to their ledgers.

On his own authority the mayor then took a detachment of soldiers and went out into the countryside to liberate a herd of hogs from Viet Cong control. "It's crazy," says the mayor's deputy (also a paratrooper), and the mayor adds, "I do not have to fight the people, I have to fight the government. Look, I am a military man." He holds up an imaginary rifle. "I'd like to be out shooting the Communists. Bang, Bang!" He laughs uproariously.

Even if the national government were interested in its civilian city problems, it would have to deal with its own incapacity for decision-making. A thousand real and imagined obstacles block the first step toward city planning. How can the municipality enforce what few zoning laws it possesses when Mme. Nguyen Van X shares her real estate profits with M. Tran Van Z? Since few civil servants can trust their staff or colleagues, suspicions run through the government like concertinas of barbed wire; on them factions set up their checkpoints to stop unfriendly appointments and unprofitable programs. For the year that the ministries of Public Works and Transport administered the Saigon bus system, 1100 to 1600 employees ran a total of seventy buses, thirty of which were almost permanently out of commission. The exact number of employees remains a matter of doubt, for such facts are, like the national budget, classified or unofficially interred.

The life of a civil servant is terribly hard. In a city that is growing as expensive as any Western city, a middle-level bureaucrat with a college degree and an army discharge makes $70 to $100 a month; a minister earns less than a prostitute. "Even if a man is honest," said one high official, sadly, "he still has to provide a house for his family and an education for his children." In effect, if a civil servant cannot or will not make a living from graft, he must have a second occupation. Along about midnight one functionary can be seen on his Vespa on Tu Do, the street of bars, picking up American soldiers to taxi them back to their barracks.

While American bureaucrats do not have the same money problems (on the contrary), they have practically insured themselves against being any more efficient than the Vietnamese. By adopting the advisory system, USAID functionaries have accepted their "counterparts" lock, stock, red tape, family connections, and box on the organizational chart. Advisers to the ministers, advisers to the mayor, advisers for urban design and public administration—all of them work on the urban jigsaw puzzle, and none of them has all of the pieces. "Why don't you go ask Jim . . . Bob . . . Bill," they say to journalists. "He's sure to have the data."

Since April, 1966, at least three people have been trying to discover how much money is spent on what in Saigon. "If you find out anything, just let us know," says one of the "coordinators" cheerily. After all these years and at least four book-length academic studies on Saigon, the U.S. Mission has not the faintest outline of urban development priorities. It loses itself in Alice-in-Wonderland details. Since large numbers of Americans first moved into Saigon, the garbage has been piling up in the streets in great rich heaps like a bachelor's laundry. Because of its inefficient, preinflation wage policies, the government could not hire drivers for the few trucks that existed. For months USAID and the U.S. Embassy, spurred on by the cries of journalists and official visitors, struggled over the Great Garbage question. After long sessions at ambassadorial levels, they produced, first, a shipment of garbage trucks which hooligans stripped to their frames in the port before the relevant ministry could collect them, and second, an extraordinary payment system violating all U.S.-Vietnam ground rules. Now two thirds more garbage is collected in the city of Saigon. But there is also two thirds more garbage to collect. And the U.S. Mission cares about garbage extraordinarily. As for the other city problems, the brutal answer seems to be that what does not bother Americans in their day-to-day lives slips unnoticed into the future indefinite.

Americans do not normally walk through the slums. Not the real slums, like those in the outlying areas (or four out of the eight districts of Saigon), beside which Bui Phat looks like paradise. Hidden within a tangle of canals, between main streets fronted with respectable houses, these slums are difficult to find, but are more revealing specimens for their isolation. Gigantic sewers, lakes full of stagnant filth, above which thatched huts rise on stilts, crammed together but connected by only a thin strip of rotting board. When Westerners walk the tightrope, women smile shyly from behind the windows and the children rush out—a hundred of them gather in an instant. They are not like the village children, these fierce, bored urchins who scream with hysterical laughter when a small boy falls in and flounders in the filth. Within a few moments they are a mob, shoving each other, clawing at strangers as if they were animals to be teased and tortured until . . . The anger comes up quickly behind the curiosity. A pebble sails out and falls gently on the stranger's back. It is followed by a hail of stones.

Slums like these cover Saigon; slowly they curl out from the back alleyways to push across the main streets and the public land. If the city's primary problem is squatters, the squatters' problem is that they have nowhere to go. Since the high ground is already crowded, they can build only one on top of the other or in the marshes of the western districts, one of which the Viet

Cong penetrate regularly in force. (The Viet Cong add somewhat to the over-crowding by moving into the city each night to avoid the bombing on the perimeter.)

On the northeast side of the city, from the airport to the American-built highway to Bienhoa, the land is either heavily settled, insecure, reserved for future military use, or restricted by a combination of these limitations. The three-volume plan for land reclamation and low-cost housing construction drawn up three years ago by Doxiades and Associates has been abandoned *in toto*. Today the mayor cannot even find the land on which to build a bus repair station or to move the squatters who block the major road to the port. Though the government possesses a law of eminent domain, it does not use it because no one has enough confidence in the future of the piaster—or indeed, in the future of the government—to begin proceedings that are certain to last for eighteen months. An enforcement of the zoning laws, ancient as they are, is equally out of the question. Except for a small area of the Eighth District, administered by a group of dedicated young volunteers, not one square inch of land is being reclaimed for settlement. The District 8 project controls the only dredge. In the Fourth District, a marshy island behind the port, yearly fires sweep through the congeries of tin-roofed houses and thatched huts. Even after these disasters—"natural" urban renewal projects—the government does not move in; the rich corner a few square feet of mud for new concrete houses, and the poor take what is left to rebuild their thatched huts.

Public housing is something of a joke, even for the Minister of Public Works. By official count, 65 percent of all structures in Saigon are substandard—substandard for Saigon. With a population growth of 5 per-cent a year, the city must build 10,000 to 15,000 houses a year just to stay even, according to official calculations. Because of the high cost of land and building materials, only 2000 dwellings can be constructed if the most favora-ble circumstances prevail, which they never do. In past practice, low-cost housing, financed by revenue from the national lottery, has turned into mid-dle-income housing for civil servants and their families—that is, until the civil servants moved in to find themselves without electricity, sewage dispos-al, or piped water, and moved out again, leaving the housing to really low-income groups. Even the District 8 project, the only self-help housing and welfare project in the city, and the government's showcase for American visi-tors, suffers from the lack of the basic city services.

In urban Giadinh Province the government has, through the Revolu-tionary Development Ministry, managed to construct an entire hamlet with water, a school, and so forth. For lack of urban experience—the name of the Ministry is "Rural Construction" in Vietnamese—it has built a true hamlet with no agricultural land, miles away from the nearest center of employment, a patch of sad, regulated country in the midst of a city.

If an American should ask what his country has done for Saigon in the way of public service projects, the two principal answers are water and electricity. Since Americans care about electricity almost more than they care about cleanliness, the Viet Cong picked the optimum target when they blew out the transmission line from the hydroelectric plant in the north in May, 1965. For several months the city browned and blacked out day after day until the U.S. Mission brought in enough power by frantic borrowings of generators and gas turbines to handle the new demand, which in a year of the U.S. troop buildup had risen 16,000 kilowatts.

"You know," said the Public Works Minister with a mocking smile, "last month we lifted the restriction on the use of air conditioners. You did not notice? Neither did I. Always the air conditioners have used up 25 to 30 percent of the city's electricity." Yet in large areas of the Sixth, Seventh, and Eighth districts, the only electricity to be seen at night is the light from the television set that Vice President Humphrey donated to the Eighth District project. Its generator alone would produce enough wattage for the whole subdistrict—if the inhabitants had enough money to install the lines and pay for the light.

Until 1966, all the water in Saigon came from forty wells within the city limits; the wells were adequate until a million extra people started to drain them so that they threatened to draw in brackish water underground from the sea. The wells were good, but the antediluvian system of pipes so fouled the water that a U.S. handbook advises government employees to boil it for an hour before using. But then, U.S. government employees live in a part of the city where there are pipes to carry the water; in most areas of the city water runs only through the public street fountains or comes in trucks at two piasters per forty liters.

To prevent imminent disaster, USAID has given the city a development loan to construct a large pump and a set of new pipes to bring water from the Bienhoa River; beginning in 1966 with the installation of three main lines across the city, this clean new system with its increased pressure will burst all of the older pipes in town. In three years' time, the new pipes will ramify into people's houses and the existing public fountains; perhaps at some future date they will reach the now waterless areas.

There are very few sewers. There are even fewer sewers that work. There are no plans to build sewers, because to build them to carry the new water supply would cost four times as much as the new water supply system itself.

Given its topography and a climate like that of New York or Washington in a perpetual summer, Saigon will never be a healthy city. Given the overcrowding, the lack of drainage, of sewage and garbage collection, it may rate as one of the least healthy cities in the world. According to the Doxiades study of 1963, not less than 10 percent of persons ten years and older has clinically significant pulmonary tuberculosis. The infant mortality rate of 36.2 percent is significantly higher in Saigon than in any other region of the country. Despite the massive inoculation program initiated by USAID and the World Health Organization, cholera, smallpox, and bubonic plague, as well as leprosy and typhoid, have become endemic to almost every population center of Vietnam, owing to the movement of refugees.

The diseases for which there are no vaccines—malaria, amoebic dysentery, eczema, worms, and an unspecific sort of swamp fever—will continue to kill people until living conditions show some improvement.

Though the city of Saigon has more hospital beds and outpatient clinics per person than any other area in the country (the proportion, however, is dropping), its facilities would collapse if its citizens recognized all of their symptoms and the benefits of Western medicine. Instead of taking the day off to wait for an examination in a government clinic, the people buy cheap, gaily-colored Chinese medicines to treat what they think might be wrong with them.

A street away from a neighborhood clinic in the Fourth District a baby lolls in the arms of its ten-year-old sister, nodding and dull, half dead from the common dirt sores that cover its head. No, says the girl, my mother is not here, she is never here during the day. She works, she has worked since my father went away. The procession continues—the district chief and subdistrict leader ahead with the two Americans, the two district social workers mincing along behind, lifting the long white skirts of their *ao dais* out of the mud and looking neither right nor left. Near the market, vendors of soup, rice dishes, and green gelatin block the already crowded alleyways, serving their customers through a screen of flies.

A few feet further into the maze the procession stops before a small classroom packed with five- and six-year-olds. The inside is black during the middle of the day, and the children, elbow to elbow, are learning to read from comic books. When they see the visitors, they swarm out, falling all over each other, shrieking and howling. It is like breaking into the middle of an ant heap. The young teacher pushes through the melee. "It's a private school," he says. "I have six classes a day from the first grade on up."

The district chief smiles blandly at the Americans. "It's a school," he explains. "We have many schools in the district. Almost all of the children go to school. As I was saying, I lived in Paris for two years—Rue M—. Do you know it?"

Saigon has a total of forty-four government primary schools which can contain 144,000 children on shifts of two to three hours a day. "Public opinion," writes the Ministry of Education, "has been most concerned about noon classes [11:00 to 2:00] because they are considered harmful to the children's health." To resolve "the acute problem of crowding in Saigon's schools," the Ministry is in the process of building 478 more classrooms, none of which will accommodate new primary students. Although no one is counting, the number of children educated in public and private schools (of which latter the ant heap is generally representative) equals no more than half of the school-age population in Saigon.

Yet the Vietnamese government and USAID are proud of their primary school program. Over the next five years they plan to add to the 4000 public schools throughout the countryside to educate 85 percent of all children, including those of the Viet Cong. The accomplishment will be the more extraordinary for the fact that most of the new schools will, like their predecessors, go into the hamlets, where the war will demolish a good percentage of them by the end of 1966. Since not so much as a design exists for an urban two-story school, the 15 percent of illiterates may be concentrated in the cities, in pure, unadulterated patches of radio and television culture.

In Vietnam the war has replaced the industrial revolution as the source of social welfare problems. With the great suddenness of urbanization, villages have disintegrated, families have splintered, and women with their children have been left to face the cities alone. In Saigon itself, educated guesses put the number of prostitutes at 29,000 and the number of juvenile delinquents at 200,000; as for the number of orphans, widows, cripples, beggars, psychotics, abandoned children, fire, traffic, and labor accident victims—the educated imagination boggles.

Confronted by this chaos, the Ministry of Social Welfare declares, "With respect to the nation, this Ministry intends to stir up by all ways and means people's patriotic and traditional virtues with a view to shoring up our national ethics, being on the verge of ruin. . . . In respect of national philanthropy this Ministry will exhort everyone to try to solve all social problems on the basis of mercy." With due respect to the Ministry, whose views represent the intellectual consensus in this part of the country, it has lined itself up on the wrong side of history, a mistake of which the Viet Cong cannot be accused. Rather than introduce a coherent frame of reference, the United States is busily putting patches in a social fabric which its own presence in this country is helping to tear warp from woof.

After months of haggling, the Mission has finally recommended that an advisory team be sent to the Ministry of Social Welfare. Just what the team is supposed to do with the Ministry's budget of $2 million—5 percent of which goes to Saigon—plus an untrained, ill-paid, and unconvinced staff, is questionable. If the team is energetic, the VIP's that trot through the Dickensian orphanages and welfare camps may succeed in raising an outcry to form a new study group to pressure the U.S. Mission to pressure Washington to finance and pressure the Ky government into doing something about it. In the meantime, the number of juvenile delinquents in Vietnam may continue to stay level with the number of American troops.

The statistics are but signals of urban metamorphosis. Though the Vietnamese can hear them, few know how to interpret them correctly. Throughout history the cities have belonged to the foreigners—to the Chinese governors, the overseas Chinese, and the French—the people of the metropolis. From Hué, the imperial city with its scale model of the Peking Summer Palace, to Cholon, the visual extension of commercial districts in Canton, to

Saigon, with its planned avenues, its French provincial architecture, the cities reflect their past. Their foreignness clings to them; the Viet Cong speak of them as "out there" as opposed to "in here in the village." The urban intellectuals—a professor, a general, a sophisticated newspaper columnist—return to their villages each year (the war permitting) to take their place in the family hierarchy and, as it were, renew the terms of their foreign engagement.

For the four million Vietnamese who live in urban complexes, the city only half exists; it is merely a place, a transparency, through which they look back to the village. For the village *was* Vietnam. Within the village, the extended clan and traditional unit of government, a dense web of custom, religion, and family relation protected the individual and bound him to a system of mutual rights and duties. Under the mandarin and the nineteenth-century French administration, the central government rested as a light superstructure over the villages. Only after World War II did the Viet Minh, and afterward, the Diem regime, begin to break into the village organism, asserting governmental authority directly over the individual. Today, having accepted the modern concept of nationhood, the national government has not yet fully accepted its concomitants, the rights of a citizen and its own responsibility. In the countryside the powerful but essentially negative bureaucracy turns the villagers back upon themselves, upon what remains of the ancient web of the community. In the cities, where the web has disintegrated, the inhabitants, but particularly the new refugees, have nowhere to turn for justice, for material help, or for a promise of security.

In a sense, the foreigners still control the cities. By its intervention in the Vietnamese war and by its military tactics, the United States has created the urban situation. Whether or not the refugees came to find jobs, they came because of the war—not the Viet Cong activity in particular, but the war itself, the air strikes, the artillery fire, the gun battles, and the blockades between field and market. Although some cities, including Saigon, have taken measures to discourage further crowding, their populations continue to rise in almost direct proportion to the escalation of American military activity.

Quite apart from the aggressiveness of the new U.S. troops, the big American machinery, the artillery and bombs, the terror of war for the rural population increases not just in degree but in kind. While the U.S. forces have managed to kill impressive numbers of Viet Cong, neither they nor the ARVN have secured much of the territory they have "swept and cleared." In Binhdinh Province, where American troops killed more than 1500 Viet Cong in a multibrigade operation last February, the Viet Cong recaptured everything but the environs of a garrisoned district headquarters. Those inhabitants of the Anlao valley who did not leave their homes have stayed only to be shot at again. Unless either of the armies can lend more men to garrison duties, the demographic shift will continue to accelerate; large areas of land will be depopulated, and the cities will be overwhelmed.

154

One solution proposed by officials is that the armies should continue to herd villagers in from the countryside and isolate the Viet Cong. Because Vietnam is still an agricultural country, the economics of this draconian formula is worth considering. Until now, American units have operated mainly in the thinly populated regions of Central Vietnam; if the Command should send a force (up to three divisions have been mentioned) into the Fourth Corps area of the Delta, the rice bowl of Vietnam, where over a third of the population lives, it will have to deal with excruciating pressures on Saigon and the southern towns.

As the American troops have formed urban centers about themselves, so they have altered the cities and the lives of their inhabitants. In a country with no industrial base, one group of U.S. Companies, RMK-BRJ—Raymond International of New York; Morrison-Knudsen of Boise, Idaho; Brown & Root of Houston, Texas; and J. A. Jones of Charlotte, North Carolina—is under contract to the U.S. Defense Department for construction projects costing more than the total Vietnamese GNP.

The combine employs 38,000 Vietnamese, more than any other organization except the Vietnamese Army. Not only in Saigon, but in all the port cities and inland bases like Bienhoa, Ankhe, and Pleiku, the American presence has transformed the economic and social structure. With the flood of new demands for the short supplies of labor, services, and goods, the inflation mounts and the economy pulls away from its old moorings on the uneven tide of new money. For the elites on the army and civil service fixed wage scales, inflation has turned corruption from a luxury into a staple. Consumer goods imported by USAID to moderate the inflation effectively check industrial development; the new rich invest in services for the Americans. The Americans bid against one another for new quarters with water and electricity, and drive the Vietnamese from the best quarters of their own cities. Although in the long run the introduction of new ideas, new techniques, a new social mobility may benefit Vietnam, the immediate influence of the U.S. Army is hallucinatory. Take one single block in Saigon with its traveling carnival of bar girls, carousing soldiers, madames, pimps, drunken merchant sailors, beggars, pickpockets, black marketeers, shoeshine boys, gun-toting MP's, and surly cyclo drivers, then multiply by the force levels announced by the Pentagon. While embassy officials stew over "social frictions" and "incipient manifestations of anti-Americanism," they view with suspicion Vietnamese proposals for an American University in Saigon. "Too much American influence here already. The Vietnamese ought to develop their own national institutions." Truly, the United States has no talent for colonialism.

Reluctant to take too overt a ro e in the management of Vietnamese affairs, the U.S. civilian agencies have played and continue to play Hamlet in the U.S. military's production of *Macbeth*. Until 1962, USAID designed its policy in Vietnam according to its general principles: (a) loaning the government capital for long-range economic and "institutional" development and (b) extending credit to restore the country's balance of payments. Called in by the Diem regime to work on the planning and execution of the Strategic Hamlet program, USAID began for the first time to operate within the governmental structure. While it hung back from assuming responsibility for the entire civil administration, USAID sent representatives to the provinces and began to initiate policies. Faced with a rural insurgency situation, planners decided that their first efforts should be given to winning over the peasants for the national government. Because at that time the urban populations were smaller, relatively isolated from the country people and from the ravages of war, they concluded that the cities could be left alone for the moment; in the countryside, they reasoned, their limited resources, unencumbered by major development projects, would stretch through a wide variety of small, inexpensive programs: school construction, pig rearing, agricultural extension, and so forth.

The planners put their faith in pacification. To support President Diem's Strategic Hamlets, General Khanh's New Life Hamlets, the Political Action Teams, and the Revolutionary Development cadre, they build bridges, pig-pens, and schools, whether or not the army (or armies) could provide them with adequate security. In most cases they were, in effect, asking the peasants to risk their lives every day for the government out of sheer gratitude. Four years later and four years heavier in experience, staff, and investment, USAID still clings to its original brief for rural development as it teeters between its horror of overinvolvement and its fear of ineffectuality. Meanwhile everything else has changed. The country under government control, following the sharp decline in security after the fall of the Diem regime, dwindled away to almost nothing by the spring of 1965; then the Americans entered the war.

At the Honolulu Conference in February, 1966, President Johnson and Premier Ky pledged their governments "to the attack on hunger, ignorance and disease" and "to the work of social revolution." Although the pledges referred to all of the Vietnamese people, they naturally applied only to those people living under government control. As the cities and provincial capitals contain 60 to 70 percent of them as well as the central redoubts of "hunger, ignorance and disease," it might have been assumed that the Honolulu Conference promised vast new urban and town development programs. From "the work of social revolution" it might have been inferred that the partner-governments planned reforms in the cities, where the progressive young leadership waits, now biding its time outside the civil service.

At his press conference of October 6, 1966, President Johnson spoke once again of the February Honolulu Conference, "which I considered very successful. At that meeting the government of South Vietnam re-enforced its determination to ... multiply efforts in health, education, and agriculture *particularly in the countryside.*" (Italics added.)

In rural Vietnam the village gates which traditionally kept out the law of the emperor still remain to bar the way of modernization and nationhood. Only in the cities, where old habits and old loyalties are giving way under the pressures of the war, can General Ky put meaning into those tired words "social revolution." Of course, if the United States and South Vietnam designed their Honolulu pledges with a mind to winning the rural population away from the Viet Cong, they might, for the sake of credibility, think to fulfill them in the areas they control. Today the cities are no longer isolated from the countryside; between the refugees and their relatives still living in the contested areas the communication is complete—and more persuasive than the radio. In the struggle against the forces of a real revolution, official unconcern for the cities can only stem from a belief that in this country where a citizen has so little to be thankful for, the twin benefits of security and safety, plus a large military force, suffice to ensure the cooperation of the urban populations.

Although the last few years have taken their toll in all of Vietnam, the refugees, more than anyone else, have understood the consequences for their country of a twentieth-century war. Driven from their lands and villages, they have dragged the full weight of their lives onto a new territory where they cannot take root. In the debris of villages around the shattered cities, they cling to the habits of a society that no longer exists; to their children, the first generation of city people in Vietnam, they can point out no alternative. Without education, without skills, without a structure for their lives, these children, if the war continues on its present course, will be the major source of internal trouble for the Republic of Vietnam.

The condition of the cities is critical, yet the Ky government and its American advisers have not looked past the old assumptions, the old incomplete programs into the whole process of urbanization. Though few Vietnamese will recognize it, the new generation of city children may look familiar to Americans who have spent time in their own city slums.

SIR: Apropos the articles on Thailand (Maynard Parker: "The Americans in Thailand") and Vietnam (Frances FitzGerald: "The Tragedy of Saigon") in the December *Atlantic:* Both articles confirm my fears about the nature, extent, and consequences of our involvement in Southeast Asia. In tandem, they are depressing and ominous—what a tragedy for all concerned.

J. W. FULBRIGHT
U.S. Senate
Washington, D.C.

Photo by Paul Avery, Empire

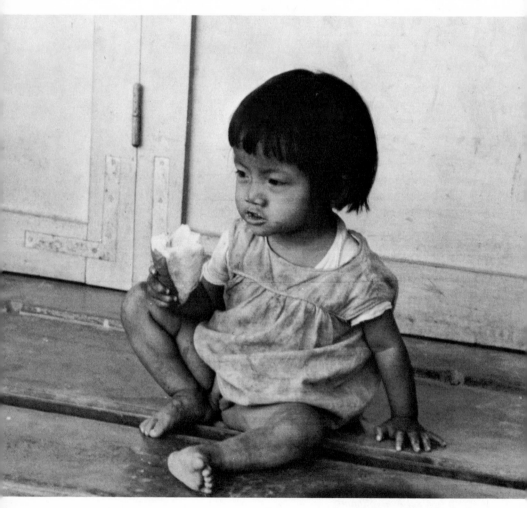

Photo by Arthur S. Doyle

How Not to Keep Them Down on the Farm*

Don Ronk

Vientiane: Methods of unconventional warfare developed in Malaya have proved to be inadequate in Vietnam. Alternative methods evolved or stumbled across in Vietnam may yet prove to be successful in Laos. What does this bode for a peasantry which rises against its government?

What is happening in Vietnam and Laos is a conscious effort by the United States to force basic socio-economic changes. The end result of both wars is to create consumer economies by contriving to raise expectations of material possession while separating the rebels from their peasant base, which Mao Tse-tung pointed out was the prime advantage of a rebel army.

To military counter-insurgency strategists like Sir Robert Thomson of Malaya the thinking and writing of Mao have a particular fascination. Well they might, as the Chinese revolution served as a prototype for most Asian revolts since. And of all the lessons put down on paper by Chairman Mao, the dictum of the fish and the water has held greatest fascination, for it is with this basic that the success or failure of a peasant based revolution rests.

Mao's dictum is far too widely known to need exploration here, but essentially says that a rebel army will be successful in a popular revolt because, being of the people, it can move among the populace with impunity, confounding the adversary, striking at will. Sir Robert believed that his experimentations in Malaya had developed the logical counter to Mao, that is, separating the fish from the water by draining off the water.

In a sense it worked in Malaya. Fortified villages were constructed and the occupants carefully watched over to ensure they provided no bodies, material or other support to the rebels. As a consequence the rebel army both literally and figuratively died. Once the insurgents had been cut off from their

*Reprinted with permission from *Far Eastern Economic Review*, July 9, 1970.

cover and sustenance it was a matter of picking them off one by one, in groups, or letting them surrender. The difference in Vietnam, the Americans were soon to find however, was that the earlier rebellion in Malaya had been carried on by an ethnic minority, the overseas Chinese, whose base of support was relatively narrow from the beginning. The ease with which the British separated rebel from non-rebel was misleadingly simple.

In Vietnam there was no such simplification of identity. The rebel army was ethnically the same as the bulk of the population and, importantly, apparently had widespread support, if only tacit support largely obtained by terror. Confounding the situation ever further was a regime with an already rapidly diminishing base of support ruthlessly attempting to force support from the mass of people. Nevertheless a programme modelled on the Malayan experiments was introduced into Vietnam as a counter to the rebellion.

Most widely known as the "Strategic Hamlet Programme," but with a lacklustre group of lesser stepchildren involving essentially the same aim, Ngo Dinh Diem's government and the United States Mission attempted to separate fish and water by penning up the population. The programme was an almost instant failure. The peasantry simply refused the rationale of moving into fortified areas, and when forced by the central government, left in droves to join the rebel army. Again, so much discussion has evolved, and so many answers given to the failure of these programmes that discussion here would be repetitious. The Malayan "solution" died ignominiously.

At best inadvertently, at worst by design, a new method of separating fish from water was discovered through the mounting use of bombardment in South Vietnam. The peasant population (some 80% of the total) under the real and potential threat of death from the sky began trekking into the cities. Another dictum of revolution had been discovered, that a population will move from the threat of death and will stay removed at least as long as the threat of death remains. Those who won't move even under this threat can be force-moved.

Thus the areas of bombardment crept across the Vietnamese countryside driving the population before them into the cities and great swathes of the land have remained "free strike zones" for years. Any movement or sign of life in a free strike zone is "fair game." The rush on the urban areas became a stampede of humans.

But short of the urban revolt, architects of "special warfare" in Vietnam got exactly what they asked for, the removal of the peasantry from much of the countryside. Everyone left "out there" then is a rebel or "aggressor."

The architects had also placed the population into a money-oriented, acquisitive milieu and played heavily upon the weaknesses of a relatively poor majority. From a subsistence existence as rice farmers, woodcutters, charcoal burners and brickmakers, the new urbanites were thrust into a milieu in which money was the beginning and end of existence, and from all appearances money supplies were endless; all one needed was the gumption to go after it.

There were half a million and more foreigners in Vietnam spending millions daily, whether for coca colas on the streets, beers and teas in the bars, to have someone make their beds, shine their shoes, wash their dishes, drive their food about or service their airplanes. An economic aid programme is spending billions yearly to ensure rising expectations, the kind of expectations that money can buy. But, at the same time Vietnam has been producing virtually nothing but consumers; once a rice exporter it became a rice importer, rubber exports dropped to nothing along with duck feathers, once a prime export. Daily the value of the local currency dropped as more is printed to meet the demands of payment in the economy.

In a moment of candour a USAID economist noted, almost facetiously, that if the aid programme could put a Honda under every military age male in the country there would be no more rebellion. Another truism of revolts, that it's hard to make a revolutionary of a young man worrying about buying, supporting and maintaining "things." Part and parcel of the new strategy of special warfare.

"How're you going to keep them down on the farm?" There's some question whether the United States wants very many of them down on the farm (even if it were possible) at least for some time to come.

In Vietnam it was crude, hit and miss, brutal, even grisly; in Laos the methodology and effects have been greatly refined and, in a relative sense, even sterile. When the Royal Lao government says a million and a half of its population is now refugee they are talking of half the Lao peoples. When the Americans say 700,000 are refugees they are still talking about one quarter of the population, and both are talking of the exodus of bomb-driven people from north and south onto the Plain of Vientiane where they are far behind the theoretical lines of government control, and most importantly, far from sustaining an insurgency by their husbands, brothers and sons.

Unlike Vietnam, these people being driven by the heaviest bombing in the history of warfare, or forcibly expelled (as US Mission personnel admit in private, not "voting with their feet" as said in public), from their ancestral homes are not rushing into the urban areas, but are being assigned unclaimed land just beyond the cities and towns.

There, it is expected, they will remain quiet farmers just close enough to a money economy and the rich, aid-supported bounty of the shops, to become good "thing-oriented" citizens.

Disclaimers and secrecy aside, it is apparent that the US developed a strategy for the decade of the Seventies to deal with peasant revolts and, importantly, has learned to go about policing the underdeveloped world with the minimum of world observation and approbation.

American architects of counter-insurgency have developed a strategy which apparently effectively counters Mao's dictum in being able to force-drain the water through which the fish swim and hold off that water while digging new channels of flow. They have also learned through the bitter lessons of a world watching Vietnam to go about their business in "low profile," with clandestine armies, without American deaths in the battlefield, by half-truth disclaimers about the presence of American military forces.

It all sounds and looks so hygienic that it's hard to bear in mind that untold masses have died, been maimed, millions are dislocated and human aspirations have been corrupted into a way of life for far too many people; but that is warfare as the underdeveloped world goes into the Seventies.

This week's question is whether variations on the strategy are now at work in Cambodia, and where next?

Health and Death in Vietnam

by Thomas Bodenheimer, M.D., and George Roth, M.D.*

South Vietnam has a population of seventeen million. Every one of those people has undergone immense suffering as a result of the war: death, disease, injury, homelessness, or separation from family. The feeble attempts of health care institutions to relieve suffering are overwhelmed by the war's capacity to produce pain and destruction.

Roughly one million South Vietnamese have been killed since 1961.[1] Three-fourths of these are civilians. In the heavily escalated war of recent years, perhaps 200,000 have died each year.[2]

Counting killed plus wounded Vietnamese, one arrives at a figure of four million,[3] close to one-quarter of the country's population. Sixty percent of civilian war injuries involve children under 16.[4] Perhaps four-fifths of all casualties are produced by U.S. bombs and fire-power.[5]

This incredible casualty rate, especially among civilians, is caused by the American techniques of waging war. Since it is of no military benefit to occupy territory in a guerilla war, the only meaningful measure of victory appears to be the number of enemy killed. Thus the U.S. military has devel-

---

*Tom Bodenheimer and George Roth are both physicians working in San Francisco. Dr. Roth has traveled to South Vietnam three times under the auspices of the Committee of Responsibility, an organization which brings war-maimed children of Vietnam to the United States for medical care.

[1]M. Lumsden, *The Vietnamese People and the Impact of War* (Denmark: Institute for Peace and Conflict Research, 1969), p. 52.

[2]Extrapolated from data in Lumsden, *op. cit*, p. 52.

[3]Lumsden, *op. cit.*, p. 53.

[4]Subcommittee to Investigate Problems connected with Refugees and Escapees, Senate Committee on the Judiciary, "Civilian Casualty, Social Welfare and Refugee Problems in South Vietnam" (Washington: GPO), 1969, p. 124.

[5]*Ibid.*

oped the "body count" philosophy, by which the success of a unit is measured by the number of dead bodies it creates. In fact, U.S. fighting units report their daily body counts to a central headquarters, and artillery and air support are ordered only to those units with sufficiently high counts.[6] The incentive, clearly, is to kill as many people as possible. The massacre at My Lai is a direct outcome of the body count philosophy, and is thus a crime committed principally by the U.S. Government, and not simply by a few deviant officers.

The value placed on piling up bodies is not only paramount among ground troops; the bombings are also directed against people rather than industrial or military installations. The saturation bombing of South Vietnam—particularly intense after the bombing halt in the North—is most concentrated in rural areas where villagers are the only targets. Most indicative of America's goal of killing people as a war strategy is the use of anti-personnel bombs. These clusters of small steel pellets explode and lodge deep inside their victims, yet have no effect whatsoever on buildings or military hardware.

Burns are an immense medical problem; in at least one hospital 25% of the patients are burn victims.[7] The burns are chiefly produced by white phosphorus bombs and gasoline. Napalm is still used extensively, but few napalm burns reach the hospital; most are already dead. Patients with burns affecting over 20% of their body surface almost invariably die of infection, usually after days or even weeks of intense pain. Those who survive may become scarred monsters, requiring delicate plastic surgery to preserve the use of their hands, mouth, or eyes.

Direct injuries caused by weapons are by no means the only health disasters brought about by the war. Contagious diseases have spread in epidemic proportion within South Vietnam. Most dramatic is the increase in bubonic plague, which was an insignificant disease in 1961.[8] Now thousands of cases are found all over the country, caused by the decline in living conditions, the increase in rats, and the disintegration of ecologic checks and balances.[9] The even more serious pneumonic plague, absent since 1940, is also reappearing. South Vietnam has become the only country in the world with a plague problem. However, other Pacific basin nations fear the spread of the disease from Vietnam.[10] Cholera has increased by 100% and is more prevalent in South Vietnam than anywhere else on the earth.[11] Polio is commonly seen, and there is no polio immunization program.

Saigon has grown ten-fold, from 350,000 to 3.5 million in a decade. People are crowded together everywhere, living in hammocks, closed on the street. Rats are ubiquitous among the crowds of people. Water is not

[6]Dr. George Roth, personal observations.
[7]W. F. Pepper, "The Children of Vietnam," *Ramparts,* January, 1967.
[8]D. Lyle, "Plague and War, 1966", *Esquire*, Sept., 1966.
[9]Lumsden, *op. cit.*, p. 61.
[10]"Vietnam: Rise Found in Plague and Cholera", *Science*, February 23, 1968.
[11]Lumsden, *op. cit.*, p. 61.

purified, and everyone has intestinal parasites. Tuberculosis has become rampant in Saigon due to the crowded conditions. The suicide rate there increased 9-12 times in two years. There are large locked wards of mental patients, with only seven Vietnamese psychiatrists in the entire country.[12] It is likely that the desperate conditions will leave many people with long-term psychiatric illness.

In Vietnam, the Americans determined to win the hearts and minds of the people. They found that in order to do this, they first had to win their bodies. To win the bodies of the Vietnamese people it was necessary to burn them, bomb them, and kill them. *The only insurmountable health problem in Vietnam, then, is the presence of the Americans.*

Medical Care in South Vietnam

Apart from the gun, the only weapon against American killing is medical care. The purpose of this care is to prevent the millions of wounded from joining the already innumerable dead. However, the medical facilities in South Vietnam—grossly inadequate even without a war—are pathetic in the face of the enormous number of casualties. The U.S. itself is in the midst of a crisis in medical manpower with one doctor per 750 inhabitants.[13] South Vietnam, by contrast, has one doctor per 16,000 people.[14] And three-fourths of these doctors are in the military, unavailable for civilian use. Worse yet, some of the 250 non-military doctors have private offices in Saigon, treating the sore throats and colds of middle-class bureaucrats.[15] Meanwhile, less than 200 doctors attempt to handle the half-million gruesome casualties which occur each year. A program of "joint utilization" was recently instituted by which South Vietnamese military doctors would do some work in civilian hospitals. On paper this program is a good one; in reality, only one military doctor could be found who gave time to civilians.[16]

South Vietnam's two medical schools are the country's only answer to the doctor shortage. The Saigon medical faculty graduated 50 per year, and Hue produced another 25.[17] However, the Saigon school was closed in 1970 due to anti-government student uprisings, and Hue's university was destroyed in the 1968 TET offensive and has not yet been rebuilt.[18] The production of doctors is now almost at a halt. Medical training in Saigon is Western oriented due to the strong influence of American doctors upon the school.[19] Thus specialization and curative medicine dominate at the expense of public health and prevention.

---

[12]*Ibid.*, p. 67.
[13]*Report of the National Advisory Commission on Health Manpower* (Washington: GPO, 1967).
[14]Dr. George Roth, interviews with Vietnamese officials.
[15]Dr. George Roth, personal observations.
[16]*Ibid.*
[17]Lumsden, *op. cit.* p. 90.
[18]Dr. George Roth, personal observations.
[19]*Ibid.*

Wounded and sick Vietnamese either receive no medical care, or seek help in Vietnamese Government medical facilities. These facilities are totally inadequate to render even the most primitive care to the vast numbers of war victims. The Saigon Government spends a mere 2% of its budget on health (60% goes to the military),[20] as compared with 10-20% for some underdeveloped countries without a health crisis.[21] One of the authors, Dr. Roth, visited a number of government hospitals, and found them to run up to 30% more patients than beds. Some beds contain two or even three patients. Other patients lie on the floor, or sit in the halls and porches.

In Tam Ki province hospital, for example, the ward is run by a minimally trained medical corpsman who, against his wishes, became an instant physician, dangerously incapable of coping with the massive problems he encounters daily. The day of the visit, a woman was lying on the floor, having waited 5 hours to be seen. She had been caught in mortar fire, and had a skull fracture, multiple penetrating wounds of the chest, many fractured ribs, and was probably bleeding into her chest cavity. All of these injuries could be corrected by surgery, yet it might have been 5 more hours before the staff could be assembled to begin the operation. She certainly died, a victim of the Americans and of the medical care system.

The Da Nang surgical hospital, with 1200 patients and 900 beds, has a dedicated Vietnamese surgeon who operates 6-8 hours each day. Over 100 patients have waited in a thatched-roof hut for up to two years to undergo corrective orthopedic surgery. However, the acutely injured receive first priority, so the waiting continues, with summer temperatures in the hut reaching 120 degrees. The burn ward, receiving large numbers of patients, is a room of horror. One woman with a 30% burn was dying of infection; the dozens of flies settling on her open, draining skin were no longer of concern to her. A nurse was delicately removing dressings from a child's badly burned chest, each tug rewarded with a scream. The trembling naked child was then washed in a large pail of dirty water. The dressings were replaced, and the endless drama began again with another child.

Vietnam has many paraplegics (from shrapnel damaging the spinal cord) and amputees (with limbs often unnecessarily amputated as the most rapid treatment of arm and leg injuries), who need rehabilitation. The National Rehabilitation Institute in Saigon has a half-finished building, with no funds available for completing and opening the center. Thus there is no hope in sight for the 750 paraplegics in Vietnam; now there are treatment facilities for only 30.[22] In April of 1970, Vietnamese war veterans, mostly amputees and paraplegics, protested the absence of medical care for themselves, and were tear-gassed by Saigon police.

---

[20]Lumsden, *op. cit.*, p. 53.
[21]*Las Condiciones de Salud en las Americas* (Washington: Pan American Health Organization, 1966), p. 87.
[22]Dr. George Roth, interview with National Rehabilitation Institute director.

American Versus NLF Health Care

The American government boasts that it has opened U. S. military hospitals to civilian war casualties. This is true to an extremely limited extent. The American hospitals care for only about 10,000 wounded per year, or less than 2% of total casualties.[23] Civilians never know which hospitals are open to them or whether beds are available. Military casualties have priority, and 35% of the beds are left empty at all times in preparation for potential emergencies.[24] In one U.S. medical officer's experience, there had never been a need for this large number of unused beds. In any case, many civilians are turned away from U.S. hospitals which are only two-thirds full. These rejects often end up on the floor of a Vietnamese hospital.

It is true that the U.S. has contributed to South Vietnam's meager health care effort by sending volunteer doctors and supplies. An absurdity: killing hundreds of thousands of people and then sending a few doctors and bandages to patch up some wounds. The doctors are recruited through an AMA program, advertised as: Visit Vietnam and take a trip around the world. The U.S. doctors experience total disillusionment upon arrival, not being trained to function without nurses, surgical instruments, laboratory or X-ray. The Vietnamese doctors with whom they work feel that the American physicians make essentially no medical impact; the program is clearly a political one.

The U.S. medical and public health aid program costs about $50 million per year, and is diminishing each year. A majority of the supplies are pocketed by corrupt administrators before they reach the hospitals, and are sold on the black market for profit. Penicillin, which may be the most important factor in saving the lives of wounded people, is nonexistent in some Vietnamese hospitals, yet it can be bought in large quantities on the streets of Saigon.

The U.S. embassy bureaucrats concerned with non-military problems such as refugees, public health, and "pacification," are overwhelmed by the chaos and totality of the shambles about them. The problems grow far faster than solutions can be devised. This situation is dealt with by creating myths: U.S. military hospitals make a significant contribution to civilian medical care, the "joint utilization" of Vietnamese military doctors is functioning, there is a meaningful immunization program in the country, Vietnamization is possible, etc. These beliefs have no basis in fact whatsoever, but Americans embrace such myths because they cannot tolerate the reality.

In direct contrast to the American orientation toward health care stands the program of the National Liberation Front. The NLF controls large areas of the South Vietnamese countryside, and has established a medical care

---

[23]Extrapolated from Subcommittee to Investigate Problems., *op. cit.*, p. 19.
[24]*Ibid.*, p. 20.

network in some of these areas.[25] The facilities are decentralized, and manpower is simply trained. Rather than placing resources into the prolonged education of a few physicians, the NLF trains a large number of sub-professionals. Thus the total health manpower in one area was increased from 3 to 200 within five years.[26] At least one health worker (nurse or auxiliary nurse) is stationed in each tiny village, under supervision by the few available doctors. Similar systems of rural health care are used in many underdeveloped countries with great success.

The U.S. military hospitals provide a good quality of care, with modern equipment and well-trained specialists. But quality is of no benefit to the tens of thousands who are not in the hospitals. Most patients are unable to travel to the centrally placed hospitals, and those who arrive may be turned away. The rudimentary facilities and manpower of the NLF are present for everyone in the villages where the injuries and diseases occur. The presence of one auxiliary nurse with a bottle of penicillin is worth more than ten modern distant hospitals.

Conclusion

Health is dead in Vietnam, and there will be no resurrection until the war is finished. Any belief that the war-caused health problems can be solved amidst the killing is sheer myth and delusion.

To restore decent health care in South Vietnam, however, will require even more than an end to the war. The totality of American cultural, educational, and medical penetration of the country must cease. A few shiny medical schools slowly graduating modern Western-type specialists will never bring health care to the Vietnamese people. Needed are large numbers of rapidly trained health workers: placed within the villages and throughout the crowded cities; supervised by doctors; concentrating on vaccination, sanitation, rat and mosquito extermination; and referring patients to hospitals only when necessary. Only in this way could South Vietnam quickly develop an adequate health care system. And only under a government which is free from U.S. influence and responsive to the people's needs will such a system emerge.

---

[25] "War and Urbanization in Indochina," Moss and Shalizyi, (Simon and Schuster, N. Y., 1970)
[25] Lumsden, *op. cit.,* p. 89.
[26] W. G. Burchett, *Vietnam: Inside Story of the Guerilla War* (International Publishers, N. Y., 1965).

The Circle of Deception — Notes on Vietnam

Robert Jay Lifton, M.D.

It is becoming increasingly apparent that the American presence in Vietnam is enclosed in a circle of deception. Distorted perceptions, false interpretations, and misguided actions have been reinforcing one another in a self-defeating process. During a recent re-visit to South Vietnam I had a chance to talk at some length with various articulate Vietnamese and Americans. Their conflicts revealed to me some of the psychological and historical dilemmas underlying our ever deteriorating military and political involvement. The subsequent elections have obscured but by no means eliminated the problem.

I

Beginning with the military situation itself. one could not help but note an element of George Orwell's "Newspeak" in official American versions: "progress" means disintegration, and "victory" stalemate. American correspondents told me how they would over the course of a year accompany American troops three or four times through the same woods or highlands, each time be informed of the impressive number of Vietcong killed, only to end up finding things back the way they were with nothing really settled, nothing held, nothing secure. Indeed the word "stalemate," so repugnant to our President and Secretary of State, if anything gives us the benefit of the doubt. It is difficult to estimate how much Americans promulgating this Newspeak believe in it, but one can say that any circle of deception involves a considerable amount of self-deception.

---

*Reprinted with permission from *Transaction Magazine*, March, 1968.

Everybody seems to agree that a major cause for these difficulties is the fact that the Vietnamese Army won't fight. When one inquires why they won't fight, Americans have a quick answer: "Lack of leadership." This explanation is put forth as though one were discussing a large machine in which a few key gears (leaders) were missing, with the implication that if *we* (Americans) could only "instill leadership" in *them* (Vietnamese), they would then fight and all would be well. This *mechanistic fallacy* pervades much of American thinking about Vietnam in general, and is a means of dismissing the more fundamental human dimensions of the problem (the National Liberation Front and the North do not seem to "lack leadership"). Americans are reluctant to look beyond the immediate "operation" into the chasm, preferring to reinforce at every point the circle of deception.

The truth is that South Vietnam is a society so dislocated and fragmented that no amount of American technology or technique, military or rehabilitative, can put it together again. The dislocation goes back at least two centuries, and includes pre-colonial, colonial, and post-colonial social conflicts, as well as certain "post-modern" confusions now found in all societies. The present war accelerates processes of breakdown at every level, especially in its annihilation of village life, the main source of social stability in Vietnam. And what is too often overlooked is the extension of these disintegrative tendencies into the realm of idea systems and images. There has been a breakdown not only of social institutions but of the shared symbols necessary to ordered existence—symbols defining rhythms of life and death, group loyalties, and the nature of reality. This "desymbolization" reaches deeply into the individual mental life and undermines collective efforts of all kinds, including that of fighting a war. Whatever success Communism has had as a cohesive social force in the North or the South has resulted from its capacity to provide meaningful new images and symbols, or to revitalize old ones.

While all South Vietnamese are involved in this process of desymbolization, one begins to appreciate its national consequences when one observes some of the convolutions in the lives and thoughts of would-be leaders. One formerly high-ranking diplomat I spoke to had a background of diverse intellectual and political allegiances (he had lived in China, Japan, and the United States), of long and close association with Diem, and of continuing leadership in a prominent religious sect (which itself combined mystical, clan-territorial, and political elements). He could speak from experience when he described to me the last thirty years of Vietnamese history as "nothing but explosions." But he went on to characterize all existing political systems—"so-called American democracy," European parliamentary methods, and the various kinds of communism and socialism—as inadequate for Vietnamese needs ("We have to find our own way"), adding somewhat vaguely, "These days all ideologies are a little outmoded." I was left with the impression of a man both knowledgeable and confused, in whom the pulls of old

Vietnamese and contemporary international images had resulted in a facile end-of-ideology perspective which covered over a more fundamental absence of any viable ideas at all. Another prominent public figure, after a strikingly uninhibited account of pervasive governmental corruption, including manipulation of the then impending elections, considered the elections nonetheless hopeful because "people were learning to play the game of the constitution." Again I had the sense of a post-modern distrust of all thought systems—of the whole thing being a "game" or "scenario" (perhaps a "bag") which had to be played out but was not to be taken seriously—in a man who, like his country, could construct little that was cohesive out of damaged old goods and tarnished new ones. (He did not remain hopeful when the elections were over: he condemned them as fraudulent.)

The American response to Vietnamese dislocation and emptiness is more and bigger war. And this of course means more deception, more claims that things are getting better and that progress is being made.

I found myself reminded of two rather terrifying psychological analogies: First the tendency of people committed to certain beliefs, when circumstances have proven their beliefs to be wrong, to refuse to surrender them but instead embrace them with renewed intensity while rationalizing their error. The second, based upon my own work relating to death imagery, that men are most apt to kill or wish to kill when they feel themselves symbolically dying—that is, overcome by images of stasis, meaninglessness, and separation from the larger currents of human life. (Nor does the actual military threat from the Vietcong invalidate these analogies.)

II

To pursue an understanding of the circle of deception is to examine more closely the nature of the American presence in Vietnam. One is immediately confronted with the theme of the impotence of American power—of the *blind giant*. This is not to say that American men and machines count for naught, but rather that America-in-Vietnam, despite its vast technological and bureaucratic dimensions (one must go to Vietnam to grasp these) is incapable, *in this situation*, of doing what it says it is doing or wants to do (defend the South against Communism, help strengthen democracy, defeat the NLF and the North or weaken them sufficiently to cause them to seek peace). Here the circle of deception works something like this: The giant has been called forth, fully equipped; one cannot admit that he is helpless. But the giant *is* helpless, not because he lacks strength or even intelligence, but because, in a psychological and historical sense, his vision is profoundly impaired. Unable to "see" the actual dimensions of the environment in which he finds himself, he resorts to blind technological saturation of it with his destructive fire-power; unable to see the enemy, he shoots blindly at elusive figures who might just as well be his wards or allies.

Yet in another sense the giant seems all-powerful. There is often the feeling in South Vietnam that if America does not take care of things nothing gets done—as well as a tendency among a dislocated people, new to Western technology, to lean on America more and more to do everything. What is beginning to become clear, however, is that Vietnamese immobilization is not relieved but increased by the giant's presence. This is so because of an unhealthy relationship between Vietnamese and Americans around psychological themes of power and dependency—or what I call a *situation of counterfeit nurturance*. Colonialism is a classical example of such a situation, but one finds the pattern also existing in association with American aid to underdeveloped countries, in Negro-white relationships within the United States, and in virtually all programs of social welfare attempted anywhere. It can develop around any one-sided relationship, and consists of feelings of special need on the part of the weak, together with strong resentment of help offered because the help is perceived as a confirmation of weakness. The key problem is the absence of a sense of autonomy—indeed, the perpetuation of a situation which makes autonomy impossible.

I constantly came upon precisely this combination of dependency and antagonism in South Vietnamese feelings toward Americans. The sense of help received as counterfeit was enhanced by the fact that the help was directly accompanied by broadening areas of destruction. Moreover, Vietnamese hold the most extreme images of Americans. They see them sometimes as an omnipotent force, a hidden manipulative hand behind everything, and at other times as ineffectual innocents repeatedly duped by a tough enemy. In a situation of counterfeit nurturance, a balanced view of Americans becomes impossible; and many aspects of the American presence perpetuate this psychological imbalance.

The majority of Americans are new to the country and relate to it mainly on the basis of the present war. One may say that for them there are "two Vietnams" in a sense different from that usually meant by the term, one of fighting and killing (the predominant American contingent concerned in one way or another with military operations) and the other with healing and rebuilding. This "second Vietnam" is made up of such people as physicians, agriculturalists, and providers of various forms of social and economic relief —of every variety of the *humane American*. But however valuable and even heroic the contributions of the humane American may be, his efforts tend to be tainted by his ultimate involvement with the first group—either because he is officially sponsored, because he must depend upon the American military (dispensers of transportation and much else in South Vietnam) to sustain himself, or simply because he is American (though a few in private medical and welfare groups struggle valiantly to avoid military or political taint, and their non-American counterparts can of course stand apart from it). In these and other ways services offered by the humane American are likely to become enmeshed in conflicts surrounding suspicion of counterfeit nurturance. Their healing efforts are in fact associated with a strange twentieth-century moral inconsistency: on the one hand the assumption (though belated and in response to outside pressure) of considerable medical and social responsibility for injured and dislocated civilians; on the other, the willingness to sacrifice these same civilians, and indeed entire villages, to the goals of war.

There are also many individual examples of what might be called the *poignant American,* who becomes increasingly aware of the larger contradiction surrounding his energetic and often compassionate reconstructive or therapeutic work. He is an entrapped idealist, and the agent of his entrapment is the official bureaucracy he serves and the mission it assigns him. He tries to cope with his situation through a form of "bureaucratic idealism," but this is likely to be heavily flawed by some version of the mechanistic fallacy mentioned before. One able young foreign service officer working in "pacification" thus said to me: "If I had three or four hundred good dedicated men, I could get the job done." When I asked him whether he meant Americans or Vietnamese, his answer—"Of course, if they could be Vietnamese that would be fine"—made it clear that he had Americans in mind. Although well informed about the historical complexities responsible for the absence in such a program of "three or four hundred good dedicated" Vietnamese, he chose to brush these complexities aside in favor of a characteristically American vision of the most efficient way to "get the job done." In the fashion of most Americans, he attributed the continuing success of the Vietcong (despite severe stresses) to their "organization"—and sought to equal that organization as a way of defeating it. But in Vietnam this kind of efficiency becomes inefficiency, especially when attempted by an alien force —a blind giant—whose vast resources can find no point of local integration, and whose actions, even on behalf of reconstruction, must be perceived as externally imposed.

These realities were impressed upon me even more forcefully by another poignant American doing similar work. Unusually well trained (he spoke both French and Vietnamese) and well regarded, his administrative position had been preceded by extensive work in the field. After outlining to me the steps in the program he and his team sought to carry out—establishment of security, evaluation of social and economic needs, institution of necessary changes—he admitted that the major impediment to the whole thing was the simple fact that security was at best tenuous because "the Vietnamese won't fight." He went on to describe how he and his group would seek out a village head and coax his participation while instructing him on necessary procedures, then rush off to the provincial office to smooth the way for the expected application, and then struggle with various forms of bureaucratic resistance (not to mention the resistance of villagers afraid of retaliation from the Vietcong). He defined his own role in all this as a "catalyst." But it was clear that under such conditions an American is less a catalyst than a *desper-*

ate energizer—one who initiates and oversees (rather than merely enhances) a reaction that is not primarily a Vietnamese one, and, for that matter, is not really taking place.

There are many varieties of the *numbed American*—intellectually aware of death and suffering but emotionally desensitized to them. Such "psychic numbing" is a useful defense in various encounters with death, but also permits man's most extreme violations of his fellows. One of its forms is a preoccupation with "professional" concerns. Emphasized to me repeatedly was the widespread awareness among Americans of the importance for professional advancement of a stint in Vietnam—whether for journalists ("the place where the story is"), foreign service officers, or career military men (it was said that a record of some form of command in Vietnam would in the future be a prerequisite for highest military appointments). And in all three groups a large percentage of men conducted themselves as "professionals" in the sense of knowing their work and performing well in adversity. In Vietnam, ordinary professional numbing perpetuates the circle of deception by enabling each to think only of "doing his job"; only occasionally does one encounter men who both "do their jobs" and transcend them—doctors who combine their healing with outspoken moral revulsion toward killing, journalists who by telling the truth lay bare the circle of deception.

I heard much of another kind of numbed American—officials who, when asked about the killing of civilians, would answer, "The numbers have been exaggerated, and anyhow civilians always get hurt in war"; and about the jailing of intellectuals: "We haven't heard about that—after all we can't keep up with everything that goes on—and besides, we are guests in this country." This last form of numbing emerges directly from the contradiction surrounding American influence in Vietnam, as well as from the deception that we are there merely to help a worthy government in its uphill fight to create a free society.

Still other forms of numbing derive from American frustration at Vietnamese immobilization, as in the case of a provincial USAID (United States Agency for International Development) representative who spoke of the dreadful predicament of "unofficial refugees" who camp along the roads in order to avoid the gunfire in the villages—and a minute or two later, when discussing a campaign to collect blood for needed transfusions, declared angrily: "No American should give a single pint of blood to the Vietnamese until they learn to do things for themselves." GI's, facing similar frustrations, sometimes with life-and-death consequences, in a strange country that seems to offer them so little and demand so much, often characterized Vietnamese as "dirty," "cowardly," "not willing to do a damn thing for themselves," and "not worth fighting for." I heard extreme attitudes emerging from combinations of numbing and rage: "We should use every single weapon we have—including nuclear weapons. We used the atomic bomb in Hiroshima, didn't we?" Nor need one dwell on the brutalization of combatants, or on patterns of "military necessity" prominent on both sides: Americans firing at "anything that moves," and Vietcong killings of those thought to collaborate with Americans or simply to possess needed equipment.

The psychological purpose of numbing is the warding off of anxiety about death, and of guilt toward the dead and dying. In the case of Americans, both in Vietnam and at home, it prevents awareness of what is happening to combatants on all sides as well as to non-combatants, but is easier to call forth in relationship to an alien non-white people than to our own dead.

The closest to the *quiet American* among those I encountered were, alas, the resident social scientists. One I talked with, a man with a considerable academic reputation who had been supervising a series of studies under government contract, exuded an unnerving enthusiasm—about the country ("a fascinating place") and his research (also "fascinating" and "rewarding"). There was an aura of unreality about this scholar's exuberance in the midst of disintegration as he discussed problems of South Vietnamese and NLF "attitudes," and then the measuring of responses of villagers to the presence of television sets provided by the Americans for experimental purposes. When I originally read the Graham Greene novel, I thought its portrait of the quiet American in Vietnam a bit overdrawn. But I think I now understand a little more about what Greene was trying to convey: a form of misplaced decency, an altruistic commitment at once naive and arrogant in its ideological presuppositions, ending up in the most disastrous actions. Certainly the social scientist in Vietnam has been much less destructive than many of his fellow countrymen, but he has a special relationship to one aspect of the circle of deception implicit in Greene's concept—the fiction that a mixture of expert technical knowledge and dedicated anticommunism would enable Americans to show the way toward a "solution" of the Vietnamese problem.

Finally, there was the *tired American*, emotionally drained by weeks, months, years of experiencing a deteriorating situation and explaining, to others and to himself, its positive possibilities. One should never underestimate the psychological work necessary to maintain illusion against continually impinging actuality. A number of Americans I met fell into this category, but it was perhaps best exemplified by a high-ranking official spokesman. He responded to my initial expression of doubt about our position in Vietnam with skillful open-mindedness: "One *should* have doubts. Nothing is clear-cut." But a distorted version of events quickly emerged: "We have always been in favor of negotiations, but no one answers the phone." And he buttressed his interpretations with a series of "scholarly" half-truths, including an ingenious justification of the American presence in the form of a discovery by an American psychologist that Vietnamese "have a strong need for a father figure" —a vulgarism impressive in its psychological, historical, and moral reach.

Even more revealing was his consistent technique of affirmation by negation. On the subject of economic suffering of Vietnamese with fixed salaries because of spiraling prices caused by American spending: "There has

as yet been no *runaway* inflation." About the poor performance of Vietnamese troops and their tendency to desert: "There has been no defection of
whole battalions." And about the burgeoning resentment of Americans:
"There have been no all-out anti-American *riots*." Here the circle of deception operated on the assumption that, since one could imagine (anticipate?)
much worse developments, things must be quite good now. About the use of
American influence to curb flagrant violations in election procedures, he
wavered between decorous restraint—"It's their country"—and sly admis-
sion that "We do, of course, talk to people." The fatigue and despair in his
voice became all the more understandable when I later learned that he had
been among the minority of top-ranking Americans in Saigon favoring
stronger support of civilian government, since he was now in the position of
daily defending the course he opposed. One must keep in mind that there are
doves and hawks of sorts among resident American officials—and that, as
one knowledgeable journalist put it to me, "Everyone but the generals wants
out." But the tired American must remain, and justify being, "in."

III

Unknown to most Americans, there are large numbers of Vietnamese
who refuse to enter the circle of deception, who are painfully aware of the
negative consequences of the situation of counterfeit nurturance. Political
leaders, university professors, and writers and editors conveyed to me in our
talks various messages of extreme dissatisfaction.

One predominant message was: *You are curing us to death.* A
prominent political candidate, who is also a physician and therefore given to
medical metaphors, referred to America as an "iron lung" now being used to
help "the patient" (Vietnam) to "breathe." Then he added, with considerable
emotion: "But this iron lung should be for the purpose of the patient learning
how to breathe by himself and becoming healthier—not to take over his
breathing for him." A newspaper editor wrote in a similar metaphor: "The
injection of a right dose—in the right place will cure, but an overdose
injected in the wrong place will kill." He went on to refer to American assistance in an even more telling idiom; "A moderate drink...once in a while will
improve health and morale. But too many drinks too often will poison the
blood, and eventually destroy the brain and the liver. Barrels of it will drown
the drinker." Here the message is: *Your "help" is poisoning (drowning) us.*

He went on to specify that "excessive and prolonged aid" would further
an already harmful tendency in South Vietnam for the city to be alienated
from the countryside, and make them both "dependent on the donor country" in a way that would "sap ... physical as well as moral strength, and
render (South Vietnam) powerless in the face of a threat to its social body
from the inside.... (and would be one of) the worst gifts ever made to this
country, for it would mean eventual destruction ... of its capacity to think,

plan and execute, and its will to work and struggle, that is to live." Here we encounter what is perceived as the most extreme form of counterfeit nurturance: help meant to be life-giving becomes deadly; in political terms, assistance meant to thwart communism speeds up its victory.

In his talk with me he emphasized not only that South Vietnam was being overwhelmed, psychologically as well as economically, by the various facets of the American presence, but lashed out at what he saw as the hypocritical nature of the American effort: "We know you are not fighting for Vietnam but against China. If you want to fight China, why not go there, to her borders, and fight?" As a Southerner, he was especially bitter about the destruction of the country ("Everyone talks about bombing of the North, but what about the bombing of the South?"), and in his writings referred to the "preposterous situation" in which Americans supply not only the military force to impose an unpopular government upon a rural population but "even . . . carry out psychological warfare and civic action to win the population over to the government side." And in our talk he also brought forth what is for an Asian intellectual the most extreme kind of condemnation, referring to his country as "like a colony but worse."

Essentially the same message was conveyed to me by a university professor in the midst of a quiet discussion over *aperitifs*, when he suddenly launched into an angry monologue about the blind giant in intellectual spheres. He compared the modest office of his university president with the suite maintained on the floor below by the resident American "advisor," complained of American dictation of educational policies in ignorance of Vietnamese needs and desires, and concluded bitterly: "Americans always think their ways, their ideas, their teaching, their food, their way of life are the best." Like the other two Vietnamese quoted above, he was by no means free of need for the Americans, but found himself humiliated, and at times paralyzed, by the form the American presence has taken.

We see, then, that the message, *You are curing us to death*, readily extends itself into: *Give us back our country!* Such was vividly the case with a young writer who had spent several years at an American university and now belonged to a loosely organized oppositional group of intellectuals—highly nationalistic and vaguely socialist, with contempt for their government and respect for the NLF ("We are against their terror but we understand them, and consider many of them patriots"). He spoke to me at length about America's takeover of South Vietnam, summing up his bitterness in the phrase: "This is not our country." Throughout our talk he struggled with feelings of humiliation, and with the quest for renewed individual and national pride. He expressed contempt for Vietnamese who had in the past become French citizens; asserted "I am Vietnamese and shall be Vietnamese until I die!"; and summed up his convictions about his country's situation as follows: "I don't care so much whether it is communist, anti-communist, nationalist, or imperialist (then, more slowly and pointedly) *as long as it is Vietnamese*"!

He resented Americans' collusion in the fraudulent situation he saw confronting Vietnamese intellectuals: "A friend of mine tried to publish an academic study of Marxism, but it was disapproved by the censor, so he wrote another book entitled *Sexual Response*, which was easily approved." He illustrated the helplessness of the blind giant in Vietnam by suddenly asking me the question, "Can you sleep at night?" I thought at first that he was raising a problem of American conscience, but he was referring to the noise of artillery fire one hears in Saigon every evening; his point was that it was occurring on the very outskirts of the city. Yet with it all he in no sense gave up on America. He recalled with great affection the warm and stimulating student community he had known there, in contrast to the "other America" of generals and bureaucrats he found in Vietnam. He seemed to be asking for a reassertion of the libertarian spirit he had associated with America in the past. He went so far as to suggest that, since "the problem is not the North but the Chinese" (a point of view of many Vietnamese nationalists), even if the North were to take over the country "it might want an American' base in Vietnam." However one might question the accuracy of this assumption of joint interest in preventing Chinese incursion, it would seem to contain a lingering wish to remain allied to America in the struggle for national independence.

But to conclude that men with this kind of intellectual and emotional tie to the West can be counted upon to support Western—or in this case American—political policies is to enter further into the circle of deception. Indeed for almost a century Asian intellectuals have been emerging from their Western experiences as revolutionaries combatting Western domination. If one looks to such examples as Chou En-lai, Krishna Menon, or Ho Chi Minh, one suspects that much of the hostility ultimately felt toward the West has to do with precisely the kind of ambivalence we observed in this young writer. The strong initial attraction, followed as it is by profound personal and political disillusionment, becomes viewed as an evil seduction which must be violently resisted in the name of individual and national integrity. And there are many "Wests" to draw upon for ideological commitments. The connection with the West is never entirely broken, but it is used mainly as a means of self-discovery.

Other frequent messages Vietnamese conveyed to me about Americans were variations of: *We feel that we need you but* ... A woman of about thirty, the daughter of a plantation owner from the North who had lived in Paris for some time, was appalled at the generally corrupt and "Americanized" atmosphere she observed upon her return to Saigon. She spoke even more bitterly about the effects of American-induced inflation upon Vietnamese civil servants and soldiers, going so far as to claim that many incidents of stealing and killing attributed to the Vietcong were actually the work of destitute members of the South Vietnamese Army—virtually attributing these crimes to American influence. Her proposed solution to these problems was a Vietnamese version of the circle of deception: a strongman to run the government who would put to death a few of those indulging in graft to set examples for the others; and more American soldiers "to fight the communists." But she seemed extremely uneasy about reports of hesitation on the part of Americans, and repeatedly asked me to tell her "what Americans think about the war." This kind of anxiety in Vietnamese seemed to stem from doubts not only about American staying power, but about the validity (in the face of the deep deterioration they know to exist in their country) of the demands they were making of Americans. And such uneasiness and guilt is always likely to increase resentment.

The combination of demand and resentment could take various symbolic forms. On a visit we made to a Saigon hospital my wife distributed little dolls to war-injured children. She had given away almost all of them when one of the parents rushed up to her, holding the head of a doll in one hand and the rest of it in the other to demonstrate that the doll had broken in half——all the while smiling with discomfort in the East Asian fashion, and making it clear that she expected the broken doll to be replaced (which it was). The incident seemed to suggest several dimensions of the situation of counterfeit nurturance: the help needed and demanded is endless; the American giver will be resented for the imperfections of his gifts; and (somewhat more abstractly) Americans are expected to put severed things and people together—because they possess such great power, and because they are largely responsible for severing them in the first place.

I encountered another symbolic expression of this demand-resentment constellation in the delusion of a young female dancer hospitalized at a psychiatric center in Saigon. She had lived for some time in London, and had returned to her country because of developing symptoms of mental illness. But she was convinced that "the Americans" had abducted her in London and carried her forcibly back to Saigon, and now wondered what I could suggest to make her better. Again, Americans are seen as all-powerful—the ultimate source of both benevolence and suffering. The pattern is of course by no means unique to Vietnam—General MacArthur frequently appeared in the delusions of Japanese mental patients during the early postwar years, in this and other ways replacing the Emperor—but it is illustrative of the American-Vietnamese relationship.

The prevailing atmosphere one senses among intellectuals is that of despair and helplessness, or *immobilisme.* Similarly, the people in general seem to react neither with enthusiasm nor opposition but rather with passive resistance: general resistance to government programs; peasants' resistance to taxes; young men's (especially students') resistance to the Army; and, of course, the Army's resistance to fighting. The general mixture of lassitude, cynicism, and aggressive self-seeking pervading Saigon is reminiscent of accounts of the atmosphere in large cities in China just before the Communist takeover (remnants of which one could observe in Taiwan shortly afterwards), suggesting that there is a certain style of American interplay with Asian corruption, of joint participation in the fiction that a highly unpopular and ineffectual government is a dynamic and virtuous force around which free men must rally. In truth, the most efficient and whole-hearted American-Vietnamese collaboration I encountered in Saigon was a bar-whorehouse featuring beautiful Vietnamese girls and elite (mainly Embassy) American clientele—with no complaints about Vietnamese "organization" or "leadership."

IV

If Vietnamese themselves reject the circle of deception, are there any authentic ideas and images to which they are capable of responding? I had the clear impression that there were three, none of them new to the world but all extremely important in this specific setting: images of nation, social transformation, and peace. To grasp their importance one must remember that the human mind lives on images, absorbing and recreating them as a basis for all understanding and action. The problem in Vietnam is less a matter of "getting the bugs out of the machine," as the fallacy of mechanism would have it, than of evolving shared world-pictures which inspire and cohere. I would suggest that the unpalatable truth concerning the American presence in Vietnam is that it radically undermines each of the three significant images I have mentioned.

We have already observed the force of the *image of nation*; it has been rendered especially compelling by the very precariousness of Vietnam's historical status as a nation, by old national struggles as well as recent dismemberment. To be considered a nationalist is to wear a badge of honor, and much of the admiration in the South for Ho Chi Minh has to do with his capacity to make psychological contact with all Vietnamese through this shared image (enhanced by his creating a form of "national Communism" with its considerable independence from larger Communist nations). Similarly, Vietnamese who feel threatened by the Vietcong are nonetheless willing to speak sympathetically of "nationalists" among them.

Many stressed to me the South's need for a leader who could, like Ho, reanimate the national image—always making clear that men who have fought on the side of the French during the struggle for independence, as did most of the present military junta, would be immediately disqualified. One young political scientist with experience in government expressed to me the opinion that Vietnamese have been searching in the wrong places for models of leadership and economic development, and advocated someone on the order of Ayub Kahn of Pakistan. Most looked toward eventual reunification of their country, though differing on how that could or should be achieved. Virtually all stressed that the American presence painfully violates the image of nation, and that this violation had direct operational significance: guerrillas with minimal military equipment can harass and outmaneuver the blind giant because he is widely identified as an alien threat to their nation.

We have of course by now become familiar with the excesses that can surround the image of nation, with aggressive national*ism*, but this should not cause us to lose sight of the profoundly integrative force exerted by a shared sense of geographical-racial-cultural destiny. The root of the word nation is the same as that of "origin" or "birth," and in our desperate need to extend the concept outward from its beginnings in clan and tribe to include all of mankind, we may too readily forget that men still require it for their sense of immortalized human continuity.

Clearly the idea of nation is not something that one people can provide for another, least of all Americans in Asia. The refrain I heard from Vietnamese again and again was that "America must take a risk" and support the kind of leaders who were sufficiently independent of her to make it likely that they would question her policies. Both sides are thus presented with an excruciating paradox which the elections have by no means resolved: the American need to support opponents of American power; and the Vietnamese need to call upon American power to help them overcome it. This is part of what the editor quoted earlier meant by the "preposterous situation" —a situation which will find no solution that does not include a reassertion of Vietnamese autonomy.

The significance of the second general image, that of *social transformation*, is attested to by the recent use of the term "Revolutionary Development" for the American-South Vietnamese village pacification program. The military regime's miserable record on all aspects of social transformation, especially the fundamental issue of land reform, renders this terminology sadly ironic. I was told by a leading legislator who studies the problem how landlords would return right behind government soldiers when territory was re-taken from the Vietcong. But a vision of major social reform remains fundamental to reversing the symbolic social death of South Vietnam and bringing about a collective sense of rebirth.

While a number of the people I spoke to condemned the Communists for their "betrayal of the revolution," there was little doubt that *some* form of revolution had to take place. Thus the same editor called for "a new army and a new civil service ... (which) would have to be built up *in the field* (italics his) away from the capital and cities, around a nucleus of revolutionary men ... living simply among the peasants." The idea sounds familiar; its proponent readily admits that it has much in common with the successful approach of the Vietcong. The American claim to have favored such transformation is very much part of the circle of deception. For while it is true that we have applied pressure upon a reluctant government in the direction of reform, our relationship to that government (not to mention the nature of that government itself) makes impossible the actual accomplishment of transformation from within. A related deception is the dismissal, as irrelevant or disruptive, of those groups which have most strongly articulated the widespread urge toward transformation—militant Buddhists, students, and younger intellectuals—and who will surely be heard from in the future.

An even more extreme deception has surrounded the American underestimation of the significance for Vietnamese of the *image of peace*. The perception of South Vietnamese as determined to continue their military struggle should have been shattered, once and for all, by the results of the recent elections. Despite the ruling generals' questionable manipulations, they drew fewer votes than the combination of three candidates who had declared themselves for peace; and the most outspoken "peace candidate" surprised everyone by coming in second. From all that I heard when I was in Vietnam I would tend to agree with the opinion expressed by journalists that the dove symbol used by the peace candidate on the ballot had much to do with his impressive showing. For anyone who has talked to Vietnamese during the past few months could readily sense something close to a groundswell of peace sentiment. What more than a dove could appeal to an electorate that is largely illiterate but by no means indifferent to the sufferings of war and the attractions of peace? The image of peace includes relief from a long and terrible cycle of death anxiety and death guilt, and—whatever the qualifications put forth about the kind of peace there would be—an opportunity to reverse the increasingly intolerable pattern of disintegration.

I had an encounter with a "former peace candidate" which, I believe, illustrates some of the complicated dimensions of the peace image. He was an economist who, though still in his late thirties, had been finance minister in three cabinets—and *his* campaign emblem was a bomb crossed out by two diagonal lines drawn over it. Since peace talk had in the recent past been associated by the military regime with such dangerous tendencies as "neutralism" and Communism, this kind of campaign by so prominent a person was creating quite a stir. At the time Americans were divided about him—on occasion one would hear him spoken of as "unrealistic" or "put up to it by someone," and at other times he would be praised for his accomplishments as finance minister and described as "one of the best minds in South Vietnam." No one was too surprised when, on the day before I went to see him, he was publicly denounced by the police as having "Communist affiliations," leaving his future as a campaigner and indeed as a free man in doubt.

He told me that he welcomed talking to me as he too wished to stress a psychological perspective. And he immediately handed me a brief essay (translated from the original French) in which he somewhat abstractly discussed the motivations of the Vietnamese as people caught up in revolution, in opposition to revolution, and now in "the powerful psychological motivation" surrounding "the desire for peace." He insisted that the elections should give the people a chance to express this desire, stressing to me his sense of the urgency of proper timing—since in the past there did not exist the necessary combination of war exhaustion and political climate for peace, and in the future there might be little left of the country to salvage. He spoke of a "war mechanism"—a self-perpetuating system—with no possibility of anyone winning but all continuing to fight "because they don't know anything else to do" (I was later reminded of this when I read John Galbraith's contention that "War turns reason into stereotype" and freezes participants in original error). He felt that the mechanism could be interrupted only by installing a government committed to peace through negotiations, that such a commitment would cut down the effectiveness of the Vietcong, who thrive on an atmosphere of war and chaos, and that it would evoke a strong general response in the Vietnamese people which would in turn impel the NLF and the North to join the South in negotiations. He thought that all of this would take time, and that American troops would remain in Vietnam during protracted negotiations, but that once the general undertaking had been initiated it would succeed in bringing peace to the country.

One could raise various issues concerning his program, but what struck me about it was the serious effort not only to rally the country round the image of peace but to evolve a workable theory of peace as well. He told me that the government was spreading false stories about him in order to prevent him from running in the election, and when I asked him why they were so determined to do so he answered, "Because the idea of peace is extremely popular." It would seem that he was right on both counts: he was officially eliminated as a candidate a short time later, and the elections proved that peace was indeed a popular idea.

But images are not eliminated as easily as candidates. Once safely established in their campaigns, a number of others (especially the peace candidate who did so well) actively committed themselves to negotiations and the search for peace, and even the military rulers themselves were forced to make very uncharacteristic obeisance in the same direction. Many elements seem to be converging—the influence of the "former peace candidate," an increasing American realization that there is no feasible course other than negotiations, strong pressure from the rest of the world—but underneath everything is the extreme power of the image of peace and its ultimate capacity to break through the circle of deception.

Ever since World War II Vietnam has been living out in the most extreme way the painful problems besetting the world at large. Thinking back to my first visit to Saigon thirteen years ago, I recall mainly scenes of ordinarily well-intentioned men—Vietnamese, French, American—arguing passionately, sometimes intelligently, always endlessly, about what should be done, behaving as men do when confronted by a terrible problem which, however approached, will not go away. What I have tried to suggest here is that the problem is being confounded rather than solved by the American presence—because that presence works against Vietnam's only viable psychological and historical possibilities. Is it not time for the giant to begin to see? Can he not recognize, and then step out of, the circle of deception?

Photo by Franz Schurmann

Photo by Paul Avery, Empire

Photo by Paul Avery, Empire

Photo by Robert Scheu, Photon West

Psychological Warfare

In addition to the massive fire power of saturation bombing and artillery, a complex array of anti-personnel and incendiary weapons have been developed in recent years for counterinsurgency warfare. These weapons are directed against individuals and small groups almost at random. The result is that

> Most of the victims of anti-personnel bombs are not killed, rather they are maimed. The pellets from anti-personnel bombs are designed to cause irregular and hard-to-cure wounds. This serves two functions. First, it means that instead of a single man dead and withdrawn from military production, six to ten people (as well as facilities and supplies) must care for him. Secondly, the sufferings of a badly wounded victim tend to have a greater demoralizing effect on the remaining population than the dead. Thus such weapons 'build a deterrent capability into conventional ordnance.' That is, they have a 'separate and distinguishable psychological impact . . . apart from the actual destruction which they caused.'*

These weapons are but part of the psychological warfare conducted against the rural population. Besides these weapons a variety of leaflets are scattered throughout the countryside designed to terrify local inhabitants enough to prevent them from cooperating with guerrilla forces.

* Aviation Week, Mar. 21, 1966.

Photo by Paul Avery, Empire

Automated War*

Derek Shearer†

Is Indochina to become a testing ground for Gen. William Westmoreland's "Army of the Future"? "I see battlefields or combat areas that are under 24-hour real or near real-time surveillance of all types," he said last October. "I see battlefields on which we can destroy anything we locate through instant communications and the almost instantaneous application of highly lethal firepower. . . ."

Now, of course, our firepower is already quite lethal. In an average month, American B-52s drop 100,000 tons of bombs on South Vietnam (500,000 tons were dropped in the Pacific theater during *all* of World War II). But with further progress towards an automated battlefield, greater efficiency in destruction is anticipated. "On the battlefield of the future," Westmoreland predicts, "enemy forces will be located, tracked and targeted almost instantaneously through the use of data links, computer assisted intelligence evaluating and automated fire control." So "the need for large forces to fix the opposition physically will be less important."

A new computer network called Seek Data II being installed in Vietnam will reduce the average time for planning day-to-day operations from two days to two hours. "It is a crucial step toward bona fide pushbutton warfare," says an article in *Air Force and Space Digest* (Feb. 1970). Seek Data II has been developed by Control Data Corporation, which has people working at the 7th Air Force Headquarters in Saigon installing it. "By comparison," *Air Force and Space Digest* says of Seek Data II, "no previous computer programming package, including those used for command and

*Reprinted with permission from the *New Republic*, May 30, 1970.
 Derek Shearer *is co-editor of a book on the Pentagon and national security to be published by Doubleday.*

control of US strategic forces, has been able to provide real-time control of situations as dynamic and ever-changing as the tactical air operations in a major theater. Issuing orders to hundreds of aircraft in rough forward areas is a most difficult command and control task. Automation of this through Seek Data II should significantly increase the efficiency of our tactical air capability.

In order to "fix" the enemy, he has to be found. Westmoreland promises that the Army is significantly "improving our capability" to find him. A *New York Times* article of Feb. 13 reported that "the Pentagon is studying a proposal to provide enough modern sensing devices so that South Vietnam could seal its entire 900 mile border against sizable enemy infiltration"; a scientist notes that "we can now provide for ground troops [the South Vietnamese who are supposed to take over the fighting] the kind of early warning systems that we long have provided in anti-submarine warfare and air defense."

This proposed sensor seal resembles the McNamara Line—land mines, barbed wire, and electronic sensors which were placed along the 39 mile demarcation line between South and North Vietnam. A number of monitoring devices are already in use there. A two-foot long cylindrical sonobuoy, used by the Navy to track enemy submarines, was dropped into the trees and brush around Khesanh, and along the Ho Chi Minh trail in Laos and Cambodia. It records the sounds of enemy troops and trucks, stores the information until special planes fly overhead and pick up the information electronically. The recordings are transmitted to a computer bank.

When the Seek Data system is completed, the US may be able to respond with massive firepower in a matter of hours to enemy movements detected by the sensors. Firepower "can be concentrated without massing numbers of troops," Westmoreland told the US Army Association last October 14. "In Vietnam where artillery and tactical air forces inflict over two-thirds of the enemy casualties, firepower is responsive as never before. It can rain destruction anywhere on the battlefield within minutes . . . whether friendly troops are present or not."

This pinpointing is also being improved through the use of laser technology. *Aviation Week and Space Technology* (Jan. 19, 1970) reports that "the success of many laser-related techniques in Southeast Asia and others now in trial in Eglin AFB and elsewhere presage widespread use of laser designator/ranger finds in at least those permissive military environments that characterize air warfare over South Vietnam and to a lesser degree prevailed over North Vietnam where the US maintained air superiority."

The Department of Defense has stated that laser-guided bombs, introduced in 1968, have led to a tenfold increase in accuracy. Laser finding equipment is being used by the Air Force to improve night bombing. The Army is developing use of lasers for illuminating night viewing and night observation devices, and as a rangefinder for helicopter weapon delivery and artillery spotting from both the air and the ground. Research and development on new technical systems designed to improve firepower capabilities in Southeast Asia is being carried out. In the fiscal year 1971 defense budget, $27.9 million is allotted for the AX attack bomber, a small turboprop plane able to operate effectively at a wide range of subsonic speeds. The AX has a short takeoff and landing capability, is armed with a variety of conventional bombs and strafing guns, and is expected to be more reliable than the F-100, F-105 and F-5 planes now in use in Vietnam. Another project in the development stage which is designed to build up US firepower is SMASH (Southeast Asia Multi-Sensor Armament System Helicopter).

Technological warfare replaces men on the field. It destroys in ways less visible, less costly to Americans—though not less costly to the Indochinese.

Photo by Franklin Levin

THE BLEEDING PIG

US forces possess a wide range of small-yield nuclear weapons in the one-to-five kiloton range for battlefield use. They can be launched from a fighter bomber or can form part of the army's medium range artillery such as the Sergeant and Honest John Rockets. Nuclear shells can be fired from certain types of howitzers. Used against concentrations of troops, nuclear weapons would be made to burst in the air up to a height of 1,500 feet, causing enormous casualties to those exposed to the blast. The other method, a ground burst, would affect a smaller area, but the destruction would be heavy and the radiation more deadly and longer lasting than in a mid-air burst.

The use of even "tactical" nuclear weapons in Indochina would be genocidal. Rain forests act as a trap for nuclear fallout. Instead of the devastation spreading through the air stream, it is contained close to the ground. Eventually the contaminants enter the ground water systems, contaminate them, and as the water flows out of the immediate area, poisons everything downstream. If such weapons were used in Cambodia, that could mean the US would virtually wipe out the populations of both Cambodia and South Vietnam throughout the Mekong Delta region.

Andrew Kopkind and James Ridgeway

*Reprinted with permission from *Hard Times*, Washington, D. C., May 25-June 1, 1970.

From *Nuclear War Games**

As of 1968 there were more than 5,500 nuclear weapons in the Southeast Asia area. Most of these weapons are aboard carriers and can be brought to Vietnam extremely rapidly. A substantial number of weapons are located on the mainland in Korea. Nuclear weapons are also located in Thailand, according to reliable reports of knowledgeable Pentagon officials and military officers.

Until 1965 the Commander in Chief of the Pacific (CINCPAC) had no plans or weapons capabilities to fight other than a nuclear war in Southeast Asia. During the Vietnam buildup both plans and weapons for non-nuclear war were developed. However, senior officers of the area still appear to subscribe to the view that nuclear weapons are "conventional." There is substantial military doctrine developed in the 1950s and early 1960s prescribing the specific circumstances under which nuclear weapons would be used in terrain such as Vietnam and their effects. In "Nuclear Weapons and Limited War," an article appearing in 1960 in Air University Review, Gen. Frederic H. Smith, Jr., writes: "We cannot afford to lose friendly nations and territories to the USSR, Red China, or their satellites under any circumstances. . . . The purpose of this article is to demonstrate that not only can the intelligent use of nuclear firepower in limited war give us the greatest possible opportunity to win such wars at minimum cost . . . but that it is highly probable that without the use of such weapons, our chances of winning in many areas are slim indeed." One of such areas described in detail is typical of Vietnam.

President Nixon appears to share the view expressed by General Eisenhower to his biographer that the threat to use nuclear weapons in Korea was instrumental in bringing an end to that war. On March 17, 1955, Mr. Nixon, then Vice President, told the Executive Club of Chicago, ". . . Our artillery and our tactical air force in the Pacific are now equipped with atomic explosives which can and will be used on military targets with precision and effectiveness.

"It is foolish to talk about the possibility that the weapons which might be used in the event war breaks out in the Pacific would be limited to the conventional Korean and World War II types of explosives. Our forces could not fight an effective war in the Pacific with those types of explosives if they wanted to. Tactical atomic explosives are now conventional and will be used against the military targets of any aggressive force."

Richard J. Barnet

Reprinted with permission from *Hard Times*, May 25-June 1, 1970, Washington, D. C.

PART 5

From the Other Side

The wheel of the law turns without pause.

After the rain, good weather. In the wink of an eye

The universe throws off its muddy clothes.

For ten thousand miles the landscape

spreads out like a beautiful brocade. Light breezes. Smiling flowers.

High in the trees, amongst the sparkling leaves,

all the birds sing at once. Men and animals rise up reborn.

What could be more natural? After sorrow, comes joy.

Ho Chi Minh

Photo by Franklin Levin

"Our People Are a Wonder"

(Pham Van Dong, March 31, 1968)

Franz Schurmann

My nineteen-day trip to the Democratic Republic of Vietnam (March 18-April 5) gave me many surprises, but none so great as the discovery of Vietnam and the Vietnamese people. For three years I had been reading about Vietnam, yet people and country remained abstract. They were a powerful force frustrating the ambitions of American militarists. I had imagined America's geopoliticians plotting the forces of world history and deciding that the "insurgency" in Vietnam had to be crushed lest it give rise to a wave of revolution in parts of the world closer to home. I could envisage generals and admirals in Honolulu and Saigon directing the most massive application of fire power in the history of mankind. Having once been a soldier, I could sense the reality of soldiers doing their service in Vietnam. From the welter of news reporting about Vietnam, I knew that the military and political schemes of the rulers of the American Empire were being shattered, one after the other. Yet the men who were defeating the schemes of the most powerful nation in history, the "Viet Cong," were faceless. Was it possible that small bands of black-pajama-clad peasants, slipping in and out of the jungle, could cause such havoc with American and A.R.V.N. military forces?

If I already had been prepared to discover the humanity of the Vietnamese, the Vietnamese showed it so fully that it was a surprise.

Yearning for Independence

I suppose political scientists "analyzing" the Vietnamese phenomenon would call it nationalism, but I doubt whether many American academics sitting in their sterile offices have much of an intuitive sense of what

Reprinted with permission from *Liberation*, April 1968.

195

nationalism is (now that it is erupting close to home in the black ghettos, maybe they can learn). Leaving labels such as nationalism and patriotism aside, I should like to try to convey the message about themselves the Vietnamese communicated to me. Again and again they spoke of their yearning for unity and independence. They are fighting for a single Vietnam and no matter how long it takes them to achieve the unity of "Hanoi-Hue-Saigon," as the flower arrangement in their Park of Unity says, they will continue to fight. Unity means much more to them than a political arrangement which will erase the 17th parallel. Decades of civil war have split families asunder, have separated people from their *terre natale* (how can this feeling of place of origin be rendered in American with our spirit of constant geographical mobility?). The sense of community and family remains very strong in Vietnam, as leaders and people several times told us. Yet unity, which will allow people to be reunited in community and family, is not enough. Unless they be independent, be free of foreign domination, they will never accept unity, on any terms. After all, they were unified under the French. This passionate desire for independence is something a great people perhaps cannot understand, and least of all the Americans, who are too far removed from their own national liberation struggle. The French, for all of their lack of racial prejudice (the Vietnamese, by the way, have none), considered them a small people. If some had big ambitions, they could always become French. The Americans pretend that they are no more than a kindly foster father coming in to help the little boy grow up. Nothing more arouses the contempt of the D.R.V. and Front leaders than pictures of Thieu and Ky with amiable Ambassador Bunker standing behind them to give them "moral support." To us, as representatives of the American people, they were generous and hospitable, as would be anyone who is master of his own home and welcomes a guest. The Americans in the South are oppressors, pure and simple, no different from the French. Yet the monstrous technological barbarism of the Americans in the South and in the North has surprised them. Repeatedly they asked me about this, and I found it difficult to explain how a people whom Ho Chi Minh had admired in 1945 and whose Declaration of Independence he emulated had spawned instruments of such mass inhuman destruction. "Let them leave Vietnam, and they can then return as friends" —so they said many times. (I suggest that much of the intense feeling behind this struggle of the Vietnamese for unity and independence is shared in their own way by the people of America's ghettos.)

In an academic paper I once defined power as the command over men and resources to achieve one's own goals. Since power is the essence of politics, their political goals for all of Vietnam are not difficult to discern: they demand that Vietnamese, not Americans, wield all power in Vietnam. They will never accept any arrangement for South Vietnam where the Americans keep behind-the-scenes control of the military and the economy, even though a more "representative" government may function in Saigon. Decades ago, Stalin controlled his satellites by getting a firm grip on a country's economy, military and secret police, while allowing them to have their own national political leaders. American imperialism throughout the world now operates in a similar fashion. For Washington, Vietnam is a desperate struggle to see whether it can continue that fashion of imperialist rule.

The Visible Spirit of the People

What Pham Van Dong meant in calling his people a wonder was their extraordinary response, both in the South and the North, to a war of unprecedented destructiveness. The swift escalation of the American involvement in 1965 surprised the leaders of the D.R.V. and the Front. They must have wondered whether their people (soldiers, peasants, professionals) would not be crushed by the intensity of the American bombardment. (After all, the Air Force had defined the destruction of "the psychosocial structure" of the enemy as one of the chief purposes of bombing.) They told me that Washington had assumed in 1965 that after three months of bombing Hanoi would be ready to knuckle under. Hence the May 1965 bombing pause. Yet three years later the D.R.V. and the Front are stronger than ever before. Throughout North Vietnam one can see large quantities of military and economic material from the entire socialist camp. The roads, bombed time and time again, are in good shape. The antiaircraft defense has already been admitted, by American military men, to be the finest in history. Yet more important than that is the visible spirit of the people. People work actively, even the peasants in remote villages. They are healthy. They smile readily. All along the road one sees units of the shock brigades, young men who have volunteered for the dangerous tasks of repairing bomb damage, defusing delayed-action bombs, keeping the lines of communication and transportation open.

Despite evacuation, family and friendship ties are evidently strong. Rather than demoralization, the bombing has produced indifference and anger—indifference in that people continue to work even during alerts, calculating probabilities that the chances of being hit are small; anger against a bombing often as meaningless as a storm. The curious fact is that the air war has actually strengthened the "psychosocial structure" of the people. Among the American military that has been called "the astonishing recoverability" of the North Vietnamese.

The central district of Hanoi, which includes the government buildings, the embassies and, fortunately, the hotel, has not yet been bombed (I might note that the mission of the N.L.F. has one of the finest shelters in Hanoi, obviously expecting one day to be surgically bombed as once were the Chinese and Cuban embassies). Beyond the central district is a band of residential area which has been sporadically bombed. In a generous mood I would be prepared to say that this bombing may have been accidental. But as soon as one goes out into the suburbs, one sees destroyed village upon destroyed village. Gia Lam, the suburb beyond the Red River, has been completely destroyed, even though the international airport has not yet been hit. Strangely enough, Catholic villages appear to be a favorite target. In fact, when the so-called "Hanoi port facilities" (Hanoi citizens laugh at this) were attacked early this year, one of the prime targets was a Catholic village. I can only assume that the pilots, playing around with their radar and detection devices in mid-air, pinpointed a sizeable structure and decided that it must be a military objective. Every Catholic village has a large church with a towering steeple.

Three Principles of Survival

Once beyond Hanoi (and the port facilities and central area of Haiphong) everything is fair game for our Air Force heroes. Bombed straw huts can be seen everywhere; bomb craters have become favorite places for raising fish; hospitals, adminstrative buildings, schools have almost all been bombed —again, I suppose, on the basis of the simple logic that any big structure must be a military target. Most barbaric of all is the steady rain of C.B.U.'s and delayed-action bombs which are strewn over the countryside. One evening our friends took Mary and myself to a popular theatre which showed a simple play about a heroic doctor, a studious student and a pretty girl. The doctor had developed new surgical methods of extracting pellets from human beings. What I found most shocking was how matter-of-factly the *bom bi* (C.B.U.'s) were treated—they had become so much a part of the everyday life of the people. Postwar surveys of the effectiveness of bombing over Germany and Japan years ago revealed that the bombing was counterproductive. Not only was the "psychosocial structure" of the people reinforced, but production even continued to climb. Three years of Air Force pounding of North Korea leveled that country to the ground, yet Korean-Chinese military power was stronger than ever when the armistice was signed. Admiral Ulysses Grant Sharp, who directs the air war over North Vietnam from his CINCPAC headquarters in Honolulu, was once described as "a great admirer of air power." It is not difficult to suppose that the "astonishing recoverability" of the Vietnamese must be driving the esteemed admiral up the walls. How have they done it? I would like to suggest three principles which the Vietnamese have followed with great success: dispersal, evacuation and decentralization.

Dispersal

Dispersal means that at no time must men and materiel be concentrated in large quantities at a single point. For example, as soon as an air-raid alert is sounded, every group of people splits into individuals running for shelterholes or trenches (the exception being Hanoi where there are larger air-raid shelters). Once, during an alert, I wanted to pull my friend Le Duy Van of the

Peace Committee into the same hole, but he later sternly lectured me that this was against the principle of taking shelter. He said simply it is better that only one of us be killed. Evacuated schools and hospitals are scattered over the countryside in widely separated peasant huts. An agricultural school in Hao Binh province, which had been bombed once, dug six kilometers of trenches for shelter. Every day the children's bedding was put into the trenches in case they had to spend the night there. One hospital in the same province had put its operating room in a cave, but the rest of the hospital was spread out over a large area. Nguyen Van Tien, chief of the N.L.F. Representation in Hanoi, explained to me that dispersal and constant mobility (as well as digging) were the key principles to the survival of N.L.F. troops in the South. N.L.F. troops operated in small mobile units, yet their communications were so good that they could be rapidly assembled for large-scale regular actions at short notice. Rapid dispersal and regroupment was the key to the military success of the Chinese Communists during their war against the Nationalists, and now the same principle is being followed by the N.L.F. troops.

Dispersal also applies to materiel. I saw an immense amount of military equipment in North Vietnam; William Baggs, in his articles, has already noted that he felt there was ten times as much as in previous years. Presumably it comes in from China and through Haiphong. The U.S. military periodically announces attacks on ammunition depots and storage areas. Nothing could be more ridiculous. The Vietnamese strew the equipment over the countryside. Below every tree is a crate or an oil drum, but never close enough together to make an inviting target. Trucks move at night, and never in convoy, always spaced far apart. Obviously the American Air Force and Navy are aware of this, and have resorted to strafing of roads. But that is not so easily accomplished. People in Hoa Binh told me of one plane which strafed the road during the day when there was no military traffic. The militia put up an intense fire and brought him down, all in a matter of less than a minute.

If the principle of dispersal has minimized the human and material damage of the bombings, it has also made everyone and everything a target. This truly is a people's war, one evidence for which is the fact that the population is armed, down to the lowliest peasant village. Thus the true target of the American air attacks are the entire Vietnamese people. It is already known that the military geopoliticians have been rapidly getting to the point of desperation where the only way they can win through their "weapons" is to envisage the extermination of all Vietnamese. One Vietnamese official related in intense anger the statement of Representative Mendel Rivers, a leading advocate of all-out technological war in Vietnam, that all of Vietnam was not worth the life of a single American soldier. The Vietnamese well know that Rivers is merely echoing statements voiced by the military.

Evacuation

Evacuation means moving the entire urban population into the rural areas. Hanoi is today a sparsely populated city; there are no children. School buildings, factories, ministries stand empty or virtually empty; their people and equipment have gone to the rural areas. But the sociological importance of evacuation has been far more important than its purposes of self-defense. In every developing country, the gap between city and country has been a terrible problem, for as cities advance, the villages stand still, rooted in their millennial traditions. In North Vietnam, the trained people of the country now live in the villages. Children are boarded with peasant families. Teachers and students live in straw huts alongside villages. Government officials rub shoulders with the peasants every day. The benefits have been mutual. The delicate city people have become stronger, more rugged, more healthy, psychologically and physically. The warmth and closeness of peasant life has made them more human; peasant simplicity has deprived them of their arrogance. Life is very hard in the villages, but life must be with and among people. Even the short visits I made to the provinces gave me the sense that a new type of community was forming in the rural areas, one not without its problems but which apparently had overcome that alienation which city life breeds.

The benefits for the peasants are not difficult to imagine. Literacy appears to be almost universal in the country. The villages are spotlessly clean, even where the houses are crude and the lanes a sea of mud. Clothing is shabby, yet clean. The evacuation of hospitals has helped create a universal medical system. Every village has, at least, a rudimentary first-aid station, and is never far away from a district dispensary or hospital. Even if one assumes that we were shown the best villages, we stopped often on the roadside where we saw the same conditions. Health, particularly among the children, seemed to be excellent. I suppose that the major effect of evacuation will be to bring the peasant into the modern world, long before great industrial installations dot the countryside. What the North Vietnamese have achieved, without much in the way of technology, is that revolution in consciousness of the poorest peasants which so many developing countries find impossible to achieve. Hanoi might well consider giving a medal to the U.S. Air Force.

Decentralization

Decentralization means the transfer of administrative powers to provinces and districts. I had several conversations with officials on this subject, but for security reasons they obviously did not go into detail. Nevertheless, from what I have read and from observations made during my visits to the provinces, I am convinced that the North Vietnamese, as a response to the war, have decentralized most administrative power away from Hanoi to preclude the possibility that a single devastating strike against the capital could disrupt the governmental system. I was struck how in the provinces, all administrative offices had been broken into mobile sections which were constantly on the move from one district to another. Obviously the fact that American planes had been systematically bombing all the provincial centers made evacuation essential. But the point is not that the offices were removed to a safe location, but that they were split up and made mobile. I had some first-hand experience with the decentralization when our friends from the Peace Committee told me that they could not just come down from Hanoi with orders in their hands but had to negotiate with the provincial authorities as equals.

That the U.S. Air Force and Navy are systematically trying to destroy the D.R.V.'s administrative structure was indicated to me in an indirect way. A French correspondent from *Le Monde* had the chance to visit the Pathet Lao areas of Laos and returned to Hanoi shaken by the trip: not only were the Americans devastating every village in the area of Sam Neua, but they were trying to destroy the administrative structure of the Pathet Lao. Even *Time* magazine has now admitted that American planes are dropping more bombs on Laos than on North Vietnam (there being less antiaircraft defense in Laos, the raids over Laos are safer for our heroic pilots).

Most remarkable about the decentralization is that the country is covered by an extraordinary communications network. No matter where the planes come from, loudspeakers in every village quickly signal their position and their distance from the village, arousing people to the possibility of an air raid. Despite their mobility, the administrative committees are in uninterrupted communication with each other. Clearly a people's war can be fought in no manner other than through decentralization. No central power can make the multitude of rapid decisions necessary as a result of bomb damage. The principle of decentralized operations and unified communications is equally followed in the South. The Madison Avenue team of Westmoreland and Komer had been grinding out glowing reports about how the Viet Cong forces were being pounded into harried bands. It turned out, of course, that those harried bands managed to stage a Tet offensive which, if nothing else, was an amazing example of coordinated operations. Of course, no decentralization will work unless it has the active support of the population. Perhaps there were men in Hanoi who, in 1965, were worried that decentralization could lead to chaos. The "wonder" proved the opposite. As so often in other times and places when people were attacked by barbaric force, the Vietnamese people responded by mounting the most amazing effort of resistance in modern history.

During bombing raids in the North, school is held in such trenches. *Photo by Franz Schurmann.*

Cylinders in Hanoi used to protect individuals from bombing. *Photo by Franz Schurmann.*

The National Liberation Front and the
Transformation of Vietnamese Society*

Mark Selden

In its reliance on popular participation and initiative, in the emphasis on the contributions of man in a context of face-to-face human struggle, in the high value placed on individual performance of multiple roles as soldiers, farmers, cadres and teachers, in its egalitarian spirit embodied in every facet of the movement—in all these ways the resistance spirit is embodied in new and fruitful definitions of Vietnamese society.

In the resistance, emphasis on popular participation—the fundamental postulate of people's war—means that strength and legitimacy rest primarily on active peasant support. This support in turn is contingent on the movement's ability to respond effectively to wartime political, economic, and security needs. As Franz Schurmann recently observed after a visit to bomb-shattered North Vietnam, the mobilization process cannot be grasped exclusively or even primarily in organizational terms. Rather "the spirit of individuals and classes is the energy that makes organization work. Without that spirit, organization can function only through nonhuman technology, which means turning men into machines as well as making use of machines."[1] Consciousness of this problem, of the danger of turning men into machines, is central to the resistance in South Vietnam. Under continuous crisis conditions, rigid and dogmatic tendencies toward elite domination and tight central control of war and administration are challenged effectively by populist and pragmatic impulses and the conviction that ultimate support and commitment require popular participation and initiative. The result is that decentralization, antagonism to bureaucratic elitism, and heavy reliance on popular creativity, characterize the guerrilla military struggle and the extraordi-

---

*The Bulletin of Concerned Asian Scholars (CCAS) Vol. 2. No. 1 Oct. 1969.

[1]"Our People Are a Wonder," Schurmann, *Liberation*, April 1968.

nary wartime efforts to transform rural life. As the peasantry *en masse* breaks the bonds of passivity and subservience, new forms of local community begin to replace those eroded steadily during a century of rural disintegration, colonial bondage and war.

These developments have a significance far beyond their important contribution to independence from foreign domination. In the course of the Vietnamese resistance a vision of social transformation and development is carried beyond local resistance communities and embodied on a national scale: That conception reaffirms the contributions of men, above all of peasants working in their own villages, rather than the efforts of a remote technological elite. It is linked with a pragmatic and practical effort implemented even while the fighting rages to advance concretely toward a day when the nation as a whole can reap the benefits of independence and development. Problems of peasant particularism, economic stagnation and elitism cannot of course be eliminated in a single sweep. What is impressive is that we see in the resistance new forms of community life and growth consonant with its ideals. The effort to resist a ruthless oppressor is communally directed toward overcoming natural and man-made barriers to progressive change. The spirit of the resistance thus suggests new possibilities of human fulfillment while grappling with the formidable problems of foreign domination, poverty, and development which stalk the Third World.

The Bombing of Vietnam*

Jon M. Van Dyke

In early May of this year, the United States launched new bombing attacks against North Vietnam. Our government reported the resumption in typical jargon, asserting that there had been no policy change. But the announcements were so similar to those of February and March, 1965 (when the first round of bombing started), that no one was fooled this time. Although three and a half years of unrelenting bombardment had failed to interfere in any significant way with North Vietnam's conduct of the war in the South, the United States government under a new President and new military leaders in in the field seemed determined to try again.

Our memories are so short that we have already forgotten the folly of the previous bombing policy. It may be useful, therefore, to illustrate some of the ways the North Vietnamese resisted the air attacks for three and a half years and thus to show why bombing is a bad tactic from even the most callously militaristic point of view.

The United States began bombing North Vietnam regularly in March, 1965. Throughout 1965 and into the first half of 1966—except for a thirty-seven-day bombing pause in December, 1965, and January, 1966—American officials instructed pilots to bomb a steadily enlarging geographical area and to hit targets closer and closer to populated areas. In late June and July, 1966, pilots began to bomb petroleum storage dumps in Hanoi and Haiphong. Although these cities had not been greatly damaged up to then, almost every other city was largely destroyed.

*Reprinted with permission from *The Center Magazine*, Vol. III, No. 4, July 1970. Mr. Van Dyke, a Visiting Fellow of the Center, recently completed a book, *North Vietnam's Strategy for Survival*. It will be published by Pacific Books later this year.

Children's griffiti in North Vienam. *Photo by Franz Schurmann.*

Within a few months, U.S. planes turned more directly to the two largest cities. Beginning with a few sporadic bombings in December, 1966, and January, 1967, and escalating into a virtually unlimited campaign from April, 1967, to March, 1968, Hanoi and Haiphong were vigorously attacked. Then, on March 31, 1968, President Johnson announced that no American planes would bomb north of the twentieth parallel in North Vietnam, and in fact after the first week of April no bombers ventured north of the nineteenth parallel. On November 1, 1968, all bombing of North Vietnam was stopped.

During this period, the United States sent over three hundred and fifty thousand planes on some one hundred and fifteen thousand different missions and dropped a million tons of bombs on North Vietnam, twice as much as the United States dropped in the Pacific Theater in World War II or on Korea in the Korean war. Yet the bombing achieved none of the goals that its advocates had sought.

The main goal, according to Secretary of Defense Robert S. McNamara, was "to make clear to the political leaders of the North" that they will "pay a price" so long as they continued "to carry on their aggression of the South." It was felt that bombing would force the North Vietnamese to come to the negotiating table and make important concessions, or better yet to give up entirely. Admiral Ulysses S. G. Sharp, then the commander-in-chief of U.S. forces in the Pacific, stated that the bombing was essentially a device to put the squeeze on the North Vietnamese leaders until they cried "uncle." General Harold K. Johnson, who was Chief of Staff of the Army, expressed similar views by saying that the bombing "is something like the repetitive strokes of a jackhammer, if you will. At some point the concrete begins to break up, and I think that it is this continuing and unrelenting pressure that will eventually bring us to a conclusion."

Other American leaders justified the bombing in terms of its ability to stop infiltration from the North. McNamara's successor, Clark M. Clifford, said, for instance, that the purpose of the bombing was "to impede the flow of men and supplies, munitions, and armaments to the South." William C. Westmoreland, when he was commander of the U.S. forces in South Vietnam, agreed with this justification: "For every bomb we drop on a truck, we destroy five hundred bombs and rockets that won't fire shrapnel and steel into the hips and bodies of American boys."

These goals have not, of course, been reached, nor do they seem any nearer now than in 1965. Although the North Vietnamese did agree to begin talks when we reduced the intensity of the bombing in 1968, they were unwilling to compromise any of their demands and have not reduced the intensity with which they are fighting in South Vietnam, Laos, and Cambodia.

Unfortunately, America's military leaders still think that North Vietnam can be bombed to the peace table. General Westmoreland, who has withdrawn from the battlefield and is now Army Chief of Staff in Washington, said in December, 1969: "It is my opinion that if we had continued to bomb, the war would be over at this time—or would be nearly over." Several days later, Admiral Sharp, now retired, called on President Nixon to serve an ultimatum on Hanoi—begin negotiating in two weeks or face "concentrated" air attacks. "If we started concentrated air attacks against Hanoi and Haiphong," he said, "I believe there would be a sudden desire by the other side to negotiate." The Nixon Administration eventually accepted this proposal. When sporadic bombings were resumed in May, 1970, Administration spokesmen said that the change in policy was made in an effort to stop all infiltration from the North and thus to force Hanoi to talk peace.

It should be evident by now, though apparently it is not, that a country determined to struggle for a cause it feels is vital to its national interests will not be deterred from this struggle by bombing of its homeland. This finding was reported by the Pentagon team that investigated the effects of bombing Germany in World War II. The same lesson was obvious after an examination of the bombing of Korea in the early nineteen-fifties. And the identical lesson should have been learned after the first three and a half years of bombing in North Vietnam.

This article is an attempt to explain to our military leaders some of the reasons why North Vietnam cannot be bombed into negotiating. I have chosen illustrations from two of the more important aspects of North Vietnam's ability to survive, the process of infiltrating men and supplies from North Vietnam to the South, and the evacuation and decentralization of the industrial base in the North. Although bombs do kill and do place obstacles in the paths of the North Vietnamese going south, they cannot block all the trails to the South Vietnamese battlefields. Although bombs can destroy factories and force laborers to work in camouflaged jungle retreats, they cannot stop a determined labor force from continuing to produce the bare essentials.

Infiltration of North Vietnamese to the South did not begin until the escalation of the war in early 1965. Prior to that time, about forty thousand of the South Vietnamese who had gone to North Vietnam after the 1954 division of Vietnam had worked their way back to the South to serve as cadre for the Vietcong, and supplies were moving regularly from North to South. Virtually no members of the North Vietnamese regular army, however, had made the trip to the South.

The infiltration situation changed in 1965, partly because the North Vietnamese thought that year would be decisive and partly because large numbers of American troops arrived in South Vietnam to thwart a communist victory. From a previous annual high of 12,900 the infiltration rose (according to U.S. estimates) to 35,300 during 1965, to eighty-nine thousand in 1966, to between fifty-nine thousand and ninety thousand in 1967, and then to one hundred and forty thousand in 1968. After the bombing of North Vietnam ended, the United States continued a round-the-clock bombardment of the Ho Chi Minh Trail in Laos and South Vietnam. But the infiltration was unaffected. About one hundred thousand to one hundred and ten thousand North Vietnamese came down to South Vietnam in 1969. In the early months of 1970, soldiers came south at the rate of four thousand per month, and in April the figure rose to over ten thousand for that month.

Trucks have moved south at a rate unrelated to the intensity of the bombing. In June, 1966, Secretary McNamara announced that the number of trucks moving from North to South Vietnam was twice as large as it had been when the bombing started. Over a year later, in August, 1967, McNamara reported that the infiltration had continued to increase. Testifying before the Senate Preparedness Subcommittee, he said that the number of trucks in the southern panhandle of North Vietnam "has increased very substantially in the early months of this year versus last year despite a very large increase in the number of air strikes during that period of time. We have seen also that [deleted] despite very, very large increases in air strikes, the amount of traffic over the roads has increased, and, as a matter of fact, the whole road network has increased." In his final report to the Senate, in January, 1968, McNamara said, "It is difficult to conceive of any interdiction campaign" that would effectively stop the flow of men and supplies to the South.

Military leaders, particularly those connected with the Air Force, vehemently disagreed with McNamara on the question of how air power ought to be used. In the summer of 1967, for instance, the Joint Chiefs of Staff convinced President Johnson to authorize unlimited bombing attacks against every conceivable target connected with transportation, including many bridges that had previously been declared off limits. The bombing effort had no effect on infiltration south. On October 26, 1967, a U.S. military spokesman reported that there had been "no significant reduction in the flow of supplies south within the last month or two." Two months later, the U.S. command in Saigon actually reported an increase in traffic down the Ho Chi Minh Trail in Laos. North Vietnamese laborers, it was reported, were working to convert the trail into an all-weather route. The official source said, "We have failed to interdict the trail and stop it from being improved," and a senior American officer commented a few days later, "There's a hell of a lot of movement."

The main reason why our bombing has never seriously interfered with North Vietnam's battle plans in the South is that the forces in the South do not need much to sustain them. Secretary McNamara reported in August, 1967, that the consensus of the U.S. intelligence community was that only fifteen tons of non-food supplies per day were required to support all the communist forces in South Vietnam. On the basis of a three-hundred-thousand-man army this averages out to less than two ounces of supplies per man per day and was rejected as much too low by most of the Senators on the Senate Preparedness Subcommittee who were listening to McNamara. The Secretary himself was mystified by the data. When the operations of the communist forces in South Vietnam are studied, however, the figure proves to be accurate.

The average Viet Cong soldier operating in the Central Highlands or the Mekong Delta fights only one or at most two days out of thirty. His weapon and ammunition requirements are therefore significantly lower than those of his American counterpart and some of the weapons—like mines—are built in factories located in South Vietnam's jungles or are captured from U.S. forces. Viet Cong rifles are designed to shoot bullets only slightly larger than those used by American soldiers, so the Viet Cong can use any ammunition captured from U.S. forces, although the reverse is not true. The reliance of the communist forces on U.S. weapons has declined, but at the end of 1968 captured weapons were still significant.

An article appearing in North Vietnam's army newspaper in October, 1968, described in detail the 66-mm. M-72 bazooka, which American troops had begun using regularly. The article concluded: "The American young gentlemen soldiers are equipped with large amounts of good weapons and ammunition but they are afraid to die and often flee, abandoning all their weapons. If we can obtain their weapons, reinspect them, and find the M-72 bazooka still good, it can be used immediately to destroy enemy armored vehicles and fortifications."

The communist troops need little petroleum because they have only a few wheeled vehicles in the South. In late 1967, the communists began using some trucks, bulldozers, and tanks in areas like the Central Highlands and the Ashau Valley, but these vehicles are still somewhat rare. The Viet Cong receive radios and medicines and perhaps some ammunition through Cambodia, and food from nearby sources. Those fighting in the Delta area, for instance, receive their food from South Vietnamese farmers. Despite U.S. efforts to deprive the Viet Cong of their food sources through chemical defoliation programs, there have never been any major shortages. The soldiers in the central highlands receive their food from Cambodia; the only serious shortage there is salt. Most of the communists fighting in South Vietnam thus receive only guns and some ammunition from the North. The soldiers who operate around the demilitarized zone are the exception to this rule; they receive all their requirements (including food) directly from North Vietnam. Secretary McNamara estimated in August, 1967, that these fighters required sixty tons of supplies per day to sustain their operations.

The rapid buildup of communist forces in the first half of 1968 changed the situation somewhat. The new troops could not get all their supplies from the traditional sources and were forced to rely more on the routes from the

North. There were some shortages of guns and ammunition among the communist forces in South Vietnam just before the summer of 1968, and occasional reports of food shortages. Vast new road complexes were quickly opened in the communist-held areas, however, and at every given moment during the first half of 1968 there were ten thousand trucks carrying supplies south through Laos and South Vietnam.

An American Army captain who was fighting in the Saigon area in September, 1968, said of the communist supply situation: "Those newer weapons they have are damned good. And don't believe anyone who tells you that they have an ammunition or food problem. They don't." Even after the buildup, the North Vietnamese had to send no more than eighty tons of supplies from the North per day to sustain their troops.

Before going south, each North Vietnamese soldier is given particularly nourishing food for a period varying from two weeks to two months to strengthen him for the arduous journey. One private who left for the South in August, 1965, said that his food allowance was quadrupled for two months so that he could eat anything he wanted, including beef, pork, fish, cake, fruits, sweets, sugar, and milk. Sometimes a soldier about to go south is granted permission to visit his family for a few days before the trip begins, but more often there is no opportunity to say goodbye. Even when a trip home is permitted, the soldier is frequently instructed not to tell his family where he is going.

A typical soldier going south travels by train or truck from his training camp to Dong Hoi, the southernmost city of any size in North Vietnam. Then he begins walking south and southwest on paved and unpaved roads—traveling only at night because of the danger of air attacks—to a settlement at the northwest corner of the demilitarized zone. At this settlement, which the American intelligence community calls "Ho Village," he rests for a few days, receives new clothing, new equipment, and new identification documents so his identity as a North Vietnamese will be camouflaged. After this pause, the infiltrator crosses into Laos, where he and his companions are guided through the hundreds of small paths and roads in the complex known as the Ho Chi Minh Trail. Here the soldiers can travel by day because of the thick jungle canopy that covers the area, and at night they stay at campsites that are situated along the paths at ten- to fifteen-mile intervals. These way stations consist of two or three huts guarded by a small squadron of soldiers. Every few stations has a storehouse full of rice.

On most days, during the march through Laos, the soldiers rise at three-thirty in the morning, march from four to eleven, and then, after a lunch break, continue marching until six in the evening. At this point, they put up hammocks, dig foxholes, cook and eat dinner, prepare their rice-ball lunches for the following day and then sleep. The marchers cover ten to fifteen miles per day and rest one day out of every five to ten. Their food during the march, as well as after they reach the South, consists of one to two pounds of rice per day, plus some vegetables, salt, and meat.

The infiltrators face some problems common to any long march. Many are provided with sandals rather than boots, and until they learn how to use the sandals they suffer blisters and sprained ankles. They carry some dry field rations, like canned meat and salt, and so they usually eat two hot and one pre-cooked meal per day. There are occasional shortages, however, and to maintain this diet the soldiers must on occasion obtain rice from the surrounding area, pick wild vegetables, and hunt animals. One infiltrator who subsequently defected reported that his group hunted deer and threw grenades into rivers to catch fish. Health is also a constant problem. Soldiers are regularly reminded to boil their water, take their anti-malaria pills, and follow anti-mosquito instructions.

Other problems are unique to this particular march. The infiltrators must carry from seventy-five to eighty-five pounds of supplies with them throughout the trip. Among the personal supplies each soldier brings with him are three shirts, three pairs of trousers, a hammock, a pair of sandals, perhaps a nylon tent and a raincoat, and a first-aid kit filled with various pills. In addition each soldier must carry a carbine, sub-machine gun, or rifle, and parts of the heavy weapons that the company transports south.

Because the United States bombed the Ho Chi Minh Trail constantly, the North Vietnamese troops must never be congested in large numbers. This raises serious logistical problems because—with all the bridges along the trail under regular aerial attack—the troops are forced to ferry across the many rivers in the area and must assemble at the ferry crossing to wait for the boat. Until November 1, 1968, one hundred and fifty U.S. planes bombed the Ho Chi Minh Trail in Laos each day. Since then the United States has shifted many more of its planes to Laos, with the result that four hundred and fifty bombing raids are now carried out in Laos every day.

Planes flying over the Ho Chi Minh Trail have since the beginning of 1967 been aided by an electronic warning system that spots infiltrators as they pass. Modern electronic gadgets are spaced along the route south to count men and trucks and to notify bombers of the infiltrators' locations. In some parts of the Trail, tiny mines have been planted by U.S. and allied forces, so that, instead of dropping a bomb, a pilot learning of the location of trucks or troops can electronically set off a mine in the area.

The electronic equipment is supplemented in much of the Trail area by trail watchers who observe men and trucks moving south. The use of these watchers—who are usually Laotians, Cambodians, and South Vietnamese Nungs of Chinese origin—was increased when the United States stopped bombing North Vietnam in late 1968 and concentrated on the Laos part of the Trail. There are also some U.S. and allied troops along the Ho Chi Minh

Trail in Laos who use counter-guerrilla tactics to interfere with the soldiers marching south.

Interrogation of captured North Vietnamese soldiers has disclosed that from ten to twenty per cent of the men sent south do not survive the two- to six-month march to the battle area. Most of those who do not make it succumb to malaria; only two per cent are casualties caused by the air attacks. The drop-out percentage has declined since early 1968 when some of the infiltrators began being transported through Laos by truck rather than on their own feet.

The soldiers who march south carry some weapons and ammunition with them. Most supplies, however, come through Laos by truck after being transported through the southern panhandle of North Vietnam either by truck or on the inland waterways. The point at which trucks enter Laos, the Mu Gia Pass, has been bombed repeatedly, but the bombs have never been able to close the road for more than a day or two. The story of how the North Vietnamese have kept this pass open is illustrative of how the people have kept traffic moving throughout the route south.

The Mu Gia Pass, about seventy-five miles north of the demilitarized zone, was selected in early 1965 as the most important and most vulnerable point in the transportation system. It is a narrow, two-and-a-half-mile-wide pass in a very mountainous region, seemingly an obvious target for effective saturation bombing. On April 12, 1966, the United States sent thirty of its eight-engine B-52 bombers there, and they dropped thousands of tons of bombs on a three-mile section of the twenty-one-mile-long pass. A spokesman in Saigon said that the aim of the raid was to "really pulverize that pass" and to close the road for a significant length of time. Many delayed-action bombs (set to go off at times varying from minutes to days after the attack) were dropped in the attack to impede the efforts of North Vietnamese crews to clear the pass. Returning pilots said that a large section of the mountain appeared to have crashed into the pass in a huge landslide.

On April 24, however, Cyrus R. Vance, then the Deputy Secretary of Defense, reported that the saturation bombing had closed the pass only briefly and that two days after the massive attack fighter-bombers had to be sent in to attack trucks that were using the reopened pass. Secretary Vance estimated that the North Vietnamese had employed one hundred and fifty thousand workers to clear the pass, but that estimate was outrageously high. Vance and the reconnaissance pilots simple overestimated the damage that could be inflicted by bombs. Trucks can and did maneuver around or over bomb craters and landslides.

When the military planners considered which spots to begin bombing in May, 1970, they again turned to the Mu Gia Pass and launched a major raid designed again to close the road. The raid was no more effective than those of four years ago, however, and the North Vietnamese continue to send men and supplies through the pass.

Once in Laos, the trucks travel south on fairly well-established if somewhat rudimentary roads. They are usually dirt, but occasionally a surface of crushed stones or logs has been laid down by the twenty-five thousand North Vietnamese army guards and fifty thousand North Vietnamese laborers who work on the Ho Chi Minh Trail. Truck parks have been built within the jungle canopy every three to twenty miles, with every third to fifth shelter containing fuel and supplies. Each park is staffed by thirty to sixty North Vietnamese soldiers who repair bombed roads and work to expand the existing network. Beginning in 1967, roads began being built from Laos into Viet Cong base camps in South Vietnam, but before then most goods were transported into South Vietnam on oxcarts, pack bicycles, elephants, or on the backs of coolies.

After the United States scaled down its bombing in 1968 the North Vietnamese became able to move supplies to the Laos border without as much subterfuge. After the partial halt of March 31, 1968, the North Vietnamese moved their main staging area from Hanoi ninety miles south to Thanh Hoa. Within three and a half months all major bridges and rail lines north of the nineteenth parallel were repaired; one American general asserted in October that war supplies that had formerly required a hundred days to be moved from Haiphong to the demilitarized zone could be moved in ten. Similarly, within five weeks after all bombing of North Vietnam was stopped on November 1st, the North Vietnamese repaired the bombed-out bridges between the seventeenth and nineteenth parallels and moved goods through that area much faster.

The fact that goods move faster when there is no bombing than they do when there is bombing does not, however, justify a new bombing campaign. The North Vietnamese have shown that they can move men and supplies to the battlefields in South Vietnam no matter how vigorously we bomb, and they have shown they are willing to make whatever sacrifices are necessary. Secretary McNamara eventually learned, and he eventually told the Senate Preparedness Subcommittee, that no amount of bombardment can stop North Vietnamese infiltration. Our leaders in uniform and our current Secretary of Defense, however, apparently have not yet come to the same realization.

While North Vietnamese throughout the southern part of the country were working to keep infiltration routes open, those in the more urbanized north were struggling to produce food and supplies to keep the country functioning economically. One of the main reasons the economy did not collapse was the willingness of socialist countries to give virtually unlimited material aid to the North Vietnamese. The North Vietnamese worked unstintingly on their own behalf, however, and will undoubtedly renew this effort should the United States begin bombing again at the 1965-68 level.

Probably not even the North Vietnamese have accurate figures on the percentage of industrial facilities they moved, but it is certain that most urban industrial establishments were transported entirely or in part to new rural sites. Although the large Thainguyen pig-iron complex and the Haiphong cement factory could not be moved, almost all smaller facilities were evacuated. A pharmaceutical factory in Hanoi that in February, 1968, employed only one-tenth of its one thousand workers at the original site is probably not unusual.

Wilfred Burchett, an Australian communist writer, waxed poetic in early 1966 about a factory he visited in the mountains: "A famous old grotto with a hundred yards or so of rock above it was inhabited by bats and a few stone statues when I last visited it. Now there was the steady hum of machinery. Galleries which led off in all directions from the mouth of the main grotto had been widened and reinforced, generators installed in some; lathes, jigs, borers, grinders, and polishers and other machines in others—an entire vital industrial unit in full production."

John Pairman Brown, an American Episcopal clergyman, described in late 1967, with somewhat less flair, a branch of the Hanoi Machinery Factory he had seen: "We visited one of those workshops, not so much camouflaged as melted into a village: a cluster of huts rising in a bamboo grove in a paddy. Washing was strung on lines, a water buffalo with a small rider astride looked into the window of a hut almost entirely filled with a humming transformer and an electric annealer. The next few huts contained dozens of sumptuous Soviet-made automatic and semi-automatic machine tools, with cutting gears resting in a bath of oil. A hundred meters away ran the truck road along which the rough-cast blanks are brought in at night; later trucks bear the finished gears away to a subassembly workshop where other machine tools are being manufactured."

The number of articles in technical journals discussing the problems of evacuation bears witness to the fact that the dispersal was extensive. An article that appeared in the North Vietnamese magazine *Telegraph, Telephone, and Broadcasting Techniques* in March, 1966, for instance, discussed the problems of moving equipment into caves. It is important that a cave chosen to be an industrial site be well-ventilated, the article said, so equipment will stay dry. The best caves are usually located at the foot of a mountain, because they tend to be large, well-ventilated, and safe. Rainy seasons present a problem, however, and if the chosen cave has either a bowl-shaped floor or a bowl-shaped ceiling, the equipment should be put on a platform to keep it dry. If any houses are to be built near the cave site, they should be carefully camouflaged, so bombers will not be drawn toward the caves.

An article appearing in the January, 1967, issue of another North Vietnamese periodical, *Common Sense Science,* went into still more detail on how to select dispersal areas and install machines at these sites. The author suggested that buildings be found that are near high-voltage power lines and fairly near sources of supply, but at least two kilometers from any strategic targets. A central factory should not disperse to widely scattered locations, because that causes problems of administration. In particular, a large factory should not place its machines in buildings more than six miles from each other and a small enterprise in buildings more than three miles apart.

When the dispersal began, this article continues, some factories sent all the machines of a particular type (for instance, all lathes) to one site and machines of each other type to its own site. Such a system proved impractical, however, because the bombing of one site ended production in the entire system. Ideally, the entire array of machines necessary to construct a completed product should be sent to each location. This causes repair difficulties and may lower efficiency in the short run, but enables the industry to last longer under heavy bombing.

The ability of the North Vietnamese to counter U.S. attacks on oil-storage dumps and electrical-power plants offers the most vivid example of how the economy has been held together. Oil and electricity are vital to the continued functioning of all other sectors of the economy, and they were, naturally enough, singled out by American bombers to be attacked with particular intensity. The North Vietnamese responded by increasing their imports of petroleum and small generators, by dispersing these items in small quantities throughout the countryside and by reducing their reliance on these sources of power. Despite numerous attacks and extensive destruction, the North Vietnamese continued to keep their trucks and small factories running.

The bombing of the oil-storage depots in unpopulated areas began in early June, 1966, followed by attacks on the large dumps near Hanoi and Haiphong on June 29. Throughout the summer of 1966, U.S. planes were given virtually free range to hit all known oil depots in what has been described by Secretary McNamara as an "unrestricted bombing campaign against petroleum." American officials at first stated optimistically that the raids had been successful. On August 25, 1966, these sources were quoted as saying that the air strikes had had a very substantial and a very serious effect on North Vietnam's oil supplies. No major tanker, the officials said, had discharged petroleum at Haiphong since the June 29 raid. Hanson Baldwin wrote in *The New York Times* in the middle of October, 1966, that "all but twenty per cent of North Vietnam's known petroleum storage facilities have been destroyed." And on December 8, Air Force Secretary Harold Brown asserted that more than two-thirds of North Vietnam's oil storage capacity had been "knocked out."

The hoped-for collapse of the transportation system never, however, occurred, because the North Vietnamese had prepared for the day when their large storage facilities would be hit. Wilfred Burchett reported that deep underground storage bins had been developed long before the summer of 1966. If this is an exaggeration, it is at least clear that many large drums had been put into villages and other decentralized storage areas to ensure that travel could continue even if the large depots were destroyed and that these decentralized areas contained enough oil to keep trucks running until more oil could be brought in from Russia.

Because the eighteen storage tanks and the plumbing equipment for unloading tankers in Haiphong were destroyed by the bombings in the summer of 1966, oil probably did not come through that port for at least a short period of time. American sources reported in August, 1966, that at least one tanker was diverted to a Chinese port, where its cargo was unloaded and then transshipped to North Vietnam by rail. Shortly thereafter, a system involving a series of transfers at sea was put into operation. Soviet tankers came to a point near the Haiphong harbor, perhaps in one of the Red River delta tributaries, and unloaded their cargo into shallow draft barges. The barges than moved slowly under cover of darkness to transport the oil to one of many concealed rendezvous points on the North Vietnamese waterways.

As a result of this effort, North Vietnam soon acquired an ample supply of oil, which was dispersed all over the country in a way that made air power almost totally ineffective against it. *Le Monde* journalist Jacques Decornoy reported seeing in late 1966 a profusion of fifty-five-gallon barrels of oil scattered all over the countryside. Harrison Salisbury confirmed this; he reported in *The New York Times* in January, 1967, that there were "oil barrels strewn all over the North Vietnamese landscape." This system of dispersion became more and more sophisticated throughout the bombing. Just before the attacks on the Red River Valley stopped on March 31, 1968, William C. Baggs, late editor of the *Miami News*, said that he had seen numerous gasoline tank trucks traveling all over the countryside.

Secretary McNamara admitted to a congressional committee in early 1967 that the attempt to deny North Vietnam oil had failed: "The bombing of the P.O.L. [Petroleum, Oil, and Lubricants] system was carried out with as much skill, effort, and attention as we could devote to it . . . and we haven't been able to dry up those supplies." When asked in a press conference in February, 1967, whether he would concede that our heavy bombing attack had failed to stop infiltration from the North, McNamara stated, "I not only concede it, I report it."

McNamara described this failure in more detail in his August, 1967, testimony: "Our P.O.L. experience is illuminating. Our air strikes on petroleum facilities did destroy the inshore P.O.L. off-loading facilities in Haiphong. However the North Vietnamese have demonstrated a capability to adjust their methods, and they now off-load P.O.L. drums into lighters and barges and bring the drums ashore at night. There is no evidence of a P.O.L. shortage and stocks on hand equal an estimated one hundred and twenty days' consumption."

North Vietnam's allies seem willing to send as much petroleum as is needed. Forty-six thousand metric tons were shipped to North Vietnam during the first six months of 1967. The United States did not interfere with foreign tankers on their way to North Vietnam and U.S. pilots were not able to find and bomb the petroleum barges after they left the side of the large tankers.

The concentrated onslaught against North Vietnam's electrical power plants did not begin until the spring of 1967, but once begun it was carried out with as much fervor as were the attacks against the oil dumps. A Pentagon statement issued in August, 1967, reported: "Fourteen power plants, having a combined capacity of 165,000 kilowatts or eighty-six per cent of the national total, including all major plants in the principal areas of Hanoi, Haiphong, Hon Gai, Thai Nguyen, Viet Tre, Bac Giang, Thanh Hoa, and Ben Thuy have been struck. All but the Hanoi power plant, which has been restored to seventy-five per cent of pre-strike capacity, are out of operation. The total national capacity has been reduced to twenty-seven per cent of the pre-strike capacity. Air strikes have also nullified interchange of power over the extensive transmission network which serves the primary military and industrial installations. Of the four hydroelectric plants, one has been [deleted] struck."

These attacks were not without effect in North Vietnam. Many factories —both large and small—were forced to use manual tools instead of automatic equipment. At the Quyet Tien Cooperative in Thai Binh Province, where a small unit was making toilet paper, the workers had to shift from using electric mills to foot-operated mills because of the power shortage. The Tien-phong Cooperative in the same province produced glassware and had to shift from using a two-ton furnace to a one-ton furnace, so they could use manual fans instead of electric fans. The Thu Do toothbrush cooperative, which moved out of Hanoi to a new location in the countryside, was obliged to mold toothbrush handles using a welding torch instead of the electric-powered automatic mold they had used before they were evacuated.

Most of the large cities suffered shortages of electricity. William C. Baggs reported in April, 1968, that Nam Dinh had very little electricity and that the villages in that area had none. Amando E. Doronila, a Filipino reporter, wrote that same month that even in Hanoi there were frequent interruptions in the electrical supply, indicating that there were strains on that city's power plants.

The American attacks did not, however, deliver a crippling blow to North Vietnam. Secretary McNamara stated in August, 1967, and again in his farewell statement of January, 1968, that "imported diesel generators are probably producing sufficient electricity for essential services."

Perhaps the most important reason why heavy American bombing of the electrical plants did not decisively disrupt North Vietnam's industry is that the country had very little electrical power to begin with. The combined value of all North Vietnam's power plants, plus its explosive plant, the Thainguyen pig-iron complex, and the Haiphong cement plant (all of which were heavily bombed) was less than forty-five million dollars. All the power plants put together produced in 1964 and 1965 only about 550,000,000 kilowatt hours of electricity, which is one-fifth the annual power output of the Potomac Electric Power Company's plant in Alexandria, Virginia. The importation of a relatively small number of small diesel generators (somewhat more than two thousand were imported by the summer of 1967) was, therefore, sufficient to compensate for the bombed power plants and to provide enough power to keep the small dispersed factories in operation.

The cooperatives in the countryside—even those equipped with small machines—made do with very rudimentary power systems. Several North Vietnamese technicians have written that if a cooperative uses its machines in rotation rather than all at once, it should be able to get by with between ten and twenty kilowatts of electric power. The agricultural cadres have, therefore, tried to exploit those sources of power that can be found in rural areas.

The least expensive way to acquire power is by building a hydrodynamic station adjacent to whatever water is in the area. Such a station involves channeling water through a turbine that directly powers the machine by a system of power passes and link belts, without creating electricity in the process. A small hydroelectric station—in which the turbine powers an electric generator—is more versatile but also more expensive. This type of station can provide power and electrification for almost any simple machine, with the limitation that it cannot transmit electricity for a distance greater than fifteen hundred meters without a transformer. Among the other sources of power that were used during periods of electricity shortages were coal, wind power, methane gas produced by soaking corn stems, and diesel engines.

These illustrations of North Vietnam's strategy for survival have been unusually detailed because the story is one of many individuals each struggling to keep in operation a large and complicated system of production and transportation. With a renewal of U.S. bombing the North Vietnamese will be forced to find—through ingenuity and persistence—new ways to support the soldiers in the South. The people in North Vietnam will be united once again by a common enemy and will once again mobilize behind their government in an effort to maximize their skill and energy. The bombing will succeed in causing hardship, but not in deterring the North Vietnamese from continuing to fight.

Bibliography

I. Chemical and Biological Warfare—with Emphasis upon the Use of Herbicides in Southeast Asia
II. Relevant U. S. Congressional Reports and Hearings
III. Major U. S. Service Periodicals
IV. Vietnam: Bibliographies
V. Vietnam: Books and Articles
VI. Vietnamese Publications
(We wish to acknowledge the assistance of Dr. Arthur Westing, Department of Biology, Windham College, Putney, Vermont, for his material utilized in Section I, and Milton Leitenberg, of the Stockholm International Peace Research Institute, Stockholm, Sweden, for materials in Sections II, III, IV, V, VI.)

I. Chemical and Biological Warfare—with Emphasis upon the Use of Herbicides in Southeast Asia

Alland, A., Jr., "War and Disease: An Anthropological Perspective," *Natural History, 76 (10)*, 1967, pp. 58-61, 70. (Also in: *Bull. Atomic Scientists, 24 (6)*, pp. 28-31.)

Beecher, W., "Chemicals vs. the Viet Cong: 'Right' or 'Wrong'?" *National Guardsman, 20 (2)*, 1966, pp. 2-6.

Boffey, P. M., "Defense Issues Summary of Defoliation Study," *Science, 159*, Feb. 9, 1968, p. 613.

Brightman, C., 'Weed Killers' and the University at the Front," *Viet-Report (Leviathan), 2 (4/5)*, 1966, pp. 9-14, 33-48.

Bunn, G., "Banning Poison Gas and Germ Warfare: Should the United States Agree?" *Wisc. Law Rev.*, 1969, pp. 375-420. (See especially pp. 406-409.)

Burchett, W. G., *Furtive War: The United States in Vietnam and Laos*, New York, International Publ., 1963, pp. 60-65.

————*Vietnam: Inside Story of the Guerilla War*, 3rd ed., New York, International Publ., 1968, pp. 207-209.

Clarke, R., "Biological Warfare," *Science Journal*, Nov. 1966, p. 76.

————*Silent Weapons*, New York, David McKay, 1968, pp. 136-157.

————*We All Fall Down*, London, Penguin Press, 1968.

Clayton, Anne, "Health in Vietnam," *Nature, 217*, Feb. 10, 1968.

Colaianni, James F., "Napalm: Made in U. S. A.," *Ramparts*, Aug. 1966.

Commission for Investigation of the American Imperialists' War Crimes in Vietnam, *American Crimes in Vietnam*, Hanoi: Democratic Republic of Vietnam, 1966, pp. 21-24.

Committee for the Denunciation of the War Crimes of the U. S., "They Are Even More Ruthless Than Hitler!" *For Viet Nam: Bull. Tricontinental Comm. of Support to the People of Viet Nam, 2 (4)*, 1967, pp. 26-35.

Cook, R. E., Haseltine, W., & Galston, A. W., "What Have We Done to Vietnam?" *New Republic, 162 (2)*, 1970, pp. 18-21.

Cookson, J., & Nottingham, J., *Survey of Chemical and Biological Warfare*, London, Sheed & Ward, 1969, pp. 26-52, 223-252.

Corson, W. R., *Betrayal*, New York, W. W. Norton, 1968, pp. 76-77.

Csatorday, K., "Use of Chemical and Biological Weapons," U. S. Arms Control & Disarmament Agency Publication No. 43903, 1966, pp. 734-740.

Direr, F., *et al.*, *Livre Noir des Crimes Américains au Vietnam*, Paris, Libraire Arthème Fayard, 1970, pp. 41-107.

Dockter, K. W., *et al.* (Midwest Research Institute, Kansas City, Missouri), *Assessment of Ecological Effects of Extensive or Repeated Use of Herbicides*, Clearing House for Federal Science and Technology, Washington, D. C., 1967.

Duffett, J., ed., *Against the Crime of Silence*, Flanders, New Jersey, O'Hare Books, 1968, pp. 327-373.

Egler, F. E., "Herbicides and Vegetation Management: Vietnam and Defoliation," *Ecology, 49,* pp. 1212-1215.

Embassy of South Vietnam, *Post War Development of Vietnam; A Summary Report* (Vietnam Documents Series V), Washington, D. C., March, 1969.

Engineering News-Record, Land Clearing Emerges as a Top Tactic of the War," *Engineering News-Record, 184 (3)*, 1970, p. 27.

Fair, Stanley D., Lt. Col., "No Place to Hide: How Defoliants Expose the Viet Cong," *Army, 14 (2),* 1963, pp. 54-55. (Also in: *Armed Forces Chemical Jour., 18 (1),* March, 1964, pp. 5-6.)

Fall. B. B., "'This Isn't Munich, It's Spain': A Vietnam Album," *Ramparts, 4 (8),* 1965, pp. 23-29.

Galston, A. W., "Changing the Environment: Herbicides in Vietnam," *Scientist & Citizen (Environment),* 9, Aug. 1967, pp. 122-129.

————"Herbicides in Vietnam," *New Republic, 157 (22),* Nov. 25, 1967, pp. 19-21.

————"Military Uses of Herbicides in Vietnam," *New Scientist, 38,* June 13, 1968, pp. 583-584.

————"Defoliants," in: Rose (1969) pp. 62-75, 196-197.

————"Plants, People, and Politics," *Bioscience, 20,* 1970, pp. 405-410. (Also in: *Plant Science Bulletin, 16 (1),* pp. 1-7.)

Gellner, C. R., & Wu, L. N., "Use of Tear Gas in War: A Survey of International Negotiations and of U. S. Policy and Practice," in: Zablocki (1970) *II,* pp. 11-41.

Goldblat, J., "Are Tear Gas and Herbicides Permitted Weapons?" *Bull. Atomic Scientists, 26 (4),* 1970, pp. 13-16.

Gonzales, A. F., Jr., "Defoliation: A Controversial U. S. Mission in Vietnam," *Data on Defense & Civil Systems, 13 (10),* 1968, pp. 12-15.

Grummer, G., *Herbizide in Vietnam,* E. Berlin, Druckerei Neues Deutschland, 1969.

Hartke, V., *American Crisis in Vietnam,* Indianapolis, Bobbs-Merrill, 1968, pp. 126-127, 161-162.

Harvey, F., "Air War in Vietnam," *Flying, 79 (5),* 1966, pp. 38-95. (See especially p. 56.)

————*Air War: Vietnam,* New York, Bantam, 1967, pp. 39-43.

Harvey, George R., & Mann, Jay D., "Picloram in Vietnam," *Scientist & Citizen* (Environment), *10,* Sept. 1968, pp. 165-171, 221.

Hersh, S. M., *Chemical and Biological Warfare: America's Hidden Arsenal,* New York, Bobbs-Merrill, 1968, pp. 97-101, 144-167, 325-328.

————"Our Chemical War," *New York Rev. Books, 10 (8),* 1968, pp. 31-36.

House, W. B., *et al.,* "Assessment of Ecological Effects of Extensive or Repeated Use of Herbicides," U. S. Dept. Defense, 1967, (DDC AC824314) [The "MRI" report]. [Reviews in: *Ecology, 49,* p. 1211; *Scientist & Citizen* (Environment) *10 (1),* p. 20; *Science, 159,* p.614; *Environmental Science & Technology, 2,* p. 176; *Chemical & Engineering News, 46 (7),* p. 12; *Science News, 93,* p. 185; etc.]

Huddle, F. P., "Technology Assessment of the Vietnam Defoliant Matter: A Case History," U. S. House of Representatives, Comm. on Science & Astronautics, 1969.

Kahn, M. F., "Vietnam," in: Rose (1969), pp. 87-98, 198-199.

Kambuja, "Grave Attack on the Cambodian Economy: Ravages Caused by the Defoliants Spread by American Aircraft Near the Frontier," *Kambuja,* Phnom Penh, *5 (50),* 1969, pp. 112-113.

Kaufman, D. D., & Kearney, P. C., *Degradation of Herbicides*, New York, Marcal Dekker, Inc., 1969.

Langer, Elinor, "Chemical and Biological Warfare: I. The Research Program. II. The Weapons and the Policies," *Science, 155*, (I) Jan. 13, 1967, (II) Jan. 20, 1967, pp. 174-179, 299-303.

————"Chemical and Biological Weapons: Once Over Lightly on Capitol Hill," *Science*, May 26, 1967, pp. 1073-1074.

Leopold, A. C., "Defoliation," *Bioscience, 18,* 1968, p. 853.

Life, "A Tiny Enemy in Vietnam," Nov. 24, 1967.

Long, Ngô Vĩnh, "Leaf Abscission?" *Thời-Báo Gà, 5,* 1969, pp. 1-8. (Also in: *Bull. Concerned Asian Scholars, 2* (2), pp. 63-72.)

Luce, D., & Sommer, J., *Viet Nam: The Unheard Voices*, Ithaca, Cornell U. Press, 1969, pp. 160-162 (see index).

Lyle, David, "Plague and War," *Esquire*, Sept. 1966.

Mayer, J., "Starvation as a Weapon: Herbicides in Vietnam," *Scientist & Citizen* (Environment), *9*, 1967, pp. 115-121.

————"Starvation as a Weapon," in: Rose (1969), pp. 76-85, 197-198.

Mayer, J., & Sidel, V. W., "Crop Destruction in South Vietnam," *Christian Century, 83,* 1969, pp. 76-85, 197-198.

McCarthy, R. D., *Ultimate Folly: War by Pestilence, Asphyxiation, and Defoliation*, New York, Knopf, 1969, pp. 74-98.

McConnell, A. F., Jr., "Mission: Ranch Hand," *Air Univ. Rev., 21* (2), 1970, pp. 89-94.

McGrady, M., *Dove in Vietnam*, New York, Funk & Wagnalls, 1968, pp. 71-88.

Medical World News, "Defoliants, Deformities: What Risk?" *Medical World News, 11 (9),* 1970, pp. 15-17.

Meselson, Matthew S., "Chemical and Biological Warfare," *Scientific American, 222,* May, 1970, pp. 15-25.

————"Chemical and Biological Weapons," *Scientific American, 222* (5), May, 1970, pp. 15-25, 148.

Minarik, C. E., "Use of Herbicides in Vietnam," Proc. NE Weed Control Conf., *22*, 1968, pp. 1-5.

National Liberation Front, *American Crimes in Vietnam*, DRV Commission for Investigation of the American Imperialists' War Crimes in Vietnam, October, 1966.

————"Genocide Crime in South Vietnam," S. Vietnam, Liberation Editions, 1963.

————*New War Crime in South Vietnam: Spraying by U. S. Planes of Toxic Chemicals*, Hanoi, 1963.

————"Nixon's Chemical Warfare in South Vietnam," *Vietnam Courier, 6* (*246*), Dec. 8, 1969.

————"*Notes from South Vietnamese Press Conference,*" Stockholm, Sweden, Dec. 12, 1969.

————"*Speech of Mr. Le Phuong, Director, at the Press Conference,*" Stockholm, Sweden, Dec. 12, 1969.

————*They Are Even More Ruthless Than Hitler! II*, South Vietnam, 1966.

————Do Xuan Sang, *U. S. Crime of Chemical Warfare in South Vietnam.* Received from the North Vietnamese Embassy, Stockholm, Sweden, Dec. 18, 1969.

————*U. S. Imperialists' "Burn All, Destroy All, Kill All" Policy in South Vietnam*, South Vietnam, 1967.

Neilands, J. B., "Vietnam: Progress of the Chemical War," *Asian Survey, 10*, 1970, pp. 209-229.

Nelson, Bryce, "Herbicides in Vietnam: AAAS Board Seeks Field Study," *Science, 163*, Jan. 3, 1969.

————"Herbicides: Order on 2,4,5-T Issued at Unusually High Level," *Science, 166*, Nov. 21, 1969, pp. 977-979.

New York Times, "Chemical Warfare—USSR Reaction," Nov. 28, 1969, 10:1.

————"Defoliant—Possible Birth Defects," Dec. 6, 1969, 3:3.

————"Dr. Tschirley Talks of Ecological Change in Vietnam," Sept. 21, 1968, 10:4.

————"Effects of War on the Ecology of S. Vietnam," Sept. 16, 1968, 16:3.

————"North Vietnamese Press Agency Charges Ecological Damage," Jan. 21, 1970, 12:4.

————"Report by French and American Scientists," Jan. 14, 1970, 4:1,2.

————"Tear Gas and Defoliants—Congress," Nov. 26, 1969, 16:5.

————"Tear Gas and Defoliants—Editorial," Nov. 26, 1969, 44:1.

————"Tear Gas and Defoliants—UN Reaction," Nov. 26, 1969, 17:7.

————"Tear Gas and Defoliants—UN Reaction," Dec. 11, 1969, 13:1.

————"Tear Gas—Use in Vietnam," Dec. 6, 1969, 3:1.

————"Tour of Quanggai Province," Nov. 26, 1969, 44:3.

————"Cambodia to Allow U. S. to Check on Defoliant Damage to Crops," June 5, 1969.

Novick, S., "The Vietnam Herbicide Experiment," *Scientist & Citizen, 10*, pp. 20-21.

Odum, H. T., "Status of Knowledge on Herbicides and Ecology," *Ecology, 49*, p. 1215.

Orians, G. H., & Pfeiffer, E. W., "Ecological Effects of the War in Vietnam," *Science, 168*, May 1, 1970, pp. 544-554.

Pfeiffer, E. W., "Chemical Warfare in Vietnam and the American Scientific Community," *Scientific World, 12* (*6*), 1968, pp. 16-19. (Also in: *Society for Social Responsibility Science Newsletter, 195,* pp. 1-3.)

"Ecological Effects of the Vietnam War," *Science Journal, 5* (*2*), Feb. 1969, pp. 33-38.

————"Defoliation and Bombing Effects in Vietnam," *Biological Conservation, 2* (*2*), 1970, pp. 149-151.

Price, D. K., *et al.*, "On the Use of Herbicides in Vietnam," *Science, 161,* 1968, pp. 252-256. [Also in: *Scientist & Citizen* (Environment), *10,* pp. 118-122.]

Pruden, W., Jr., "Defoliating the Jungles in Vietnam," *Nat'l. Observer, 5* (*9*), 1966, pp. 1, 10.

Quimby, F. H., & Carlin, M. E., "Chemical and Biological Weapons: Some Possible Approaches for Lessening the Threat and Danger," U. S. Senate, Comm. on Labor & Public Welfare, 1969.

Rose, Steven, ed., *CBW: Chemical and Biological Warfare,* Boston: Beacon, 1969, pp. 62-98.

————*CBW: London Conference on Chemical and Biological Warfare,* London, George Harrap and Co., 1968,

Rothschild, J. H., *Tomorrow's Weapons*, New York, McGraw-Hill, 1964.

Sakka, M., *Vietnam: La Guerre Chimique et Biologique*, Paris, Editions Sociales, 1967.

Sang, Do Xuan, "U. S. Crime of Chemical Warfare in South Viet Nam," in: *Juridical Sciences Inst.,* 1968. U. S. War Crimes in Viet Nam. Hanoi, Viet Nam State Commission of Social Sciences, 1968, pp. 217-249.

Sartre, Jean Paul, *On Genocide*, Boston, Beacon Press, 1968.

Science, "Defoliation; AAAS Study Delayed by Resignations from Committee," *159*, Feb. 23, 1968.

Science Policy Research Division, *A Technology Assessment of Vietnam Defoliant Matter: A Case History*. A report to the Subcommittee on Science, Research and Development of the Committee on Science and Astronautics, U. S. House of Representatives. Legislative Reference Service: Library of Congress, Aug. 8, 1969.

Scientific Research, "Mission to Vietnam," *Scientific Research*, (+), *4* (*12*), pp. 22-30; (*13*), pp. 26-30; (*15*), p. 5.

Scientists' Institute for Public Information, "Chemical and Biological Warfare," *Scientist & Citizen (Environment)*, *9* (*7*), Aug., Sept., 1967.

Shade, R. A., "Management of the Department of Defense Vietnam Herbicide Program," George Washington Univ., M. S. thesis, 1969.

Stanford Biology Group, *"The Destruction of Indochina,"* Calif. Tomorrow, San Francisco, June, 1970.

Thant, U., *et al.*, *Chemical and Bacteriological (Biological) Weapons and the Effects of Their Possible Use*, New York, United Nations, 1969, pp. 13, 37, 71-72.

Tschirley, F. H., *An Assessment of Ecological Consequences of the Defoliation Program in Vietnam*. A report prepared at the request of the U. S. Dept. of State, April 12, 1968.

————"Research Report: Response of Tropical and Subtropical Woody Plants to Chemical Treatments," U. S. Agricultural Research Serv. Publ. No. CR-13-67, 1968.

————"Defoliation in Vietnam," *Science, 163,* Feb. 21, 1969, pp. 779-786. (Also in: *Science, 161,* Feb. 21, 1969.)

————"Ecological Effects of Extensive or Repeated Use of Herbicides," *Ecology, 49,* pp. 1211-1212.

Tuoc, Tran Huu, "Intervention," in: *U. S. Military Adventure in South Vietnam,* Hanoi, Foreign Languages Publ. House, 1962, pp. 46-49.

U. S. Department of Army, "Employment of Riot Control Agents, Flame, Smoke, Antiplant Agents, and Personnel Detectors in Counter-guerrilla Operations," U. S. Dept. Army Training Circular No. TC 3-16, 1969, pp. 62-68, 80-81.

U. S. Department of Army, "Military Chemistry and Chemical Agents," U. S. Dept. Army Technical Manual No. TM 3-215, 1967.

U. S. Departments of the Army, Navy, and Air Force, *Employment of Chemical and Biological Agents*, FM 3-10, March, 1966.

Westing, A. H., "Poisoning Plants for Peace," *Friends Journal, 16,* 1970, pp. 193-194. (Also in: *Vermont Freeman, 2 (4),* pp. 7-9.

Westing, A. H., *et al.*, "Report on Herbicidal Damage by the United States in Southeastern Cambodia," Phnom Penh, 1969. (Also in: *Defoliation* by T. Whiteside, Ballantine, New York, 1970, pp. 117-132.)

White, P. T., "Saigon: Eye of the Storm," *Nat'l Geographic Mag., 127,* 1965, pp. 834-872. (See especially p. 838.)

Whiteside, Thomas, *Defoliation*, New York, Ballantine, 1970. (See also *New Yorker, 45 (51),* pp. 32-69; *46 (4),* pp. 24-129; and *New Yorker,* June 18, 1970.)

Wolfle, Dael, "AAAS Council Meeting 1966," *Science, 155,* Feb., 1967.

Woodwell, G. M., "Effects of Pollution on the Structure and Physiology of Ecosystems," *Science, 168,* April 24, 1970, pp. 429-433.

World Health Organization, Executive Board, *Epidemiological Situation in Vietnam,* 41st session, agenda item 2.8, Jan. 23, 1968.

World Health Organization, *Health Aspects of Chemical and Biological Weapons*, Geneva, World Health Org., 1970, pp. 55-57.

Zablocki, C. J., ed., "Chemical-Biological Warfare: U. S. Policies and International Effects." (I) Hearings. (II) Report. U. S. House of Representatives, Comm. Foreign Affairs, 1970.

II. Relevant U. S. Congressional Reports and Hearings

U. S. CONGRESSIONAL HEARINGS (probably only a small sample of extant hearings, reports or Committee Prints on Vietnam)

The Vietnam Conflict: The Substance and The Shadow. Report of Senators Mansfield, Muskie, Inouye, Aiken, and Boggs to the Senate Committee on Foreign Relations, U. S. Senate, Washington, D. C., January 6, 1966.

United States Policy Toward Asia. Report of the House Subcommittee on the Far East and the Pacific of the (House) Committee on Foreign Affairs, U. S. House of Representatives, Washington, D. C., May 19, 1966.

Background Information Relating to Southeast Asia and Vietnam; 2nd ed. Senate Committee on Foreign Relations, U. S. Senate, Washington, D. C., March, 1966.

Supplemental Foreign Assistance Fiscal Year 1966—Vietnam. Hearings before the Senate Committee on Foreign Relations, U. S. Senate, 89th Congress, 2nd Session, Washington, D. C., 1966.

Civilian Casualty and Refugee Problems in South Vietnam. Findings and Recommendations of the Subcommittee to Investigate Problems Connected with Refugees and Escapees of the Committee on the Judiciary, U. S. Senate, Washington, D. C., May 9, 1968.

Civilian Casualty, Social Welfare, and Refugee Problems in South Vietnam. Hearing before the Subcommittee to Investigate Problems Connected with Refugees and Escapees of the Committee on the Judiciary, U. S. Senate, 90th Congress, 1st Session. May, August, September, October, 1968, and June 24 and 25, 1969.

Background Information Relating to Southeast Asia and Vietnam. Committee on Foreign Relations: U. S. Senate, 89th Congress, 1st Session. Washington, D. C., January 14, 1965.

Review of the Vietnam Conflict and Its Impact on U. S. Military Commitments Abroad. Report of the Special Subcommittee on National Defense Posture of the Committee on Armed Services: U. S. House of Representatives, 90th Congress, 2nd Session, under authority of H. Res. 124. Washington, D. C., August 24, 1968.

Background Information Relating to Southeast Asia and Vietnam, 4th ed. rev. Committee on Foreign Relations: U. S. Senate, 90th Congress, 2nd Session, Washington, D. C., March 1968.

The Gulf of Tonkin, the 1964 Incidents. Hearings before the Committee on Foreign Relations: U. S. Senate, 90th Congress, 2nd Session, Washington, D. C., February 20, 1968.

Rural Development in Asia, Pts. I and II. Hearings before Subcommittee on Asian and Pacific Affairs, (House) Committee on Foreign Affairs, February-May, 1967.

The Future US Role in Asia and in the Pacific. Hearings before Subcommittee on Asian and Pacific Affairs, (House) Committee on Foreign Affairs, February-April, 1968.

Measuring Hamlet Security in Vietnam. Report of a Special Study Mission by Hon. J. V. Tunney, California, (House) Committee on Foreign Affairs, House Report 91-25, February 25, 1969.

Report of the Special Study Mission to East and Southeast Asia. (House) Committee on Foreign Affairs, House Report 91-30, March 6, 1969.

Report of the Special Study Mission to East and Southeast Asia. Hon. E. R. Roybal, California, (House) Committee on Foreign Affairs, February 18, 1969.

Report of the Special Study Mission to South and Southeast Asia. Hon. Robert Taft, Jr., Ohio, (House) Committee on Foreign Affairs, May 5, 1969.

Report on the War in Vietnam (as of June 30, 1968). *Section I*: Report on Air and Naval Campaigns against North Vietnam and Pacific Command-Wide Support of the War, June 1964-July 1968, by Admiral U. S. G. Sharp, USN Commander-in-Chief, Pacific: *Section II*: Report on Operations in South Vietnam, January 1964-June 1968, by General W. C. Westmoreland, USA Commander, U. S. Military Assistance Command, Vietnam.

III. Major U. S. Service Periodicals

The following Armed Forces' publications provide invaluable information about American military presence in Southeast Asia. Probably the best source is *Aviation Week and Space Technology*, a private publication.

1. *Aerospace International*

2. *Air Force and Space Digest*

3. *Army*

4. *Army Aviation Magazine*

5. *Armed Forces Management*

6. *Army Information Digest*

7. *Aviation Week and Space Technology*

8. *Military Review*

9. *Naval Aviation News*

10. *Naval Review (Yearbook)*

11. *Navy*

12. *Ordnance*

13. *Our Navy*

14. *U. S. Naval Institute Proceedings*

IV Vietnam: Books and Articles

American Friends Service Comm., *Peace in Vietnam: A New Approach in South East Asia*, New York, Hill & Wang, 1966.

Aptheker, H., *Mission to Hanoi*, New York, International Publishers, 1966.

Arlen, M. J., *Living-Room War*, New York, The Viking Press, 1960.

Armbruster, E., R. D. Gatsil, H. Kahn, W. Pfaff, E. & Stillman E., *Can We Win In Vietnam?* New York, Praeger Publishers, 1968.

Bain, C. A., *Vietnam: The Roots of the Conflict*, Englewood Cliffs, N. J., Prentice-Hall, 1967.

Bator, V., *Vietnam: A Diplomatic Tragedy*. Dobbs Ferry, N. Y., Oceana Publishers, 1965.

Beal, C. W., *The Realities of Vietnam*, Prepared under the auspices of the Ripon Society, Washington, D. C., Public Affairs Press, 1967.

Bodard, L., *The Quicksand War: Prelude to Vietnam*, Boston,   Little, Brown & Co., 1967.

Bouscaren, A. T., *The Last of the Mandarins: Diem of Vietnam*, Pittsburgh, Duquesne University Press, 1965.

Brass, A., *Bleeding Earth*, Melbourne, Heinemann, 1968.

Bromley, D. D., *Washington and Vietnam: An Examination of the Moral and Political Issues*, Dobbs Ferry, N. Y., Oceana Publications, 1966.

Broughton, J., *Thud Ridge*, Philadelphia, J. B. Lippincott, 1969.

Brown, Robert M., A. J. Heschel, and M. Novak, *Vietnam: Crisis of Conscience*, New York, Association Press, 1967.

Browne, M., *The New Face of War*, Indianapolis, Bobbs Merrill, 1965.

Burchett, W., *Vietnam: Inside Story of a Guerilla War*, New York, International Publishers, 1965.

The Furtive War: The United States in Vietnam & Laos, New York, International Publishers, 1963.

Vietnam North, London, Lawrence and Wishart, 1966.

Mekong Upstream, Hanoi, Reed River Publishing House, 1957.

Vietnam Will Win, New York, Monthly Review Press, 1968.

Buttinger, J., *The Smaller Dragon: A Political History of Vietnam*, New York, Praeger Publishers, 1958.

Vietnam: A Dragon Embattled, 2 vols. New York Praeger Publishers, 1967, London, Pall Mall Press, 1970.

Butwell, R., *Southeast Asia Today and Tomorrow*, New York, Praeger Publishers, 1964.

Cady, J. F., *The Roots of French Imperialism in Eastern Asia*, Ithaca, N. Y., Cornell University Press, 1954.

Southeast Asia: Its Historical Development, New York, McGraw-Hill, 1964.

Cameron, J., *Here Is Your Enemy: James Cameron's Report from North Vietnam*, New York, Holt, Rinehart & Winston, 1966 (Also published in England as: *Witness: The Complete Story of James Cameron's Journey to North Vietnam*, London, Victor Gollancz, Ltd., 1966.

Chi, Hoang Van, *From Colonialism to Communism*, New York, Praeger Publishers, 1964.

Child, F. C., *Essays on Economic Growth, Capital Formation, and Public Policy in Viet-Nam, Saigon* (Michigan State University Vietnam Advisory Group), May, 1961.

Clubb, O. E., *The United States & the Sino-Soviet Bloc in Southeast Asia*, Washington, D. C., Brookings Institute, 1962.

Coe, C., *Young Men in Vietnam*, New York, Four Winds Press, 1968.

Coedes, G., *The Making of Southeast Asia*, translated by H. M. Wright, Berkeley, University of California Press, 1966.

Cole, A. B., ed., *Conflict in Indo China & International Repercussions: A Documentary History 1945-1955*, Ithaca, N. Y., Cornell University Press, 1956.

Corson, W. R., *The Betrayal*, New York, Norton, 1968.

Critchfield, R., *The Long Charade: Political Subversion in the Vietnam War*, New York, Harcourt, Brace & World, 1968.

Crozier, B., *South-East Asia In Turmoil*, Baltimore, Penguin Books, 1965.

Dang, N., *Vietnam: Politics & Public Administration*, Honolulu, East-West Center Press, June 1966.

Davenport, S., F. Maher, J. McGregor, W. Pepper, A. Reich, Vietnam Curriculum, 4 vols., *Introductory Unites; History and Issues; Impact of the War; American Attitudes and Values,* New York, New York Review.

Devillers, P. and J. Lacouture, *End of A War: Indochina 1954* New York, Praeger Publishers.

The Diablo Press, *We Accuse: The Vietnam Day Protest in Berkeley*, Berkeley, California, 1965.

Dobby, E. H. G., *Southeast Asia*, London, University of London Press (U.S. distribution by Verry), 1950.

Dommen, A. J., *Conflict in Laos*, New York, Praeger Publishers, 1965.

Donlon, R. H. C., *Outpost of Freedom*, New York, McGraw-Hill, 1965.

Draper, T., *Abuse of Power*, New York, The Viking Press, 1970.

Drendel, L., *The Air War in Vietnam*, New York, Arco, 1968.

Duncan, D. D., *This is War* (photographs), Bantam, 1967.

Duncan, Donald, *The New Legions*, New York, Random House, 1967.

Eastlake, W., *The Bamboo Bed*, New York, Simon & Schuster.

Eden, A., *Toward Peace in Indochina*, Boston, Houghton Mifflin, 1966.

Full Circle. London, Cassell, 1960.

Evans, Barbara, *Caduceus in Saigon*, London, Hutchinson, 1968.

Fall, B. B., *Anatomy of a Crisis: The Laotian Crisis of 1960-1961*, Garden City, New York, Doubleday & Co., 1969.

Hell in a Very Small Place: The Siege of Dien Bien Phu, Philadelphia, J. B. Lippincott, 1966.

Last Reflections on a War, New York, Doubleday, 1967.

On Revolution: Selected Writings of Ho Chi Minh 1920-1966, New York, Praeger Publishers, 1967.

Street Without Joy: From the Indo China War to the War in Vietnam, Harrisburgh, Pa., Stackpole Co., 1964.

The Two Vietnams: A Political & Military Analysis, New York, Praeger Publishers, 1963 & 1964.

Vietnam Witness: 1953-1966, New York, Praeger Publishers, 1966.

Field, Michael, *The Prevailing Wind*, London, Methuen, 1965.

Fifield, R. H., *Southeast Asia in United States Policy*, New York, Praeger Publishers, 1963.

Fischel, W., ed., *Problems of Freedom—South Vietnam Since Independence*, New York, Free Press of Glencoe, 1961.

Fischer, A., *South-East Asia: A Social, Economic, and Political Geography*, London, Methuen; and New York, E. P. Dutton & Co., 1965.

Fulbright, J. W., *The Arrogance of Power*, New York, Random House, 1967.

The Vietnam Hearings, New York, Random House, 1966.

Garfield, B., *The Last Bridge*, New York, McKay, 1966.

Gettlemen, M., ed., *Vietnam: History Documents and Opinions on a Major World Crisis*, Greenwich, Conn., Fawcett, 1965.

Gerassi, J., *North Vietnam*, London, Allen and Unwin, 1968.

Gian, T. V. and L. V. Chat, *The South Vietnam Liberation National Front*, Hanoi, 1962.

Giap, V. N., *Big Victory, Great Task* (North Vietnam's Minister of Defense Assesses the Course of the War), Introduction by D. Schoenbrun. New York, Praeger Publishers, 1968.

Dien Bien Phu, 3rd ed. rev., Hanoi, Foreign Languages Publishing House, 1962.

People's War, People's Army, New York, Praeger Publishers, 1961.

Goodwin, R., *Triumph or Tragedy: Reflections on Vietnam*, New York, Random House, 1966.

Goulden, J. C., *Truth Is the First Casualty. The Gulf of Tonkin Affair: Illusion and Reality*, Chicago, Rand McNally & Co.

Greene, F., *Vietnam! Vietnam!* Palo Alto, Calif., Fulton Publishing Co., 1966.

Gruening, E. and H. B. Beaser, *Vietnam Folly*, Washington, D. C., The National Press, 1968.

Gurtov, M., *The First Vietnam Crisis. Chinese Communist Strategy and United States Involvement*, 1953-1954, New York, Columbia University, 1967.

Halberstam, D., *The Making of a Quagmire*, New York, Random House, 1965.

Hall, D. G. E., *A History of Southeast Asia*, London, MacMillan, 1955.

Hammer, E. J., *The Struggle for Indochina*, Stanford, Stanford University Press, 1954.

Vietnam: Yesterday & Today, New York, Holt, Rinehart, & Winston, 1966.

Hanh, T. N., *Vietnam: Lotus in a Sea of Fire*, New York, Hill & Wang.

Hartke, V., *The American Crisis in Vietnam*, Indianapolis, Bobbs-Merrill, 1968.

Harvey, F., *Air War: Vietnam*, New York, Bantam, 1968.

Hempstone, S., *A Tract of Time*, Boston, Houghton Mifflin Co., 1966.

Hendry, J., *The Study of a Vietnamese Rural Community*, Saigon, M. S. U. G., 1959.

The Small World of Khanh Hau, Chicago, Aldine, 1964.

Herman, E. S. and R. B. DuBoff, *America's Vietnam Policy: The Strategy of Deception*, Washington, D. C., Public Affairs Press, 1966.

Hickey, G. C., *Village in Vietnam*, New Haven, Conn., Yale Univ. Press, 1964.

Higgins, M., *Our Vietnam Nightmare*, New York, Harper & Row Publishers, 1965.

Honey, P. J., ed., *North Vietnam Today*, New York, Praeger Publishers, 1962.

Communism in North Vietnam: Its Role in the Sino-Soviet Dispute, Cambridge, Mass., M. I. T. Press, 1963.

Jacoby, E. H., *Agrarian Unrest in Southeast Asia*, New York, Columbia University Press, 1949.

Just, Ward S., *To What End; Report from Vietnam*, Boston, Houghton Mifflin, 1968.

Kahin, George McTurnam, ed. *Governments and Politics of Southeast Asia*, Ithaca, N. Y., Cornell University Press, 1964.

and J. W. Lewis, *The United States in Vietnam*, New York, The Dial Press, 1967.

Kastenmeier, R. W., *Vietnam Hearings: Voices from the Grassroots*, New York, Doubleday, 1965.

Kennedy, D. E., *The Security of Southern Asia*, New York, Praeger Publishers, 1965.

Knoebl, K., *Victor Charlie: The Face of War in Vietnam*, London, Pall Mall Press, 1967.

Kraslow, D., and S. H. Loory, *The Secret Search for Peace in Vietnam*, New York, Random House, 1968.

Labin, S., *Sellout in Vietnam?*, Arlington, Va. Crestwood Books, 1966.

Lacouture, J., *Ho Chi Minh: A Political Biography*, New York, Random House, 1968.

Vietnam Between Two Truces, New York, Random-Vintage, 1966.

Lam, Truong-bun, *Patterns of Vietnamese Response to Foreign Intervention: 1858-1900*, Monograph Series No. 11, New Haven, Conn., Yale University, 1967.

Lancaster, D., *The Emancipation of French Indochina*, London, Oxford Univ. Press, 1961.

LaPalombara, J., *Bureaucracy and Political Development*, Princeton, N. J., Princeton University Press, 1963.

Lawyer's, "The Committee on American Policy Towards Vietnam," *Vietnam and International Law: An Analysis of the Legality of the U. S. Military Involvement*, O'Hare Books.

Lederer, W. J., *Our Own Worst Enemy*, New York, Norton, 1968.

Lindholm, R. W., ed., *Vietnam: The First Five Years, An International Symposium*, Lansing, Mich., Michigan State University, 1959.

Lucas, J. G., *Dateline Vietnam*, New York, Award House, Crown Publishers, 1966.

Luce, D., and J. Sommer, *Vietnam: The Unheard Voices*, Ithaca, N. Y., Cornell University Press, 1969.

Lynd, S., and T. Hayden, *The Other Side*, New York, The New American Library, 1967.

Mallin, J., *Terror in Vietnam*, Princeton, N. J., Van Nostrand, 1966.

Manning, R., and M. Janeway, eds, *Who We Are: An Atlantic Chronicle of the United States and Vietnam*, Atlantic-Little, Brown, 1969.

Marshall, S. L. A., *Battles in the Monsoon: Campaigning in the Central Highland, South Vietnam, Summer 1966*, New York, Morrow, 1967.

Bird, New York, Cowles Book Co., 1968.

West to Cambodia, New York, Cowles Book Co., 1968.

McAleavy, H., *Black Flags in Vietnam*, New York, Macmillan, 1968.

McAlister, J. T., *Vietnam: The Origins of Revolution (1885-1946)*, Washington, D. C., American Univ. for the U. S. Army AD-680 211.

McCarthy, Eugene, *The Limits of Power*, New York, Holt, Rinehart and Winston, 1967.

McCarthy, M., *Hanoi*, New York, Harcourt, Brace and World, 1968.

Reports from Vietnam, New York, Harcourt, Brace and World.

Vietnam, New York, Harcourt, Brace and World, 1967.

Mecklin, J., *Mission in Torment*, Garden City, N. Y., Doubleday, 1965.

Menashe, L., and R. Radosh, eds., *Teach-Ins USA: Reports, Opinions, Documents*, New York, Praeger Publishers, 1967.

Mohn, A. H., *Vietnam*, Oslo, Gyldendal, Norsk Forlag, 1965.

Montgomery, J. D., *The Politics of Foreign Aid: American Experience in Southeast Asia*, New York, Praeger Publishers, 1962.

Moore, R., *The Green Berets*, New York, Avon, 1964.

Morgenthau, H. J., *Vietnam & the United States*, Washington, D. C., Public Affairs Press, 1965.

Mulligan, H. A., *No Place to Die*, New York, Morrow, 1967.

Murray, Robin, *Vietnam*, London, Eyre & Spottingwoode, 1965.

Murti, B. S. N., *Vietnam Divided: The Unfinished Struggle*, New York, Asia Publishing House, 1964.

Newman, Bernard, *Background to Vietnam*, London, R. Hale, 1966.

Nighswonger, W. A., *Rural Pacification in Vietnam*, New York, Praeger Publishers, 1967.

O'Neill, R. J., *General Giap, Politician and Strategist*, New York, Praeger Publishers, 1969.

Vietnam Task, Australia, Cassell, 1968.

Osborne, M. E., *Strategic Hamlets in South Viet-Nam: A Survey and a Comparison*, Ithaca, N. Y., Cornell Southeast Asia Program, 1965.

Parks, D.,*G. I. Diary*, New York, Harper and Row, 1968.

Pepper, W. F., "The Children of Vietnam," *Ramparts, Berkeley, Calif., 1967.* Perlo, V. and K. Goshal,

Perlo, V. and K. Goshal, *Bitter End in South East Asia*, New York, Marzani & Munzell, 1964.

Pfeffer, R. M., ed., *No More Vietnams? The War and the Future of American Foreign Policy,* New York, Adlai Stevenson Institute of International Affairs, Harper Colophon Books, 1968.

Pickerell, J., *Vietnam in the Mud*, Indianapolis, Bobbs-Merrill, 1966.

Pike, D., *War, Peace, and the Viet Cong*, Cambridge, Mass., The M. I. T. Press, 1966.
Viet Cong: The Organization and Techniques of the National Liberation Front, Cambridge, Mass., The M. I. T. Press, 1966.

Pruden, W., Jr., *Vietnam: The War*, New York, Dow Jones, 1965.

Purcell, V., *The Chinese in Southeast Asia*, London-New York, Oxford University Press, 1965.

Pustay, J. S., *Counterinsurgency Warfare*, New York, The Free Press, 1965.

Raskin, M., and B. B. Fall, *The Vietnam Reader: Articles and Documents on American Foreign Policy and the Viet-Nam Crisis*, New York, Vintage, 1965.

Ray, Michele, and J. Murray, *The Two Shores of Hell*, New York, D. McKay Co., 1968.

Ray, S., ed., *Vietnam Seen from East and West*, Melbourne, T. Nelson, 1966.

Reed, D., *Up Front in Vietnam*, New York, Funk and Wagnalls, 1967.

Reischauer, E. O., *Beyond Vietnam: The United States and Asia*, New York, Vintage Books.

Robequain, C., *The Economic Development of French Indochina*, London-New York, Oxford University Press, 1939 & 1944.

Robinson, F. M., and E. Kemp, eds., *The Truth About Vietnam: Report on the U. S. Senate Hearings*, San Diego, Greenleaf Classics, 1966.

Rostow, W., *The Two Major Communist Offensives*, Washington, D. C., Department of State, 1964.

Roy, Jules, *The Battle of Dien Bien Phu*, New York, Harper & Row Publishers, 1965.

Russell, B., *War Crimes in Vietnam*, New York, Monthly Review Press, 1967.

Salisbury, H. E., *Behind the Lines—Hanoi: December 23, 1966-January 7, 1967*, New York, Harper & Row Publishers, 1967.

Sardesai, D. R., *Indian Foreign Policy in Cambodia, Laos and Vietnam 1947-1964*, Berkeley, University of California Press, 1968.

Scalapino. R. A., ed., *The Communist Revolution in Asia: Tactics, Goals and Achievements*, Englewood Cliffs, N. J., Prentice Hall, 1965.

Schell, J., *The Military Half: An Account of Destruction in Quang Ngai and Quang Tin*, New York, Alfred A. Knopf Co., 1968.

The Village of Ben Suc, New York, Alfred A. Knopf Co., 1967.

Schlesinger, A. M., *The Bitter Heritage: Vietnam and American Democracy 1941-1966*, Boston, Houghton Mifflin, 1967.

Schurman, F., et al., *The Politics of Escalation in Vietnam*, Boston, Beacon Press, 1966.

Scigliano, R., *South Vietnam: Nation Under Stress*, Boston, Houghton Mifflin, 1963.

and Fox, G. H., *Technical Assistance in Vietnam: The Michigan State University Experience*, New York, Praeger Publishers, 1965.

Shaplen, R., *The Lost Revolution*, New York, Harper & Row Publishers, 1965. *Time Out of Hand: Revolution and Reaction in Southeast Asia*, New York, *t Asia*, Harper & Row Publishers.

Sheehan, S., *Ten Vietnamese*, New York, Alfred L. Knopf.

Sheer, R., *How the United States got Involved in Vietnam*, Santa Barbara, Calif., Center for the Study of Democratic Institutions, 1965.

Smith, Ralph, *Vietnam and the West*, London, Heinemann, 1968.

Starobin, J., *Eyewitness in Indo-China*, New York, Cameron & Kahn, 1954.

Steel, Ronald, *Pax Americana*, New York, The Viking Press, 1967.

South Vietnam: Liberation Publishing House, *South Vietnam: On the Road to Victory*, 1965.

Taber, R., *The War of the Flea*, New York, Lyle Stuart Inc., 1965.

Tanham, G. K., *Communist Revolutionary Warfare: The Vietminh in Indo China*, New York, Praeger Publishers, 1961.

War Without Guns, American Civilians in Rural Vietnam, New York, Praeger Publishers, 1966.

Taylor, Maxwell D., *Responsibility and Response*, New York, Harper & Row Publishers, 1967.

Thai, N., *Is South Vietnam Viable?*, Manila, Carmelo and Bauermann, 1962.

Thompson, R., *Defeating Communist Insurgency: The Lessons of Malaya and Vietnam* (Maps), New York, Praeger Publishers.

No Exit from Vietnam, New York, McKay.

Thompson, V., *French Indochina*, New York, Macmillan Co., 1942.

Trager, F. N., ed., *Marxism in Southeast Asia*, Stanford, Stanford University Press, 1959.

Why Vietnam?, New York, Praeger Publishers, 1966.

Tregaskis, R., *Vietnam Diary*, New York, Holt, Reinhart, Winston—Popular Library, 1963.

United States Senate Republican Policy Committee, *The War in Vietnam*, Washington, D. C., Public Affairs Press, 1967.

United States Department of State, *Aggression from the North. The Record of North Viet-Nam's Campaign to Conquer South Viet-Nam*, Washington, D. C., 1965.

Vandenbosch, A., and R. Butwell, *The Changing Face of Southeast Asia*, Lexington, University of Kentucky Press, 1966.

Vien, N. C., *Seeking the Truth*, New York, Vintage, 1967.

Vuglen, S. M., *National Liberations Movements: Communist Conspiracies or Political Realities?* New York, O'Hare Books, 1968.

Warner, D., *The Last Confucian* (Ngo Dinh Diem), New York, Penguin, 1964.

Weil, C. A., *Curtains Over Vietnam*, Jericho, N. Y., Exposition Press, 1969.

Weinstein, F. B., *Vietnam's Unheld Elections: The Failure to Carry Out the 1956 Reunification Elections and the Effect on Hanoi's Present Outlook*, Ithaca, N. Y., Cornell Southeast Asia Program, 1966.

West, R., *Sketches from Vietnam*, London Cape, 1968.

White, R. K., *Nobody Wanted War*, Garden City, N. Y., Doubleday, 1968.

Wilson, W., *The LBJ Brigade*, New York, Pyramid Books.

Zinn, H., *Vietnam: The Logic of Withdrawal*, Boston, Beacon Press, 1967.

V. Vietnam Bibliographies

1. *University of California Library Holdings on Vietnam*, Center for Southeast Asia Studies, U. of C., Berkeley, California. May, 1968.

2. *What to Read on Vietnam. A Selected Annotated Bibliography.* Compiled by Staff Members of the Vietnam Project; Michigan State University: Institute of Pacific Relations, New York, 1959.

3. *South and Southeast Asia: A Bibliography of Bibliographies*, G. Raymond Nunn. Honolulu: East-West Center, University of Hawaii, 1966.

4. *Vietnam: A Select Reading List*, Rennie C. Jones. Melbourne, Australia, State Library of Victoria, 1966.

5. *Journal of Asian Studies.* Yearly: September issue.

6. *Southeast Asia: An Annotated Bibliography of Selected Reference Sources in Western Languages.* Compiled by Cecil Hobbs. Library of Congress, Washington, D. C., 1964 (earlier edition 1952).

VI. Vietnamese Publications

1. *The American Crime of Genocide in South Vietnam.* Giai Phong Publishing House, South Vietnam, 1968.

2. *American Crimes in Vietnam*, Democratic Republic of Vietnam, October, 1966.

3. Committee to Denounce the United States Puppets' War Crimes in South Vietnam, "Communiqué on their Crimes in 1969." Issued January 5, 1970, South Vietnam.

4. Committee to Denounce the U. S. Puppets' War Crimes in South Vietnam, "Special Communiqué Listing the Crimes Perpetrated by the United States Aggressors and Their Henchmen Against the South Vietnamese People So Far, Under the Nixon Administration from January 20, 1969 to September 30, 1969." Issued Sept. 30, 1969, South Vietnam.

5. Dinh Ba Thi (Deputy Chief of the Provisional Revolutionary Government of the Republic of South Vietnam), "Statement by Dinh Ba Thi, at the 50th Plenary Session of the Paris Conference on Vietnam," January 15, 1970.

6. Dinh Ba Thi (Deputy Chief of the Provisional Revolutionary Government of the Republic of South Vietnam), "Statement by Dinh Ba Thi, at the 56th Plenary Session of the Paris Conference on Vietnam," Feb. 26, 1970.

7. *Genocide Crime in South Vietnam*, Liberation Editions, South Vietnam, March, 1963.

8. *Hai Thu: North Vietnam Against U. S. Air Force*. Foreign Languages Publishing House, Hanoi, 1967.

9. Minister Mme. Nguyen Thi Binh (Chief of the Delegation of the Provisional Revolutionary Government of the Republic of South Vietnam), "Statement by Minister Mme. Nguyen Thi Binh, at the 57th Plenary Session of the Paris Conference on Vietnam," Mar. 5, 1970.

10. Minister Mme. Nguyen Thi Binh (Chief of the Delegation of the Provisional Revolutionary Government of the Republic of South Vietnam, "Statement by Minister Mme. Nguyen Thi Binh, at the 57th Plenary Session of the Paris Conference on Vietnam," Mar. 5, 1970.

11. Neo Lao Haksat, ed., "Memorandum du comité central du front patriotique Lao concernant l'intensification, depuis debut de Novembre 1968, des bombardements par l'U. S. Air Force de la zone sous controle du front patriotique Lao et des forces neutralistes patriotiques Lao," 1969.

12. *New War Crime in South Vietnam. Spraying by U. S. Planes of Toxic Chemicals*, Hanoi, 1963.

13. Nguyen Khac Vien, ed., *South Vietnam. Data and Prospects,* Vietnamese Studies, no. 18-19, Sept. 1968.

14. *South Vietnam. A Month of Unprecedented Offensive and Uprising*, Giai Phong Publishing House, March 1968.

15. South Vietnam Committee to Denounce U. S. Puppets' War Crimes, *U. S. Puppet Massacres of the Population in South Vietnam (from 1965-1969)*. Issued Dec. 1969.

16. *They Are Even More Ruthless Than Hitler!* Volume II, Liberation Editions, South Vietnam, 1966.

17. *U. S. Imperialists' "Burn All, Destroy All, Kill All" policy in South Vietnam*. Giai Phong, Liberation Editions, South Vietnam, 1967.

18. *U. S. War Crimes in Vietnam*. Juridical Sciences Institute under the Vietnam State Commission of Social Sciences, Hanoi, 1968.

19. *The U. S. War of Aggression in Vietnam. A Crime Against the Vietnamese People, Against Peace and Humanity,* Democratic Republic of Vietnam, October 1966.

70 71 72 73 74   9 8 7 6 5 4 3 2 1